Shedding for Life:

The Science and Flavor of Healthy Weight Loss

By
Ashlee C. Whitney

DISCLAIMER

Introduction

Welcome to a journey that goes beyond the confines of mere diets and fads, a journey where the transformative power of healthy eating is unveiled. In a world saturated with contradictory nutrition advice, "Eat Well, Slim Smart" aims to be your guiding light, bringing clarity to the crucial role of nutrition in achieving and sustaining weight loss.

1.1 Embarking on the Journey

Consider this not just a book but a roadmap to a healthier, more vibrant you. As you embark on this journey, we invite you to explore the profound impact that mindful and nutritious eating can have on your well-being. This is more than a quest for a number on the scale; it's a holistic approach to nourishing your body and soul.

1.2 The Crucial Role of Nutrition

Let's debunk the myths and cut through the noise. Nutrition is the cornerstone of your weight loss journey. What you eat affects not only your physical health but also your mental and emotional well-being. We delve into the science behind the food choices you make, empowering you to make informed decisions that resonate with your body's needs.

1.3 Overview of the Book's Approach

"Eat Well, Slim Smart" is not just another diet book; it's a fusion of science and flavor. We understand that taste matters just as much as nutritional content. Throughout these pages, we weave together the principles of healthy eating with the joy of savoring delicious meals. It's an approach designed to make your journey enjoyable, sustainable, and, above all, successful.

1.4 Key Principles for Success

Success in achieving and maintaining a healthy weight is grounded in certain key principles. We outline these principles, providing you with a solid foundation for your transformation. From portion control to mindful eating, we address the factors that contribute to a balanced and sustainable approach to weight loss.

1.5 Your Roadmap to a Healthier You

Consider this book your roadmap, guiding you through the intricacies of nutrition and lifestyle. Each chapter is a stepping stone, building on the last, bringing you closer to your wellness goals. As you navigate through these pages, you'll discover practical insights, flavorful recipes, and actionable advice that aligns with your unique journey.

1.6 Why Now?

In a world where the pace of life seems ever-accelerating, prioritizing your health has never been more critical. We explore why now is the opportune moment to make positive changes, aligning your choices with the wellness you deserve.

1.7 Setting Personal Goals

This is not just about the collective journey; it's about your journey. Take a moment to set personal goals, reflecting on what achieving a healthier lifestyle means to you. Your goals are the compass that will guide you through the challenges and triumphs that lie ahead.

1.8 Inviting Engagement

Your engagement is key to your success. Throughout the book, you're invited to participate actively. Engage in reflection, embrace challenges, and celebrate victories. This isn't a passive read; it's an interactive experience designed to enhance your understanding and commitment.

1.9 Closing Thoughts

As we embark on this journey together, let these introductory words catalyze the positive changes awaiting you. "Eat Well, Slim Smart" is more than a book; it's a companion on your path to a healthier, more fulfilling life. Let's uncover the power of healthy eating and embark on this transformative adventure together.

Chapter One

Unveiling the Power of Healthy Eating

The power of healthy eating lies in its profound impact on both physical and mental well-being. A nutrient-dense diet is not just a means to manage weight; it is a cornerstone for overall health. The body relies on a balanced intake of essential nutrients to function optimally, supporting vital processes such as metabolism, immune function, and cellular repair. Beyond the physiological benefits, healthy eating contributes to sustained energy levels and mental clarity, fostering a sense of vitality that transcends the limitations of mere calorie counting.

Moreover, healthy eating is a potent preventive measure against a myriad of chronic diseases. Scientific evidence consistently demonstrates the role of nutrition in reducing the risk of conditions such as heart disease, diabetes, and certain cancers. By adopting a diet rich in fruits, vegetables, whole grains, and lean proteins, individuals actively engage in their long-term well-being. This preventive aspect underscores the transformative power of food choices, positioning healthy eating as a proactive and empowering strategy for a healthier future.

The power of healthy eating is not confined to physical health; it extends to mental and emotional resilience. Nutrient-rich foods, coupled with mindful eating practices, contribute to stable mood regulation and cognitive function. Omega-3 fatty acids, found in abundance in foods like salmon and walnuts, have been linked to improved mental well-being.

Additionally, embracing a healthy diet can positively influence one's relationship with food, fostering a more mindful and balanced approach that emphasizes enjoyment rather than restriction. In essence, the power of healthy eating transcends the immediate benefits, creating a foundation for a robust and harmonious life.

Understanding the Crucial Role of Nutrition in Weight Loss

Understanding the crucial role of nutrition in weight loss is pivotal to achieving lasting and meaningful results. At its core, weight loss is a complex interplay between the calories consumed and the energy expended. Nutrition serves as the linchpin in this equation, determining not only the quantity but also the quality of the calories that fuel the body.

Nutrition is the cornerstone of the energy balance equation, where the calories consumed through food must align with the calories expended through physical activity and metabolic processes. It's not just about counting calories; it's about the quality of those calories and the nutrients they provide. A well-balanced diet ensures that the body receives the necessary vitamins, minerals, and macronutrients for optimal functioning, supporting overall health while pursuing weight loss goals. A diet rich in whole, nutrient-dense foods provides the necessary building blocks for bodily functions, ensuring that the body has the energy and resources it needs to thrive. This understanding sets the foundation for a sustainable and health-focused weight loss journey.

The role of nutrition in weight loss extends beyond simple calorie arithmetic. Certain foods can influence metabolic processes, promoting fat-burning and satiety. For instance, a diet rich in fiber helps regulate blood sugar levels and keeps individuals feeling fuller for longer periods, reducing the likelihood of overeating.

For instance, protein-rich foods support muscle maintenance and contribute to a feeling of fullness, aiding in appetite control. The strategic inclusion of complex carbohydrates and healthy fats provides sustained energy, helping individuals adhere to their weight loss plans over the long term. By comprehending the science behind these nutritional choices, individuals can tailor their eating habits to optimize metabolism and enhance the efficiency of their weight loss endeavors. Understanding these nuances empowers individuals to make informed choices about the composition of their meals, fostering a sustainable and enjoyable approach to weight management.

Moreover, recognizing the role of nutrition goes hand in hand with dispelling myths surrounding weight loss. Fad diets often propagate misleading information, promoting quick fixes that rarely result in sustained success. A nuanced understanding of nutrition empowers individuals to distinguish between evidence-based recommendations and fleeting trends. It encourages a shift in focus from restrictive and temporary measures to a lifestyle centered around balanced, enjoyable, and health-promoting food choices.

The journey to a healthier weight is not merely about shedding pounds but fostering a holistic well-being that extends beyond the scale. Nutrition plays a crucial role in supporting mental and emotional health, influencing mood, cognition, and overall vitality. Nutrient-rich foods, such as those high in omega-3 fatty acids and antioxidants, have been linked to improved mood and cognitive function. Understanding this intricate connection between nutrition and mental well-being underscores the significance of cultivating a positive and sustainable relationship with food throughout the weight loss journey.

In essence, understanding the crucial role of nutrition in weight loss is akin to unlocking the secrets of a balanced and effective approach to healthy living. It involves appreciating the multifaceted impact of dietary choices, from basic energy balance to the intricacies of metabolism and mental well-being. Armed with this knowledge, individuals can embark on a transformative journey that not only leads to weight loss but also cultivates a lasting foundation for optimal health and vitality.

Chapter Two

The Science Behind Weight Loss

The science behind weight loss involves a comprehensive understanding of the body's complex metabolic processes and the interplay of various factors that influence energy balance. At its core, weight loss is achieved by creating a caloric deficit, where the calories expended through basal metabolic rate and physical activity exceed those consumed through food. This intricate process is influenced by factors such as genetics, hormones, and the thermic effect of food. Additionally, the type and composition of the diet play a crucial role, in influencing satiety, nutrient absorption, and the body's utilization of stored energy. A nuanced grasp of these scientific principles empowers individuals to make informed dietary and lifestyle choices, ensuring a holistic and evidence-based approach to achieving and maintaining a healthy weight.

Exploring the Metabolic Processes and Scientific Foundations of How the Body Processes Nutrients

The body's intricate metabolic processes form the backbone of understanding how it processes nutrients, ultimately influencing weight management and overall health. At the cellular level, the body extracts energy from nutrients through a series of metabolic reactions. Carbohydrates are broken down into glucose, the primary energy source, through processes like glycolysis. Fats are metabolized into fatty acids and glycerol, while proteins are broken down into amino acids. These processes occur in various organs, primarily the liver, where nutrients are either utilized for energy, stored, or transformed into other molecules vital for bodily functions.

The scientific foundations of nutrient metabolism extend to the hormonal regulation of energy balance. Insulin, for example, plays a key role in glucose metabolism, facilitating its uptake by cells for energy or storage as glycogen in the liver and muscles. Leptin and ghrelin are hormones that influence appetite and satiety, impacting food intake and energy expenditure. Understanding these hormonal mechanisms helps elucidate how the body regulates its weight and responds to dietary changes.

Moreover, the thermic effect of food (TEF) contributes to the scientific intricacies of nutrient processing. TEF represents the energy expended during digestion, absorption, and processing of nutrients. Protein, for instance, has a higher TEF compared to fats and carbohydrates, implying that the body expends more energy digesting and assimilating protein. This knowledge underscores the significance of dietary composition in influencing the body's energy expenditure and, consequently, weight management.

The Thermic Effect of Food (TEF)

The Thermic Effect of Food (TEF) refers to the energy expenditure associated with the digestion, absorption, and processing of nutrients consumed through food. In simpler terms, it represents the calories the body expends to break down and utilize the nutrients from a meal. Each macronutrient—carbohydrates, proteins, and fats—requires a certain amount of energy for digestion, and TEF varies depending on the composition of the diet.

- **Carbohydrates:** About 5-10% of the energy content of ingested carbohydrates is expended during digestion and absorption. The body uses energy to break down complex carbohydrates into simpler forms like glucose, which can then be absorbed into the bloodstream.
- **Proteins:** Proteins have a higher thermic effect, with approximately 20-30% of the calories from protein being utilized during digestion and absorption. This is because proteins need to be broken down into amino acids, a process that demands more energy.
- **Fats:** The thermic effect of dietary fats is lower than that of proteins, typically ranging from 0-5% of the energy content. Fats are broken down into fatty acids and glycerol, requiring less energy for digestion compared to proteins.

The cumulative thermic effect contributes to the overall energy expenditure of an individual. This phenomenon is one reason why different macronutrients can have varying effects on metabolic rate. For instance, a meal higher in protein may result in a higher postprandial energy expenditure compared to a meal higher in fats or carbohydrates. Incorporating a mix of macronutrients in a diet can influence the overall energy balance, potentially playing a role in weight management strategies.

Understanding the thermic effect of food is important for individuals seeking to optimize their dietary choices and manage weight effectively. It highlights that the body expends energy not only through physical activity but also during the digestion and processing of the food we consume.

Understanding the Role of Calories, Macronutrients, and Micronutrients in Weight Management

The Role of Calories in Weight Management

Understanding the role of calories in weight management is fundamental to developing effective strategies for achieving and maintaining a healthy weight. A calorie, or kilocalorie (kcal), is a unit of measurement for energy. The basic premise of weight management is the balance between the calories consumed through food and beverages and the calories expended through basal metabolic rate (BMR), physical activity, and the thermic effect of food (TEF).

1. **Energy Balance:**
    - At its core, weight management is governed by the principle of energy balance. If the number of calories consumed equals the number of calories expended, the body weight remains stable. If there is a caloric surplus (more calories consumed than expended), the excess energy is stored as fat, leading to weight gain. Conversely, a caloric deficit (more calories expended than consumed) results in the body utilizing stored energy, leading to weight loss.
2. **Caloric Expenditure:**
    - The total calories expended by the body can be categorized into three main components:

- **Basal Metabolic Rate (BMR):** This is the energy expended at rest to maintain basic physiological functions such as breathing, circulation, and cell production. BMR accounts for the majority of daily caloric expenditure.
- **Physical Activity:** This includes both planned exercise and daily activities like walking, cleaning, and standing. The intensity and duration of physical activity significantly impact caloric expenditure.
- **Thermic Effect of Food (TEF):** As discussed earlier, TEF represents the calories burned during the digestion, absorption, and processing of nutrients from food.

3. **Caloric Intake:**
   - The calories consumed come from the macronutrients in our diet: carbohydrates, proteins, and fats. Each gram of these macronutrients provides a certain number of calories:
     - Carbohydrates: 4 calories per gram
     - Proteins: 4 calories per gram
     - Fats: 9 calories per gram
   - Micronutrients, such as vitamins and minerals, contribute negligible calories but are essential for overall health.
4. **Dietary Choices and Nutrient Density:**
   - Weight management is not solely about counting calories; the quality of those calories matters. Choosing nutrient-dense foods that provide essential vitamins, minerals, and other beneficial compounds supports overall health. Nutrient-dense foods, such as fruits, vegetables, lean proteins, and whole grains, provide more essential nutrients per calorie compared to processed and calorie-dense foods.
5. **Individual Variability:**

   - It's crucial to recognize that individual factors, such as genetics, age, gender, and body composition, influence BMR and caloric needs. What works for one person may not be suitable for another, highlighting the importance of personalized approaches to weight management.
6. **Sustainable Lifestyle Changes:**
   - While short-term calorie restriction may lead to weight loss, sustainable weight management involves adopting healthy lifestyle habits that can be maintained in the long term. This includes a balanced and varied diet, regular physical activity, and mindful eating practices.

Hence, the role of calories in weight management revolves around achieving a balance between caloric intake and expenditure. Understanding this dynamic equation empowers individuals to make informed dietary and lifestyle choices that support their unique health and weight goals.

The Role of Macronutrients in Weight Management

The role of macronutrients—carbohydrates, proteins, and fats—in weight management is crucial, as these nutrients not only provide energy but also play distinct roles in metabolism, satiety, and overall health. Understanding how each macronutrient influences the body can aid in making informed dietary choices for effective weight management.

1. **Carbohydrates:**
   - *Energy Source:* Carbohydrates are the body's primary source of energy. When consumed, they are broken down into glucose, which fuels various bodily functions, especially during physical activity.
   - *Blood Sugar Regulation:* Choosing complex

carbohydrates with fiber, such as whole grains, fruits, and vegetables, helps regulate blood sugar levels and promotes sustained energy release.

- *Satiety:* Including fiber-rich carbohydrates in meals promotes feelings of fullness, potentially reducing overall caloric intake.

2. **Proteins:**
   - *Muscle Maintenance and Repair:* Proteins are essential for the maintenance and repair of tissues, particularly muscles. Adequate protein intake is crucial for preserving lean body mass, especially during weight loss.
   - *Satiety:* Protein-rich foods promote a feeling of fullness, potentially reducing the desire for additional snacking.
   - *Energy Expenditure:* The body expends more energy (calories) digesting and processing proteins compared to fats and carbohydrates, known as the thermic effect of food (TEF).
3. **Fats:**
   - *Energy Storage:* Fats serve as an efficient energy storage form in the body, providing a concentrated source of calories. However, excessive fat intake can contribute to weight gain.
   - *Nutrient Absorption:* Fats are necessary for the absorption of fat-soluble vitamins (A, D, E, K) and certain phytonutrients. Including healthy fats in the diet supports overall nutrient absorption.
   - *Satiety:* Like proteins, fats contribute to feelings of satiety, potentially reducing the overall caloric

intake.

4. **Balancing Macronutrients for Weight Management:**
   - *Caloric Intake and Expenditure:* While each macronutrient has unique roles, the overall caloric balance remains fundamental to weight management. Consuming more calories than the body expends leads to weight gain and a caloric deficit results in weight loss.
   - *Personalized Approach:* The optimal macronutrient distribution varies among individuals based on factors such as age, gender, activity level, and health status. Tailoring macronutrient intake to individual needs supports sustainable weight management.
5. **Mindful Eating and Portion Control:**
   - *Quality Matters:* Focusing on the quality of macronutrients is essential. Opting for whole, nutrient-dense sources of carbohydrates, lean proteins, and healthy fats ensures a well-balanced diet.
   - *Mindful Choices:* Being mindful of portion sizes and paying attention to hunger and fullness cues can help prevent overeating and promote a healthy relationship with food.

In essence, the role of macronutrients in weight management involves understanding the distinct functions of carbohydrates, proteins, and fats and striking a balance that aligns with individual health goals. A well-rounded approach, considering both macronutrient composition and overall caloric balance, contributes to sustainable and effective weight management.

The Role of Micronutrients in Weight Management

Micronutrients, often referred to as the "tiny heroes" of nutrition, are a group of essential vitamins and minerals that play a profound and irreplaceable role in the overall health and functioning of the human body. Unlike macronutrients—carbohydrates, proteins, and fats—which are required in larger quantities for energy production, micronutrients are needed in smaller amounts, yet their impact is immense. These microscopic components act as catalysts, facilitators, and guardians in a multitude of biochemical processes, ensuring the seamless operation of intricate physiological pathways that sustain life.

Micronutrients are a diverse array of compounds, each with its unique capabilities. Vitamins, such as vitamin A, B-complex vitamins, vitamins C, D, E, and K, function as organic compounds that regulate numerous biological processes, from supporting vision and immune function to bone health and blood clotting. On the mineral front, essential elements like iron, calcium, magnesium, zinc, and others serve as inorganic building blocks, contributing to the structural integrity of bones, the conductivity of nerves, and the maintenance of fluid balance.

At the cellular level, micronutrients are akin to skilled conductors orchestrating a symphony of biochemical reactions. They participate in enzymatic activities, ensuring that cellular processes, such as energy metabolism, DNA synthesis, and antioxidant defense, proceed harmoniously. For instance, the B vitamins act as coenzymes, facilitating the conversion of food into energy, while minerals like selenium and copper play pivotal roles in antioxidant enzymes that neutralize harmful free radicals, protecting cells from oxidative stress.

Micronutrients are not merely sustenance for survival; they are the architects of optimal health. Beyond preventing deficiencies that lead to conditions like scurvy or rickets, micronutrients contribute to the prevention of chronic diseases, immune system modulation, and cognitive function. Omega-3 fatty acids, although classified as a type of fat, are considered a micronutrient and are celebrated for their cardiovascular benefits and influence on brain health.

While the significance of micronutrients is undeniable, achieving a delicate balance is crucial. Insufficient intake can lead to deficiencies and associated health issues, while excessive consumption can result in toxicity. Achieving an optimal balance involves embracing a varied and nutrient-dense diet, rich in fruits, vegetables, whole grains, nuts, seeds, and lean proteins.

The role of micronutrients in weight management is critical, as these essential vitamins and minerals play key roles in various physiological processes that influence metabolism, energy production, and overall health. While macronutrients (carbohydrates, proteins, and fats) provide the energy needed for bodily functions, micronutrients are vital for supporting the metabolic pathways that regulate energy utilization, nutrient absorption, and overall well-being.

1. **Metabolic Regulation:**
    - Micronutrients such as B vitamins (e.g., B6, B12, folate) and minerals like magnesium and zinc are integral components of metabolic pathways. They facilitate the breakdown of macronutrients into energy, supporting the body's energy metabolism. A well-functioning metabolism is crucial for maintaining a healthy weight.
2. **Hormone Regulation:**
    - Certain micronutrients, including vitamin D, play a role in hormonal regulation. Vitamin D, for example, is involved in insulin sensitivity, which is essential for the proper utilization of glucose and the prevention of insulin resistance—a factor linked to obesity.
3. **Energy Production:**
    - Micronutrients, particularly those involved in the

electron transport chain (such as iron and copper), contribute to energy production within cells. Adequate levels of these micronutrients are necessary for efficient energy generation, supporting overall vitality and preventing fatigue that might hinder physical activity.

4. **Appetite Regulation:**
   - Some micronutrients influence appetite and satiety. For instance, adequate levels of vitamin C have been associated with lower body weight and reduced feelings of hunger. Additionally, maintaining optimal levels of certain minerals like chromium may help regulate blood sugar levels and curb cravings.
5. **Nutrient Absorption:**
   - Micronutrients are essential for the absorption of macronutrients and other nutrients. For example, vitamin D is crucial for calcium absorption, and supporting bone health. Proper nutrient absorption ensures that the body efficiently utilizes the energy derived from macronutrients.
6. **Anti-Inflammatory Effects:**
   - Chronic inflammation is associated with conditions like obesity and metabolic syndrome. Micronutrients with anti-inflammatory properties, such as omega-3 fatty acids and antioxidants (vitamins A, C, and E), contribute to reducing inflammation and supporting overall health.
7. **Cellular Health:**
   - Micronutrients are critical for maintaining the health of cells and tissues. For example, vitamin A supports the health of epithelial cells, which line

various surfaces in the body, including the digestive tract. A healthy digestive system is crucial for nutrient absorption and overall metabolic health.

8. **Stress Management:**
    - Micronutrients like B vitamins play a role in the body's response to stress. Chronic stress can contribute to weight gain, and adequate levels of these micronutrients support the nervous system, potentially helping in stress management and weight control.

In conclusion, micronutrients are integral to various aspects of weight management, including metabolism, hormonal regulation, appetite control, and overall health. A well-balanced and nutrient-dense diet that provides a variety of vitamins and minerals is essential for supporting these functions and promoting effective and sustainable weight management.

Chapter Three

Building Your Plate: Crafting a Balanced Diet

Building your plate is a creative and empowering endeavor, where each choice becomes a brushstroke in the vibrant canvas of a balanced diet. Just as an artist carefully selects colors to create a masterpiece, you can curate a palette of nutrients, textures, and flavors to nourish your body. A balanced plate embraces the harmony of macronutrients and micronutrients, featuring an array of colorful vegetables, lean proteins, wholesome grains, and healthy fats. It's a mindful composition that not only fuels the body but also satisfies the senses, creating a sustainable and enjoyable approach to nourishment. With each meal, you have the opportunity to craft a culinary work of art that fosters well-being and supports the journey toward a healthier and more vibrant life.

Practical Tips on Creating Well-balanced Meals to Support Weight Loss

Creating well-balanced meals that support weight loss involves thoughtful planning, portion control, and selecting nutrient-dense foods. Here are practical tips to guide you in crafting meals that contribute to your weight loss goals:

1. **Embrace Variety:**
    - Include a variety of foods from all food groups: fruits, vegetables, lean proteins, whole grains, and healthy fats. This ensures a diverse range of nutrients and flavors, making meals more enjoyable.
2. **Prioritize Vegetables:**
    - Fill half your plate with colorful vegetables. They are low in calories and high in fiber, promoting satiety and providing essential vitamins and minerals.
3. **Choose Lean Proteins:**
    - Opt for lean protein sources such as poultry, fish,

tofu, legumes, and low-fat dairy. Protein helps maintain muscle mass and contributes to a feeling of fullness, reducing the likelihood of overeating.

4. **Incorporate Whole Grains:**
    - Choose whole grains like quinoa, brown rice, oats, and whole wheat bread over refined grains. Whole grains provide more fiber, promoting digestive health and offering sustained energy.
5. **Mindful Portion Control:**
    - Be mindful of portion sizes to avoid overeating. Use smaller plates, bowls, and utensils, and listen to your body's hunger and fullness cues.
6. **Include Healthy Fats:**
    - Incorporate sources of healthy fats, such as avocados, nuts, seeds, and olive oil. These fats contribute to satiety and support nutrient absorption.
7. **Limit Added Sugars and Processed Foods:**
    - Minimize the intake of added sugars and highly processed foods. These often contribute empty calories and may not provide the nutritional value needed for weight loss.
8. **Stay Hydrated:**
    - Drink plenty of water throughout the day. Sometimes, the body can interpret thirst as hunger, leading to unnecessary calorie consumption.
9. **Plan and Prep:**
    - Plan your meals ahead of time and consider meal prepping. Having healthy, ready-to-go options reduces the likelihood of opting for less nutritious choices when time is limited.
10. **Be Mindful of Liquid Calories:**
    - Be aware of liquid calories from sugary drinks and

alcoholic beverages. Choose water, herbal tea, or other low-calorie options to stay hydrated without adding extra calories.

11. **Enjoy Treats in Moderation:**
    - Allow yourself occasional treats, but practice moderation. Incorporate indulgences without derailing your overall healthy eating habits.
12. **Listen to Your Body:**
    - Pay attention to hunger and fullness cues. Eat when you're hungry and stop when you're satisfied, rather than finishing everything on your plate.
13. **Regular, Balanced Meals:**
    - Aim for regular meals and snacks throughout the day to maintain energy levels and prevent excessive hunger that might lead to unhealthy food choices.

By incorporating these practical tips into your daily routine, you can create well-balanced meals that not only support weight loss but also contribute to overall health and well-being. Remember that sustainable changes in eating habits are key to long-term success.

Portion Control Strategies and Mindful Eating Techniques

Portion Control Strategies:

1. **Use Smaller Plates and Bowls:**
    - Downsizing your dinnerware can create the illusion of larger portions, helping to satisfy visual cues for a full meal.
2. **Divide Your Plate:**
    - Mentally divide your plate into sections: devote half to vegetables, one-quarter to lean proteins, and one-quarter to whole grains. This encourages a balanced and portioned meal.
3. **Pre-Portion Snacks:**

   - Instead of eating directly from a bag or container, pre-portion snacks into smaller servings to avoid mindless overeating.
4. **Single-Serve Packaging:**
   - Opt for single-serving packages or portion out larger packages into smaller containers. This helps control intake and prevents overindulgence.
5. **Be Mindful of Liquid Calories:**
   - Use smaller glasses for beverages and be conscious of liquid calories, including those from sugary drinks and alcoholic beverages.
6. **Practice the Half-Plate Rule at Restaurants:**
   - When dining out, consider splitting entrees or following the half-plate rule by asking for half of the meal to be boxed up before it even reaches the table.

Mindful Eating Techniques:

1. **Eat Without Distractions:**
   - Avoid eating in front of the TV, computer, or while scrolling through your phone. Focus on the sensory experience of eating to enhance awareness.
2. **Savor Each Bite:**
   - Take the time to appreciate the flavors, textures, and aromas of your food. Eating slowly allows your body to recognize fullness cues.
3. **Listen to Hunger and Fullness Cues:**
   - Pay attention to your body's signals. Eat when you're hungry, and stop when you're satisfied, rather than finishing everything on your plate.
4. **Chew Thoroughly:**
   - Chew each bite thoroughly, savoring the taste and texture of the food. This not only aids digestion but

also allows you to eat more mindfully.

5. **Use All Your Senses:**
   - Engage all your senses while eating. Notice the colors, smells, and sounds of your meal. This heightened awareness enhances the eating experience.
6. **Take Breaks Between Bites:**
   - Put your utensils down between bites. This simple action can slow down your eating pace and give your body time to recognize fullness.
7. **Check in with Yourself:**
   - Pause during the meal and check in with your hunger levels. Ask yourself if you're still hungry or if you're eating out of habit or boredom.
8. **Mindful Portion Estimation:**
   - Before serving yourself, estimate appropriate portion sizes based on your hunger level. This mindful approach helps prevent overeating.
9. **Express Gratitude:**
   - Begin your meal with a moment of gratitude. Taking a moment to appreciate your food can create a positive mindset around eating.
10. **Practice Mindful Breathing:**
    - Incorporate mindful breathing exercises before and during meals to center yourself and bring awareness to the present moment.

By integrating these portion control strategies and mindful eating techniques into your daily routine, you can foster a healthier relationship with food, enhance satisfaction, and support your weight management goals.

Chapter Four

Flavorful Foundations: Herbs, Spices, and Smart Cooking

Flavorful Foundations: Herbs, Spices, and Smart Cooking serve as the culinary charm that transforms a meal from a mere necessity into a delightful and healthful experience. Embracing a palette of herbs and spices not only enhances the taste of dishes but also allows for a reduction in added salt, sugar, and unhealthy fats, contributing to smart and nutritious cooking. From the zesty kick of fresh herbs to the warmth of aromatic spices, these elements infuse complexity and depth into meals, encouraging a diverse and satisfying culinary journey. Moreover, employing smart cooking techniques, such as grilling, roasting, and steaming, preserves the nutritional integrity of ingredients while intensifying their natural flavors. This flavorful symphony not only captivates the palate but also empowers individuals to savor the joy of nourishing, delicious meals, making the quest for a balanced and health-conscious diet both enticing and achievable.

How Herbs and Spices Enhance the Taste of Healthy Meals

Herbs and spices are not only culinary companions but also powerful tools that elevate the taste of healthy meals, turning them into delightful gastronomic experiences. Their ability to enhance flavors is not just about adding zest but also about enriching the overall sensory appeal of a dish.

1. **Complex Flavor Profiles:**

- Herbs like basil, cilantro, and parsley, and spices such as cumin, coriander, and paprika, contribute complex flavor profiles that go beyond basic taste sensations. They add layers of depth, creating a harmonious blend of sweet, savory, bitter, and umami notes.

2. **Reduced Reliance on Salt and Sugar:**

    - Incorporating herbs and spices allows for a reduction in the use of salt, sugar, and unhealthy fats without compromising taste. This is particularly significant for those aiming to maintain a heart-healthy and low-sodium diet, as the robust flavors from herbs and spices provide a satisfying alternative.

3. **Aromatic Aesthetics:**

    - The aromatic qualities of herbs and spices tantalize the olfactory senses, enhancing the overall eating experience. Fragrant herbs like rosemary and thyme or spices like cinnamon and cardamom not only infuse dishes with enticing scents but also stimulate appetite and evoke a sense of culinary pleasure.

4. **Freshness and Vibrancy:**

    - Fresh herbs, such as mint and cilantro, bring a burst of freshness and vibrancy to meals. This liveliness not only enhances the taste but also contributes to the visual appeal of dishes, making them more enticing and enjoyable.

5. **Culinary Versatility:**

    - Herbs and spices offer incredible versatility in the kitchen, allowing for creativity in flavor combinations. From the warmth of cinnamon in oatmeal to the zing of ginger in stir-fries, their adaptability makes healthy cooking an exploration of diverse and enticing tastes.

6. **Health Benefits Beyond Flavor:**

- Beyond their flavor-enhancing role, many herbs and spices boast health benefits. For example, turmeric is celebrated for its anti-inflammatory properties, garlic supports cardiovascular health, and ginger aids digestion. Integrating these ingredients not only adds depth to taste but also contributes to overall well-being.

7. **Global Culinary Adventure:**

- Herbs and spices invite individuals on a global culinary adventure, allowing them to explore the diverse flavors of different cuisines. From the boldness of Mexican chili to the subtlety of French tarragon, incorporating herbs and spices enriches the palate with a world of tastes.

8. **Smart Cooking Choices:**

- Combining herbs and spices with smart cooking techniques, such as grilling, roasting, and steaming, maximizes their impact on taste without compromising the nutritional integrity of the ingredients. This synergy transforms healthy meals into a symphony of flavors that captivate the senses and foster a love for nourishing foods.

In essence, the integration of herbs and spices into healthy meals transcends the realm of taste, offering a holistic approach to culinary satisfaction. Their ability to add complexity, reduce reliance on less healthy ingredients, and contribute to overall well-being makes them invaluable allies in the pursuit of a flavorful and health-conscious diet.

Cooking Techniques that Maximize Flavor Without Compromising Nutritional Value

Maximizing flavor without compromising nutritional value involves choosing cooking techniques that enhance taste while preserving the nutritional integrity of ingredients. Here are some cooking techniques that achieve this balance:

1. **Grilling:**
   - Grilling imparts a smoky flavor and caramelization to food without the need for excessive fats. Choose lean proteins like chicken, fish, or vegetables, and marinate them with herbs, spices, and healthy oils to enhance flavor.
2. **Roasting:**
   - Roasting vegetables and meats intensifies their natural flavors. Use heart-healthy oils, such as olive oil, and season with herbs and spices. Roasting preserves nutrients and brings out rich, savory tastes.
3. **Steaming:**
   - Steaming is a gentle cooking method that retains the color, texture, and nutrients of vegetables. It's an excellent way to cook vegetables without adding extra fats, preserving their inherent freshness and flavors.
4. **Sautéing:**
   - Sautéing involves cooking food quickly in a small amount of oil over medium to high heat. Use heart-healthy oils like olive or avocado oil and incorporate aromatic herbs and spices for added flavor. It's a versatile method for vegetables, lean proteins, and grains.
5. **Baking:**
   - Baking is a dry heat cooking method that preserves the nutritional content of ingredients while enhancing flavors. Choose whole grains for baked

goods, experiment with herbs, spices, and natural sweeteners, and include ingredients like nuts and seeds for added texture and nutrients.

6. **Poaching:**
   - Poaching involves gently simmering food in a flavorful liquid. It's a technique often used for delicate proteins like fish or eggs. Use a broth infused with herbs, spices, and aromatics to impart taste without added fats.
7. **Broiling:**
   - Broiling exposes food to high heat from above, creating a caramelized exterior while maintaining moisture. It's a quick method suitable for lean proteins and vegetables. Season with herbs and spices for enhanced flavor.
8. **Use Fresh Herbs and Spices:**
   - Incorporating fresh herbs and spices is a simple way to add depth and complexity to dishes. Fresh herbs like basil, cilantro, and parsley, along with spices such as cumin, paprika, and garlic, contribute flavor without extra calories.
9. **Marinating:**
   - Marinating proteins before cooking not only infuses them with flavor but can also tenderize tougher cuts of meat. Choose marinades with herbs, spices, and acid sources like citrus or vinegar for a flavorful and health-conscious option.
10. **Layering Flavors:**
    - Build layers of flavor by adding ingredients at different stages of cooking. For example, start with sautéed aromatics like onions and garlic, then add herbs and spices, followed by liquids like broth or

wine. This method intensifies taste without relying on excessive fats or salt.

11. **Use Citrus and Vinegar:**
    - Citrus fruits and vinegar add brightness and acidity to dishes, enhancing flavors without the need for excess salt or unhealthy fats. Incorporate lemon or lime zest, or use vinegar-based dressings to impart tangy notes to salads and proteins.
12. **Experiment with Umami:**
    - Umami, the fifth taste, adds depth and savory richness to dishes. Ingredients like mushrooms, tomatoes, soy sauce, and Parmesan cheese are rich in umami. Experiment with these ingredients to enhance the overall flavor profile of your meals.

By incorporating these cooking techniques into your culinary repertoire, you can create delicious and nutritious meals that satisfy the taste buds without compromising your commitment to a healthy diet. Experimenting with a variety of herbs, spices, and cooking methods allows you to discover a plethora of flavors while prioritizing nutritional value.

Chapter Five

Mindful Eating: Savoring Every Bite

Mindful eating is a transformative approach to nourishment that transcends the act of consuming food; it is a conscious and intentional engagement with every aspect of the eating experience. By savoring every bite, mindful eating encourages you to cultivate a profound awareness of the flavors, textures, and aromas present in each morsel. It involves being fully present in the moment and appreciating the journey of food from plate to mouth. This practice extends beyond taste to embrace the sensory symphony of a meal, fostering a deeper connection with the act of eating and an enhanced understanding of one's body and its hunger and fullness cues. In the realm of mindful eating, each bite becomes an opportunity for gratitude, pleasure, and self-awareness, transforming the simple act of nourishment into a mindful, enriching, and holistic experience.

The Importance of Mindful Eating in Weight Loss: A Holistic Approach

Mindful eating has emerged as a powerful and holistic tool in the realm of weight loss, offering more than just a strategy for controlling calorie intake. Its significance lies in fostering a mindful and intentional relationship with food, addressing various aspects that contribute to successful and sustainable weight management.

1. Heightened Awareness of Hunger and Fullness:

- Mindful eating encourages individuals to reconnect with their body's natural hunger and fullness cues. By tuning into these signals, people can avoid overeating and develop a more intuitive understanding of when to start and stop eating, contributing to weight loss through portion control.

2. Emotional and Stress Eating Management:

- Mindful eating addresses the emotional and stress-related aspects of food consumption. Rather than turning to food as a coping mechanism, individuals learn to identify and manage emotional triggers. This shift promotes healthier responses to stress, reducing the likelihood of impulsive, comfort-driven eating that can contribute to weight gain.

3. Breaking Unhealthy Eating Patterns:

- Many weight-related challenges stem from unhealthy eating patterns, such as mindless snacking, emotional eating, or consuming meals too quickly. Mindful eating disrupts these patterns by encouraging a deliberate and conscious approach to each meal, helping individuals recognize and change detrimental habits.

4. Enhanced Enjoyment of Food:

- Mindful eating emphasizes savoring the sensory experience of eating. By truly appreciating the flavors, textures, and aromas of each bite, individuals find greater satisfaction in their meals. This enhanced enjoyment can lead to a decreased desire for unnecessary, empty-calorie snacks, contributing to a more balanced and controlled diet.

5. Prevention of Binge Eating:

- Mindful eating practices reduce the risk of binge eating episodes by promoting a non-judgmental awareness of cravings and impulses. Understanding and accepting these urges without succumbing to them allows individuals to make conscious choices, preventing the cycle of guilt and overconsumption often associated with binge eating.

6. Improved Digestion and Nutrient Absorption:

- Mindful eating encourages slower and more deliberate eating, aiding digestion and promoting optimal nutrient absorption. This can contribute to overall health and well-being, as the body efficiently utilizes nutrients from food, potentially influencing weight loss.

7. Sustainable Lifestyle Change:

- Mindful eating is not a temporary diet but a sustainable lifestyle change. It equips individuals with valuable skills that extend beyond specific meal plans, creating a lasting foundation for healthier eating habits. This long-term perspective is crucial for sustained weight loss and overall well-being.

8. Mind-Body Connection:

- Developing a strong mind-body connection is at the core of mindful eating. Understanding how different foods affect one's body and acknowledging the impact of emotional and environmental factors on eating habits empowers individuals to make informed choices, promoting a balanced and healthier lifestyle.

The importance of mindful eating in weight loss lies in its holistic approach to the complex relationship between individuals and food. By fostering awareness, addressing emotional aspects of eating, and promoting intentional choices, mindful eating contributes not only to weight loss but also to the development of a healthier and more sustainable approach to nourishment and well-being.

Techniques to Foster a Healthy Relationship with Food and Prevent Overeating

1. **Practice Mindful Eating:**
   - Mindful eating involves being fully present during meals and paying attention to the sensory experience of eating. Chew slowly, savor each bite, and be aware of hunger and fullness cues. This technique helps prevent overeating by promoting a deeper connection with the act of eating and fostering a more conscious approach to food.
2. **Keep a Food Journal:**
   - Maintain a food journal to track eating patterns, emotions associated with food, and portion sizes. This self-awareness can help identify triggers for overeating, allowing for targeted strategies to address specific challenges and promote healthier choices.
3. **Listen to Hunger and Fullness Cues:**
   - Learn to recognize and respond to your body's hunger and fullness signals. Eat when you're hungry, and stop when you're satisfied. Avoid eating based on external cues, such as the time of day or emotional triggers, and tune into your body's natural rhythms.
4. **Portion Control:**
   - Be mindful of portion sizes to prevent overeating. Use smaller plates, bowls, and utensils, and consider pre-portioning snacks to avoid mindless eating. Focus on serving reasonable portions, and pay attention to feelings of fullness during meals.
5. **Eat with Intention:**

- Before eating, take a moment to set an intention for your meal. Consider the nutritional value of the food, how it will nourish your body, and the pleasure it will bring. Eating with intention promotes a more thoughtful and purposeful approach to food, reducing the likelihood of mindless overeating.

6. **Stay Hydrated:**
   - Often, feelings of thirst can be mistaken for hunger, leading to unnecessary eating. Stay hydrated throughout the day by drinking water or other low-calorie beverages. Before reaching for a snack, consider whether you might be thirsty instead.
7. **Identify Emotional Triggers:**
   - Recognize emotional triggers that may lead to overeating, such as stress, boredom, or sadness. Develop alternative coping mechanisms like exercise, meditation, or engaging in a hobby to address these emotions without turning to food for comfort.
8. **Incorporate Variety:**
   - Enjoy a variety of foods to satisfy different taste sensations and nutritional needs. A diverse diet can prevent boredom with repetitive meals and reduce the temptation to overeat in search of flavor variety.
9. **Plan Meals and Snacks:**
   - Plan your meals and snacks ahead of time to avoid impulsive and unhealthy choices. Having a structured eating schedule helps regulate food intake and prevents excessive hunger that can lead to overeating.
10. **Savor Your Food:**

- Take time to savor and enjoy your food. Eating too quickly can lead to overeating as your body may not have enough time to register fullness. Put down your utensils between bites, engage in conversation, and appreciate the flavors and textures of each bite.

11. **Practice Gentle Nutrition:**
    - Shift the focus from rigid diet rules to practicing gentle nutrition. Choose foods that nourish your body and bring you joy. Avoid labeling foods as "good" or "bad," and allow yourself to enjoy a balanced and varied diet without guilt.
12. **Get Support:**
    - Seek support from friends, family, or a professional if you're struggling with overeating. Discussing your challenges and goals with others can provide valuable insights, encouragement, and accountability on your journey to fostering a healthy relationship with food.

By incorporating these techniques into your lifestyle, you can cultivate a healthier relationship with food, prevent overeating, and support your overall well-being. It's essential to approach these practices with patience and a willingness to embrace positive changes gradually.

Chapter Six

Fitness Fusion: Exercise and Nutrition Synergy

Fitness Fusion is the dynamic synergy between exercise and nutrition, a holistic approach that recognizes the interconnected relationship between these two pillars of health. It goes beyond viewing them as separate entities, instead embracing the idea that optimal well-being is achieved when exercise and nutrition work in tandem. By combining regular physical activity with a balanced and nourishing diet, Fitness Fusion creates a powerful synergy that enhances overall health, promotes sustainable weight management, and cultivates a robust foundation for vitality. This harmonious integration acknowledges that what we eat profoundly influences our ability to perform, recover, and thrive physically, while regular exercise enhances the body's capacity to absorb and utilize nutrients effectively. In the realm of Fitness Fusion, exercise and nutrition become not only complementary but inseparable partners, fostering a comprehensive and sustainable approach to a healthy, active lifestyle.

Integrating Physical Activity with a Healthy Diet for Optimal Weight Loss: A Comprehensive Approach

1. **Set Realistic Goals:**
    - Establish achievable and specific fitness and nutrition goals tailored to your weight loss objectives. Whether it's a certain number of workout sessions per week or incorporating more whole foods into your diet, realistic goals provide a roadmap for success.
2. **Balanced Nutrition:**
    - Focus on a balanced and nutrient-dense diet that supports your energy needs and weight loss goals. Include a variety of fruits, vegetables, lean proteins,

whole grains, and healthy fats. Consider consulting with a registered dietitian to create a personalized nutrition plan that aligns with your physical activity routine.

3. **Prioritize Protein Intake:**
    - Include an adequate amount of protein in your diet to support muscle maintenance and repair, especially when engaging in regular physical activity. Protein-rich foods like lean meats, beans, legumes, and dairy contribute to a feeling of fullness and assist in preserving lean body mass during weight loss.
4. **Timing Matters:**
    - Coordinate your meals and snacks with your workout schedule. Fuel your body with a combination of carbohydrates and protein before and after exercise to optimize energy levels, aid recovery, and support muscle growth.
5. **Stay Hydrated:**
    - Proper hydration is crucial for both physical activity and weight loss. Drink water throughout the day and consider the additional fluid needs associated with your workouts. Staying hydrated supports optimal performance and helps control appetite.
6. **Combine Cardiovascular and Strength Training:**
    - Integrate a mix of cardiovascular exercise and strength training into your routine. Cardio activities like running, cycling, or swimming enhance calorie burn, while strength training builds lean muscle mass, boosting your metabolism. Aim for a well-rounded fitness program that includes both components.
7. **Create a Consistent Exercise Routine:**

- Establish a consistent workout schedule that aligns with your daily routine and preferences. Consistency is key for sustainable weight loss and overall health benefits. Choose activities you enjoy to make exercise a positive and lasting part of your lifestyle.

8. **Mix Up Your Workouts:**
    - Keep your fitness routine engaging by incorporating a variety of exercises. This not only prevents boredom but also challenges different muscle groups, contributing to overall fitness and weight loss. Try a mix of cardio workouts, strength training, and flexibility exercises.
9. **Practice Portion Control:**
    - Be mindful of portion sizes to manage calorie intake effectively. While exercise is beneficial, it's crucial not to use it as a justification for overeating. Practice portion control and listen to your body's hunger and fullness cues.
10. **Monitor Progress and Adjust:**
    - Regularly assess your progress and make necessary adjustments to your fitness and nutrition plan. This may involve tweaking your workout intensity, reassessing your dietary choices, or modifying your goals based on your evolving needs and achievements.
11. **Prioritize Recovery:**
    - Allow your body adequate time to recover between workouts. Prioritize sleep, incorporate rest days, and consider activities like yoga or stretching to enhance flexibility and reduce the risk of injury. Adequate recovery supports optimal performance and long-

term adherence to your fitness plan.

12. **Seek Professional Guidance:**
    - Consider consulting with fitness professionals, such as personal trainers or nutritionists, to receive personalized guidance. Their expertise can help you create a well-rounded plan that aligns with your weight loss goals, fitness level, and individual preferences.

Integrating physical activity with a healthy diet for optimal weight loss requires a holistic and individualized approach. By combining a balanced nutrition plan with a diverse and consistent exercise routine, you create a synergistic foundation that not only supports weight loss but also cultivates a sustainable and health-conscious lifestyle.

Tailoring Exercise Routines to Complement Dietary Goals

Tailoring your exercise routines to complement dietary goals involves aligning your workout plan with specific nutritional objectives, whether it's weight loss, muscle gain, or overall well-being. Here are strategies to help you achieve this synergy:

1. **Identify Your Goals:**
    - Clearly define your dietary goals, whether it's weight loss, muscle building, or overall health improvement. Understanding your objectives provides a framework for tailoring your exercise routine.
2. **Caloric Balance:**
    - Adjust your exercise routine based on your caloric needs. If you aim to lose weight, create a caloric deficit by burning more calories through exercise than you consume. For muscle gain, ensure a caloric surplus to support growth.
3. **Cardiovascular Exercise for Weight Loss:**

- Incorporate cardiovascular exercises like running, cycling, or high-intensity interval training (HIIT) to enhance calorie burn and support weight loss. Aim for a mix of moderate and high-intensity cardio sessions to keep your metabolism elevated.

4. **Resistance Training for Muscle Gain:**
   - Include resistance training, such as weightlifting or bodyweight exercises, to promote muscle growth. Focus on compound movements that engage multiple muscle groups, and gradually increase resistance to stimulate muscle development.
5. **Balance Cardio and Strength Training:**
   - Find the right balance between cardiovascular exercise and strength training based on your goals. A combination of both contributes to overall fitness, weight management, and muscle development. Customize the ratio based on your preferences and objectives.
6. **Exercise Frequency and Duration:**
   - Tailor the frequency and duration of your workouts to align with your dietary goals. For weight loss, consider more frequent sessions with a mix of shorter and longer durations. For muscle gain, allow adequate recovery between strength training sessions.
7. **Pre- and Post-Workout Nutrition:**
   - Adjust your pre-and post-workout nutrition to support exercise performance and recovery. Consume a balanced meal or snack with carbohydrates and protein before workouts for energy, and refuel with a combination of protein and carbohydrates afterward to support muscle

repair.

8. **Nutrient Timing:**
   - Consider nutrient timing based on the timing of your workouts. For morning workouts, prioritize a balanced breakfast. If you exercise later in the day, plan meals and snacks to fuel and recover appropriately.
9. **Hydration:**
   - Adequate hydration is crucial for exercise performance and overall health. Tailor your fluid intake based on the intensity and duration of your workouts. Consider electrolyte-rich beverages for intense sessions or prolonged exercise.
10. **Listen to Your Body:**
    - Pay attention to how your body responds to different exercises and adjust your routine accordingly. If certain activities lead to discomfort or fatigue, modify your approach to prioritize sustainability and enjoyment.
11. **Progressive Overload:**
    - Implement the principle of progressive overload in your strength training routine. Gradually increase the intensity, volume, or resistance to continually challenge your muscles and support ongoing adaptation.
12. **Consult with Professionals:**
    - Seek guidance from fitness professionals, such as personal trainers or nutritionists, to tailor your exercise routine more effectively. They can provide personalized advice based on your specific goals, fitness level, and any underlying health considerations.

By customizing your exercise routine to complement your dietary goals, you create a harmonious approach that maximizes the benefits of both components. Consistency, adaptability, and a holistic mindset are key to achieving lasting success in your fitness and nutritional journey.

Chapter Seven

Superfoods for Super You: Nutrient-Packed Options

"Superfoods for Super You: Nutrient-Packed Options" unveils a vibrant palette of nutritionally dense foods that transcend ordinary sustenance, offering a powerhouse of essential nutrients to elevate your well-being. From the antioxidant-rich allure of blueberries to the omega-3 fatty acids in chia seeds and the vibrant kaleidoscope of vitamins found in dark leafy greens, these superfoods are not just ingredients; they are a symphony of health. Packed with vitamins, minerals, and antioxidants, these culinary wonders go beyond mere nourishment, aiming to optimize your health, boost immunity, and contribute to sustained vitality. This exploration into the realm of superfoods invites you to embrace a nutrient-packed journey that empowers you to become the best version of yourself, one vibrant and wholesome bite at a time.

Nutrient-rich Superfoods that Support Weight Loss

Nutrient-rich superfoods play a crucial role in supporting weight loss by providing essential vitamins, minerals, fiber, and other compounds that contribute to overall health and satiety. Here are some detailed examples of nutrient-rich superfoods that can support weight loss:

1. **Leafy Greens (e.g., Spinach, Kale, Swiss Chard):**
    - Leafy greens are low in calories and high in fiber, making them excellent for weight loss. They provide essential nutrients like vitamins A, C, and K, along with minerals like iron and calcium. The fiber content promotes satiety and aids in digestion, while the vitamins and minerals support overall health.
2. **Berries (e.g., Blueberries, Strawberries, Raspberries):**
    - Berries are rich in antioxidants, fiber, and vitamins. Their natural sweetness satisfies cravings for sweets

without the added calories. The fiber content helps control blood sugar levels and promotes a feeling of fullness, making them a valuable addition to a weight loss diet.

3. **Avocado:**
   - Avocado is a nutrient-dense superfood that provides healthy monounsaturated fats, which contribute to feelings of satiety. It also contains fiber, vitamins (such as B vitamins and vitamin K), and minerals (including potassium). Despite being calorie-dense, the nutritional richness and healthy fats in avocados make them a satisfying and nourishing choice.
4. **Quinoa:**
   - Quinoa is a whole grain that offers a complete protein source, making it an excellent option for plant-based diets. It is rich in fiber, providing sustained energy and promoting a feeling of fullness. Quinoa also contains essential amino acids, vitamins, and minerals, contributing to overall nutritional balance.
5. **Chia Seeds:**
   - Chia seeds are packed with fiber, omega-3 fatty acids, and protein. When mixed with liquid, they form a gel-like substance that expands in the stomach, promoting a feeling of fullness. The combination of nutrients in chia seeds supports energy levels and helps control cravings, making them a valuable ally in weight loss.
6. **Salmon:**
   - Salmon is fatty fish rich in omega-3 fatty acids, which have been linked to improved weight loss outcomes. The protein content helps maintain

muscle mass during weight loss, and the healthy fats contribute to a sense of satisfaction. Additionally, salmon provides essential vitamins and minerals.

7. **Greek Yogurt:**
    - Greek yogurt is a protein-packed dairy product that supports weight loss by promoting satiety and preserving lean muscle mass. It also contains probiotics, which contribute to gut health. Choose plain, unsweetened Greek yogurt to avoid added sugars.
8. **Broccoli:**
    - Broccoli is a nutrient powerhouse, rich in fiber, vitamins (such as C and K), and minerals (including potassium). Its low-calorie content and high fiber make it an excellent choice for weight loss. The fiber promotes digestive health and helps control appetite.
9. **Oats:**
    - Oats are whole grain that provides complex carbohydrates and soluble fiber. The fiber content contributes to a feeling of fullness and helps regulate blood sugar levels. Oats also offer vitamins and minerals, making them a nutritious and satisfying choice for weight loss.
10. **Lentils:**
    - Lentils are a plant-based source of protein, fiber, and various essential nutrients. The combination of protein and fiber promotes satiety, making lentils a valuable component of a weight-loss diet. They are also low in calories and versatile in various dishes.

Incorporating these nutrient-rich superfoods into a well-balanced and calorie-conscious diet can support weight loss efforts by providing essential nutrients, promoting satiety, and contributing to overall health. It's essential to focus on a diverse and colorful array of whole foods to ensure a comprehensive and sustainable approach to weight management.

Incorporating These Foods into Everyday Meals for Maximum Health Benefits

Incorporating nutrient-rich superfoods into your everyday meals can be both delicious and rewarding. Here's a guide on how to integrate the mentioned foods into your daily diet for maximum health benefits:

1. **Leafy Greens (Spinach, Kale, Swiss Chard):**
    - **Morning Smoothie:** Blend a handful of leafy greens with berries, Greek yogurt, and a splash of almond milk for a nutrient-packed breakfast.
    - **Salads:** Toss spinach, kale, or Swiss chard with colorful vegetables, avocado, and grilled chicken or salmon for a satisfying lunch or dinner.
2. **Berries (Blueberries, Strawberries, Raspberries):**
    - **Yogurt Parfait:** Layer Greek yogurt with mixed berries and a sprinkle of granola for a nutritious and delicious parfait.
    - **Oatmeal Topping:** Add a handful of berries to your morning oatmeal or cereal for a burst of antioxidants and natural sweetness.
3. **Avocado:**
    - **Toast Topper:** Spread mashed avocado on whole-grain toast and sprinkle with chili flakes or a dash of lemon juice for a quick and filling breakfast.
    - **Salad Enhancement:** Dice avocado and add it to salads, providing creaminess and healthy fats to enhance the overall flavor.

4. **Quinoa:**
    - **Quinoa Bowl:** Create a colorful bowl with quinoa, roasted vegetables, lean protein (chicken, tofu, or beans), and a drizzle of olive oil for a balanced and satisfying meal.
    - **Stuffed Peppers:** Use quinoa as a base for stuffed peppers with a mixture of vegetables, herbs, and lean ground turkey or beef.
5. **Chia Seeds:**
    - **Chia Pudding:** Mix chia seeds with almond milk and let it sit overnight for a nutritious and filling pudding. Top with berries for added flavor.
    - **Smoothie Booster:** Add a tablespoon of chia seeds to your smoothies for an extra boost of fiber, omega-3s, and a satisfying texture.
6. **Salmon:**
    - **Grilled Salmon Salad:** Top a bed of leafy greens with grilled salmon, avocado, cherry tomatoes, and a light vinaigrette for a nutrient-packed salad.
    - **Baked Salmon:** Season salmon fillets with herbs and bake them with a side of quinoa and roasted vegetables for a well-rounded meal.
7. **Greek Yogurt:**
    - **Fruit Parfait:** Layer Greek yogurt with fresh fruit, a drizzle of honey, and a sprinkle of nuts for a tasty and protein-rich dessert or snack.
    - **Smoothie Base:** Use Greek yogurt as the base for your smoothies to add creaminess and a protein boost.
8. **Broccoli:**

- **Stir-Fry:** Incorporate broccoli into a colorful vegetable stir-fry with tofu, chicken, or shrimp, and serve it over brown rice or quinoa.
- **Roasted Broccoli:** Toss broccoli florets with olive oil, garlic, and lemon zest before roasting for a flavorful and nutritious side dish.

9. **Oats:**
   - **Overnight Oats:** Mix oats with Greek yogurt, milk, and your favorite toppings (such as berries and nuts) for a convenient and nutritious breakfast.
   - **Homemade Granola:** Bake oats with honey, nuts, and dried fruits to create a wholesome and customizable granola.
10. **Lentils:**
    - **Lentil Soup:** Prepare a hearty lentil soup with vegetables, herbs, and broth for a satisfying and protein-rich meal.
    - **Lentil Salad:** Mix cooked lentils with diced vegetables, feta cheese, and a lemon vinaigrette for a refreshing and filling salad.

Incorporating these superfoods into your meals not only enhances the nutritional content but also adds variety and flavor to your daily menu. Experiment with different recipes and combinations to find what suits your taste preferences and makes healthy eating a delightful and sustainable lifestyle.

Incorporating These Foods into Everyday Meals for Maximum Health Benefits

Incorporating nutrient-rich superfoods into your everyday meals can be both delicious and rewarding. Here's a guide on how to integrate the mentioned foods into your daily diet for maximum health benefits:

1. Leafy Greens (Spinach, Kale, Swiss Chard):

• **Morning Smoothie:** Blend a handful of leafy greens with berries, Greek yogurt, and a splash of almond milk for a nutrient-packed breakfast.

• **Salads:** Toss spinach, kale, or Swiss chard with colorful vegetables, avocado, and grilled chicken or salmon for a satisfying lunch or dinner.

2. Berries (Blueberries, Strawberries, Raspberries):

• **Yogurt Parfait:** Layer Greek yogurt with mixed berries and a sprinkle of granola for a nutritious and delicious parfait.

• **Oatmeal Topping:** Add a handful of berries to your morning oatmeal or cereal for a burst of **antioxidants and natural sweetness.**

3. Avocado:

• **Toast Topper:** Spread mashed avocado on whole-grain toast and sprinkle with chili flakes or a dash of lemon juice for a quick and filling breakfast.

• **Salad Enhancement**: Dice avocado and add it to salads, providing creaminess and healthy fats to enhance the overall flavor.

4. Quinoa:

• Quinoa Bowl: Create a colorful bowl with quinoa, roasted vegetables, lean protein (chicken, tofu, or beans), and a drizzle of olive oil for a balanced and satisfying meal.

• **Stuffed Peppers:** Use quinoa as a base for stuffed peppers with a mixture of vegetables, herbs, and lean ground turkey or beef.

5. Chia Seeds:

• **Chia Pudding:** Mix chia seeds with almond milk and let it sit overnight for a nutritious and filling pudding. Top with berries for added flavor.

• **Smoothie Booster:** Add a tablespoon of chia seeds to your smoothies for an extra boost of fiber, omega-3s, and a satisfying texture.

6. Salmon:

• **Grilled Salmon Salad:** Top a bed of leafy greens with grilled salmon, avocado, cherry tomatoes, and a light vinaigrette for a nutrient-packed salad.

• **Baked Salmon:** Season salmon fillets with herbs and bake them with a side of quinoa and roasted vegetables for a well-rounded meal.

7. Greek Yogurt:

• **Fruit Parfait:** Layer Greek yogurt with fresh fruit, a drizzle of honey, and a sprinkle of nuts for a tasty and protein-rich dessert or snack.

• **Smoothie Base:** Use Greek yogurt as the base for your smoothies to add creaminess and a protein boost.

8. Broccoli:

• **Stir-Fry:** Incorporate broccoli into a colorful vegetable stir-fry with tofu, chicken, or shrimp, and serve it over brown rice or quinoa.

• **Roasted Broccoli**: Toss broccoli florets with olive oil, garlic, and lemon zest before roasting for a flavorful and nutritious side dish.

9. Oats:

• Overnight Oats: Mix oats with Greek yogurt, milk, and your favorite toppings (such as berries and nuts) for a convenient and nutritious breakfast.

• **Homemade Granola:** Bake oats with honey, nuts, and dried fruits to create a wholesome and customizable granola.

10. Lentils:

• **Lentil Soup:** Prepare a hearty lentil soup with vegetables, herbs, and broth for a satisfying and protein-rich meal.

• **Lentil Salad:** Mix cooked lentils with diced vegetables, feta cheese, and a lemon vinaigrette for a refreshing and filling salad.

Incorporating these superfoods into your meals not only enhances the nutritional content but also adds variety and flavor to your daily menu. Experiment with different recipes and combinations to find what suits your taste preferences and makes healthy eating a delightful and sustainable lifestyle.

Chapter Eight

Smart Snacking: Tasty Bites Without the Guilt

Smart snacking is a delectable journey that embraces the art of mindful indulgence, offering tasty bites without the burden of guilt. It's a conscious choice to nourish the body with snacks that not only satiate cravings but also contribute to overall well-being. From nutrient-packed almonds and vibrant, antioxidant-rich berries to the creamy delight of Greek yogurt with a drizzle of honey, smart snacking transcends mere convenience, becoming a flavorful exploration of wholesome choices. This approach encourages the inclusion of protein-rich options like hummus and crisp vegetables, creating a satisfying crunch that satisfies hunger without compromising health. With a focus on portion control and nutrient density, smart snacking transforms moments of munching into a guilt-free celebration of flavor, ensuring that every bite contributes to a balanced and energized lifestyle.

Snack Ideas that are Delicious and Contribute to Weight Loss Goals

1. **Greek Yogurt Parfait:**
   - Layer Greek yogurt with fresh berries, a sprinkle of chia seeds, and a drizzle of honey for a protein-packed and antioxidant-rich parfait.
2. **Vegetable Sticks with Hummus:**
   - Enjoy the crunch of colorful vegetable sticks (carrots, cucumber, bell peppers) paired with a portion-controlled serving of hummus for a satisfying and nutritious snack.
3. **Almonds and Dark Chocolate:**
   - Create a delightful mix of almonds and a small amount of dark chocolate for a satisfying

combination of healthy fats and antioxidants.

4. **Apple Slices with Nut Butter:**
    - Slice an apple and pair it with a tablespoon of almond or peanut butter for a tasty and fiber-rich snack that combines sweetness with protein.
5. **Hard-Boiled Eggs:**
    - Prepare a batch of hard-boiled eggs in advance for a convenient and protein-rich snack that helps keep you feeling full.
6. **Cottage Cheese with Pineapple:**
    - Combine low-fat cottage cheese with fresh pineapple chunks for a delicious blend of protein and sweetness.
7. **Whole Grain Crackers with Cheese:**
    - Choose whole grain crackers and pair them with a serving of your favorite cheese for a satisfying and balanced snack.
8. **Yogurt-Covered Berries:**
    - Dip fresh berries in Greek yogurt and freeze them for a refreshing and guilt-free treat that satisfies sweet cravings.
9. **Cherry Tomatoes with Mozzarella:**
    - Enjoy the classic combination of cherry tomatoes and fresh mozzarella for a flavorful and portion-controlled snack.
10. **Popcorn with Nutritional Yeast:**
    - Air-pop popcorn and sprinkle it with nutritional yeast for a savory and low-calorie snack that provides fiber.
11. **Edamame:**
    - Boil or steam edamame and sprinkle them with a pinch of sea salt for a protein-rich and satisfying

snack.

12. **Sliced Cucumber with Tuna:**
    - Top cucumber slices with a small amount of tuna salad for a crunchy and protein-packed snack that's also low in calories.
13. **Trail Mix with Nuts and Seeds:**
    - Create a customized trail mix with a mix of nuts, seeds, and a small number of dried fruits for a nutrient-dense and satisfying option.
14. **Avocado Toast on Whole Grain Bread:**
    - Mash avocado on whole grain toast and add a sprinkle of black pepper or red pepper flakes for a creamy and satisfying snack.
15. **Green Smoothie:**
    - Blend spinach, kale, banana, and almond milk for a nutrient-packed green smoothie that provides vitamins and minerals without excess calories.

Remember to practice portion control and be mindful of your overall calorie intake, even when choosing healthy snacks. These options offer a balance of nutrients to keep you energized and support your weight loss goals.

Strategies for Combating Cravings and Making Smart Snack Choices

Combatting cravings and making smart snack choices involves a combination of psychological strategies, nutritional knowledge, and planning. Here are some strategies to help you make healthier snack choices and manage cravings:

Psychological Strategies:

1. **Mindful Eating:**
    - Pay attention to the sensory aspects of eating, such as taste, texture, and smell.

- Eat slowly and savor each bite. This can help you feel more satisfied with smaller portions.

2. **Identify Triggers:**
    - Recognize situations or emotions that trigger cravings. Understanding the root cause can help you address the underlying issue.
3. **Distraction Techniques:**
    - Engage in activities that divert your attention away from cravings, such as going for a walk, reading a book, or doing a quick workout.
4. **Positive Affirmations:**
    - Remind yourself of your health and wellness goals. Positive self-talk can help you stay focused and motivated.

Nutritional Strategies:

1. **Balanced Snacks:**
    - Choose snacks that include a combination of protein, healthy fats, and fiber to help keep you satisfied for longer.
2. **Portion Control:**
    - Pre-portion your snacks to avoid overeating. Use small containers or snack-sized bags for easy control.
3. **Hydration:**
    - Drink water throughout the day. Sometimes, feelings of hunger are signs of dehydration.

Planning and Preparation:

1. **Healthy Alternatives:**
    - Identify healthier alternatives to your favorite snacks. For example, choose air-popped popcorn instead of chips or fresh fruit instead of candy.

2. **Meal Planning:**
   - Plan balanced meals to avoid extreme hunger, which can lead to unhealthy snacking. Include a mix of protein, vegetables, whole grains, and healthy fats.
3. **Smart Substitutions:**
   - Substitute healthier ingredients in your favorite recipes. For instance, use Greek yogurt instead of sour cream or whole grain crackers instead of regular ones.

Environment:

1. **Stock Healthy Options:**
   - Keep your home and workplace stocked with healthy snacks, making it easier to make nutritious choices when cravings strike.
2. **Remove Temptations:**
   - Limit the availability of unhealthy snacks in your environment. If they're not easily accessible, you're less likely to indulge.

Lifestyle:

1. **Adequate Sleep:**
   - Ensure you're getting enough sleep. Lack of sleep can affect hunger hormones and increase cravings for unhealthy foods.
2. **Regular Meals:**
   - Aim for regular, balanced meals to maintain stable blood sugar levels and reduce the likelihood of intense cravings.
3. **Seek Support:**
   - Share your goals with friends or family members who can provide support and encouragement.

Remember, making sustainable changes to your snacking habits is a gradual process. Experiment with different strategies to find what works best for you, and don't be too hard on yourself if you occasionally indulge—balance is key.

Chapter Nine

Recipes for Success: Delicious and Nutritious Meal Plans

Creating meal plans that balance science and flavor involves considering nutritional principles, portion control, and a variety of tastes and textures. Here's a sample day of meals that incorporate scientific nutritional principles while ensuring a delightful culinary experience:

(A) Nutrient Harmony Delight Plan

Breakfast: Protein-Packed Power Bowl

Ingredients:

- 1/2 cup rolled oats (complex carbohydrates)
- 1 cup almond milk (vitamin E, healthy fats)
- 1 tablespoon chia seeds (omega-3 fatty acids, fiber)
- 1/2 cup mixed berries (antioxidants)
- 1 tablespoon almond butter (protein, healthy fats)
- Optional: a sprinkle of cinnamon (metabolism regulation)

Preparation:

1. Combine rolled oats, almond milk, and chia seeds in a bowl. Let it sit in the fridge overnight for a convenient grab-and-go breakfast.
2. Top with mixed berries, a dollop of almond butter, and a sprinkle of cinnamon before serving.

Mid-Morning Snack: Greek Yogurt Parfait

Ingredients:

- 1 cup Greek yogurt (high protein)
- 1/2 cup granola (complex carbohydrates)

- 1/4 cup sliced almonds (healthy fats)
- 1/2 cup fresh mango cubes (vitamin C, natural sweetness)
- Drizzle of honey (antioxidant properties)

Preparation:

1. Layer Greek yogurt, granola, sliced almonds, and fresh mango cubes in a glass.
2. Drizzle with honey for added sweetness and antioxidant benefits.

Lunch: Grilled Chicken Salad
Ingredients:

- Grilled chicken breast (lean protein)
- Mixed greens (fiber, vitamins, minerals)
- Cherry tomatoes (lycopene)
- Cucumber slices (hydration)
- Quinoa (complete protein, fiber)
- Avocado slices (monounsaturated fats)
- Balsamic vinaigrette dressing (flavor without excessive calories)

Preparation:

1. Arrange mixed greens on a plate and top with grilled chicken, cherry tomatoes, cucumber slices, quinoa, and avocado.
2. Drizzle with balsamic vinaigrette dressing for a burst of flavor.

Afternoon Snack: Hummus and Vegetable Platter
Ingredients:

- Hummus (plant-based protein)
- Carrot and cucumber sticks (fiber, vitamins)
- Cherry tomatoes (lycopene)
- Whole-grain pita chips (complex carbohydrates)

Preparation:

1. Arrange hummus in a bowl and surround it with carrot and cucumber sticks, cherry tomatoes, and whole-grain pita chips for a satisfying and nutrient-rich snack.

Dinner: Baked Salmon with Quinoa and Roasted Vegetables

Ingredients:

- Baked salmon fillet (omega-3 fatty acids, protein)
- Quinoa (complete protein, fiber)
- Roasted sweet potatoes (vitamin A)
- Asparagus spears (fiber, vitamins)
- Lemon wedges (vitamin C)

Preparation:

1. Bake salmon with lemon wedges, and season with herbs and spices.
2. Serve over a bed of cooked quinoa, alongside roasted sweet potatoes and asparagus.

Dessert: Berry and Dark Chocolate Parfait

Ingredients:

- Mixed berries (antioxidants, vitamins)
- Dark chocolate shavings (antioxidants)
- Greek yogurt (optional, for creaminess)

Preparation:

1. Layer mixed berries with dark chocolate shavings in a glass.
2. Optionally, add a spoonful of Greek yogurt for creaminess.

This meal plan incorporates a variety of nutrient-dense foods, balances macronutrients, and incorporates a range of flavors for a satisfying culinary experience. Adjust portion sizes based on individual dietary needs and goals. Always consult with a healthcare professional or a registered dietitian before making significant changes to your diet.

(B) Vitality Boost Balanced Eating Plan

Breakfast: Avocado Toast with Poached Eggs

Ingredients:

- Whole-grain bread (complex carbohydrates, fiber)
- Avocado (healthy fats, vitamins)
- Poached eggs (protein)
- Cherry tomatoes (vitamin C)
- Sprinkle of black pepper (metabolism regulation)

Preparation:

1. Toast whole-grain bread and spread mashed avocado on top.
2. Place poached eggs on the avocado, garnish with cherry tomatoes, and sprinkle with black pepper.

Mid-Morning Snack: Berry and Almond Smoothie
Ingredients:

- Mixed berries (antioxidants, vitamins)
- Almond milk (vitamin E, healthy fats)
- Greek yogurt (protein)
- Handful of spinach (fiber, vitamins)
- Almond butter (healthy fats, protein)

Preparation:

1. Blend mixed berries, almond milk, Greek yogurt, spinach, and a tablespoon of almond butter until smooth.

Lunch: Quinoa and Black Bean Bowl
Ingredients:

- Cooked quinoa (complete protein, fiber)
- Black beans (plant-based protein, fiber)
- Sliced bell peppers (vitamin C)
- Avocado slices (healthy fats)
- Salsa (flavor without excess calories)

Preparation:

1. Mix cooked quinoa and black beans in a bowl.
2. Add sliced bell peppers, and avocado slices, and top with salsa for added flavor.

Afternoon Snack: Cottage Cheese and Pineapple
Ingredients:

- Cottage cheese (protein, calcium)
- Fresh pineapple chunks (vitamin C, natural sweetness)
- Sprinkle of chia seeds (omega-3 fatty acids, fiber)

Preparation:

1. Combine cottage cheese and fresh pineapple chunks in a bowl.
2. Sprinkle with chia seeds for added texture and nutritional benefits.

Dinner: Stir-fried tofu with Broccoli and Brown Rice
Ingredients:

- Firm tofu (plant-based protein)
- Broccoli florets (fiber, vitamins)
- Brown rice (complex carbohydrates, fiber)
- Soy sauce (low-sodium for flavor)
- Sesame oil (healthy fats)

Preparation:

1. Stir-fry tofu and broccoli in sesame oil.
2. Serve over cooked brown rice and drizzle with low-sodium soy sauce for flavor.

Dessert: Dark Chocolate and Mixed Nuts
Ingredients:

- Dark chocolate squares (antioxidants)
- Mixed nuts (healthy fats, protein)
- Fresh berries (optional)

Preparation:

1. Enjoy a few squares of dark chocolate with a handful of mixed nuts.
2. Add fresh berries for a burst of sweetness.

This meal plan emphasizes whole, nutrient-dense foods, provides a mix of macronutrients, and incorporates a variety of flavors.

(C) Energize & Thrive Balanced Meal Plan

Breakfast: Spinach and Feta Omelette with Whole-Grain Toast

Ingredients:

- Eggs (protein)
- Fresh spinach (fiber, vitamins)
- Feta cheese (calcium, protein)
- Whole-grain bread (complex carbohydrates, fiber)
- Cherry tomatoes (vitamin C)
- Fresh herbs (flavor without excessive calories)

Preparation:

1. Make an omelet with eggs, fresh spinach, and feta cheese.
2. Serve with whole-grain toast, and cherry tomatoes on the side, and garnish with fresh herbs.

Mid-Morning Snack: Apple Slices with Almond Butter

Ingredients:

- Apple slices (fiber, vitamins)
- Almond butter (healthy fats, protein)

Preparation:

1. Dip apple slices in almond butter for a satisfying and nutritious snack.

Lunch: Quinoa Salad with Chickpeas and Lemon-Tahini Dressing

Ingredients:

- Cooked quinoa (complete protein, fiber)
- Chickpeas (plant-based protein, fiber)
- Mixed greens (vitamins, minerals)
- Cucumber and red onion slices (hydration)

- Cherry tomatoes (lycopene)
- Lemon-tahini dressing (flavor, healthy fats)

Preparation:

1. Mix quinoa, chickpeas, mixed greens, cucumber, red onion, and cherry tomatoes in a bowl.
2. Drizzle with a lemon-tahini dressing for a burst of flavor.

Afternoon Snack: Greek Yogurt with Berries and Walnuts
Ingredients:

- Greek yogurt (protein)
- Mixed berries (antioxidants, vitamins)
- Walnuts (omega-3 fatty acids, protein)

Preparation:

1. Top Greek yogurt with mixed berries and crushed walnuts for a satisfying and nutritious snack.

Dinner: Baked Chicken Breast with Sweet Potato and Steamed Broccoli
Ingredients:

- Baked chicken breast (lean protein)
- Roasted sweet potato wedges (vitamin A)
- Steamed broccoli (fiber, vitamins)
- Olive oil and lemon zest (flavor, healthy fats)

Preparation:

1. Bake chicken breast with olive oil and lemon zest.
2. Serve with roasted sweet potato wedges and steamed broccoli.

Dessert: Mango and Coconut Chia Pudding
Ingredients:

- Chia seeds (omega-3 fatty acids, fiber)
- Almond milk (vitamin E, healthy fats)
- Fresh mango cubes (vitamin C)
- Shredded coconut (flavor, healthy fats)

Preparation:

1. Mix chia seeds with almond milk and let it sit until it thickens.
2. Layer with fresh mango cubes and top with shredded coconut for a delicious and nutritious dessert.

(D) Vibrant Wellness Balanced Meal Plan

Breakfast: Blueberry Almond Overnight Oats
Ingredients:

- Rolled oats (complex carbohydrates, fiber)
- Almond milk (vitamin E, healthy fats)
- Fresh blueberries (antioxidants)
- Almonds (healthy fats, protein)
- Greek yogurt (protein)

Preparation:

1. Mix rolled oats with almond milk and refrigerate overnight.
2. In the morning, top with fresh blueberries, sliced almonds, and a dollop of Greek yogurt.

Mid-Morning Snack: Banana and Peanut Butter Smoothie
Ingredients:

- Banana (potassium, vitamins)
- Peanut butter (healthy fats, protein)
- Low-fat milk or a dairy-free alternative (calcium)
- Ice cubes

Preparation:

1. Blend banana, peanut butter, and milk with ice cubes for a creamy and satisfying smoothie.

Lunch: Lentil and Vegetable Stew with Quinoa
Ingredients:

- Cooked lentils (plant-based protein, fiber)
- Mixed vegetables (vitamins, minerals)
- Quinoa (complete protein, fiber)
- Vegetable broth (flavor without excess calories)

- Fresh herbs (flavor, antioxidants)

Preparation:

1. Combine cooked lentils, mixed vegetables, and quinoa in a stew with vegetable broth.
2. Garnish with fresh herbs for added flavor.

Afternoon Snack: Celery Sticks with Hummus
Ingredients:

- Celery sticks (fiber)
- Hummus (plant-based protein, healthy fats)

Preparation:

1. Dip celery sticks in hummus for a crunchy and satisfying snack.

Dinner: Grilled Salmon with Roasted Brussels Sprouts and Quinoa
Ingredients:

- Grilled salmon fillet (omega-3 fatty acids, protein)
- Roasted Brussels sprouts (fiber, vitamins)
- Quinoa (complete protein, fiber)
- Lemon wedges (vitamin C)

Preparation:

1. Grill salmon with lemon wedges for flavor.
2. Serve with roasted Brussels sprouts and a side of quinoa.

Dessert: Yogurt Parfait with Mixed Berries and Granola
Ingredients:

- Greek yogurt (protein)

- Mixed berries (antioxidants, vitamins)
- Granola (complex carbohydrates, fiber)
- Drizzle of honey (natural sweetness)

Preparation:

1. Layer Greek yogurt with mixed berries and granola.
2. Drizzle with honey for a sweet and satisfying dessert.

(E) Nourish and Energize a Balanced Meal Plan

Breakfast: Sweet Potato and Black Bean Breakfast Bowl

Ingredients:

- Sweet potato (fiber, vitamins)
- Black beans (plant-based protein, fiber)
- Avocado slices (healthy fats)
- Poached egg (protein)
- Salsa (flavor without excessive calories)

Preparation:

1. Roast sweet potato cubes and mix with black beans.
2. Top with avocado slices, a poached egg, and a spoonful of salsa.

Mid-Morning Snack: Cottage Cheese and Pineapple Boat

Ingredients:

- Cottage cheese (protein, calcium)
- Fresh pineapple chunks (vitamin C)
- Chopped mint leaves (flavor)

Preparation:

1. Serve cottage cheese in a bowl or a halved pineapple, topped with fresh mint leaves.

Lunch: Turkey and Veggie Wrap

Ingredients:

- Whole-grain wrap (complex carbohydrates, fiber)
- Sliced turkey breast (lean protein)
- Hummus (plant-based protein, healthy fats)
- Mixed greens (fiber, vitamins)
- Sliced cucumber and bell peppers (hydration)
- Cherry tomatoes (lycopene)

Preparation:

1. Spread hummus on a whole-grain wrap.
2. Layer with sliced turkey, mixed greens, cucumber, bell peppers, and cherry tomatoes. Roll into a wrap.

Afternoon Snack: Kale Chips and Guacamole

Ingredients:

- Kale leaves (fiber, vitamins)
- Olive oil (healthy fats)
- Sea salt
- Guacamole (healthy fats)

Preparation:

1. Toss kale leaves with olive oil and sea salt, then bake until crispy.
2. Enjoy with a side of guacamole for dipping.

Dinner: Shrimp Stir-Fry with Brown Rice

Ingredients:

- Shrimp (lean protein)
- Mixed vegetables (fiber, vitamins)
- Brown rice (complex carbohydrates, fiber)
- Soy sauce (low-sodium for flavor)
- Sesame oil (healthy fats)
- Fresh ginger and garlic (flavor)

Preparation:

1. Stir-fry shrimp and mixed vegetables in sesame oil with fresh ginger and garlic.
2. Serve over cooked brown rice, drizzled with low-sodium soy sauce.

Dessert: Baked Apple with Cinnamon and Walnuts
Ingredients:

- Apple (fiber, vitamins)
- Cinnamon (metabolism regulation)
- Crushed walnuts (omega-3 fatty acids)

Preparation:

1. Core an apple and sprinkle with cinnamon.
2. Bake until tender and top with crushed walnuts.

(F) Revitalize and Savor a Balanced Meal Plan

Breakfast: Greek Yogurt Parfait with Berries and Almonds
Ingredients:

- Greek yogurt (protein)
- Mixed berries (antioxidants, vitamins)
- Almonds (healthy fats, protein)
- Honey (natural sweetness)

Preparation:

1. Layer Greek yogurt with mixed berries and almonds.
2. Drizzle with honey for sweetness.

Mid-Morning Snack: Whole Grain Crackers with Hummus
Ingredients:

- Whole grain crackers (complex carbohydrates, fiber)
- Hummus (plant-based protein, healthy fats)

Preparation:

1. Enjoy whole grain crackers with a side of hummus for a satisfying snack.

Lunch: Quinoa Salad with Chickpeas, Spinach, and Feta
Ingredients:

- Cooked quinoa (complete protein, fiber)
- Chickpeas (plant-based protein, fiber)
- Fresh spinach (fiber, vitamins)
- Feta cheese (calcium, protein)
- Cherry tomatoes (lycopene)
- Balsamic vinaigrette dressing (flavor without excessive calories)

Preparation:

1. Mix quinoa, chickpeas, fresh spinach, feta cheese, and cherry tomatoes in a bowl.
2. Drizzle with balsamic vinaigrette dressing for added flavor.

Afternoon Snack: Orange Slices with Dark Chocolate
Ingredients:

- Fresh orange slices (vitamin C)
- Dark chocolate squares (antioxidants)

Preparation:

1. Enjoy fresh orange slices with a couple of squares of dark chocolate for a delightful snack.

Dinner: Grilled Chicken Breast with Roasted Vegetables and Quinoa

Ingredients:

- Grilled chicken breast (lean protein)
- Mixed vegetables (fiber, vitamins)
- Quinoa (complete protein, fiber)
- Olive oil and herbs (flavor, healthy fats)
- Lemon wedges (vitamin C)

Preparation:

1. Grill chicken with olive oil, herbs, and lemon wedges.
2. Serve with roasted mixed vegetables and a side of cooked quinoa.

Dessert: Mango and Coconut Chia Seed Pudding

Ingredients:

- Chia seeds (omega-3 fatty acids, fiber)
- Coconut milk (healthy fats)
- Fresh mango cubes (vitamin C)
- Shredded coconut (flavor, healthy fats)

Preparation:

1. Mix chia seeds with coconut milk and let it sit until it thickens.
2. Layer with fresh mango cubes and top with shredded coconut.

(G) Balanced Blissful Bite Meal Plan
Breakfast: Spinach and Mushroom Egg Scramble
Ingredients:

- Eggs (protein)
- Fresh spinach (fiber, vitamins)
- Mushrooms (fiber, antioxidants)
- Feta cheese (calcium, protein)
- Whole-grain toast (complex carbohydrates, fiber)

Preparation:

1. Scramble eggs with fresh spinach, mushrooms, and feta cheese.
2. Serve with a side of whole-grain toast.

Mid-Morning Snack: Apple Slices with Peanut Butter
Ingredients:

- Apple slices (fiber, vitamins)
- Peanut butter (healthy fats, protein)

Preparation:

1. Dip apple slices in peanut butter for a satisfying and nutritious snack.

Lunch: Lentil and Vegetable Wrap
Ingredients:

- Whole-grain wrap (complex carbohydrates, fiber)
- Cooked lentils (plant-based protein, fiber)
- Mixed vegetables (vitamins, minerals)
- Hummus (plant-based protein, healthy fats)

- Fresh herbs (flavor)

Preparation:

1. Spread hummus on a whole-grain wrap.
2. Fill with cooked lentils, mixed vegetables, and fresh herbs. Roll into a wrap.

Afternoon Snack: Greek Yogurt with Berries and Granola
Ingredients:

- Greek yogurt (protein)
- Mixed berries (antioxidants, vitamins)
- Granola (complex carbohydrates, fiber)

Preparation:

1. Mix Greek yogurt with fresh berries and a sprinkle of granola.

Dinner: Baked Cod with Quinoa and Roasted Brussels Sprouts
Ingredients:

- Baked cod fillet (lean protein)
- Quinoa (complete protein, fiber)
- Roasted Brussels sprouts (fiber, vitamins)
- Olive oil and lemon juice (flavor, healthy fats)

Preparation:

1. Bake cod with a drizzle of olive oil and lemon juice.
2. Serve with cooked quinoa and roasted Brussels sprouts.

Dessert: Dark Chocolate and Berry Parfait
Ingredients:

- Dark chocolate squares (antioxidants)

- Mixed berries (antioxidants, vitamins)
- Greek yogurt (optional, for creaminess)

Preparation:

1. Layer dark chocolate squares with mixed berries.
2. Optionally, add a spoonful of Greek yogurt for creaminess.

(H) Vibrant Fuel Harmony Meal Plan
Breakfast: Berry and Spinach Smoothie Bowl
Ingredients:

- Mixed berries (antioxidants, vitamins)
- Fresh spinach (fiber, vitamins)
- Greek yogurt (protein)
- Chia seeds (omega-3 fatty acids, fiber)
- Granola (complex carbohydrates, fiber)

Preparation:

1. Blend mixed berries, fresh spinach, and Greek yogurt until smooth.
2. Pour into a bowl and top with chia seeds and granola.

Mid-Morning Snack: Rice Cake with Almond Butter and Banana Slices
Ingredients:

- Brown rice cake (complex carbohydrates, fiber)
- Almond butter (healthy fats, protein)
- Banana slices (potassium, vitamins)

Preparation:

1. Spread almond butter on a rice cake.
2. Top with banana slices for a satisfying and energy-boosting snack.

Lunch: Quinoa and Black Bean Stuffed Bell Peppers
Ingredients:

- Bell peppers (fiber, vitamins)
- Cooked quinoa (complete protein, fiber)
- Black beans (plant-based protein, fiber)
- Diced tomatoes and onions
- Mexican spices (cumin, chili powder)
- Avocado slices (healthy fats)

Preparation:

1. Mix cooked quinoa, black beans, diced tomatoes, onions, and spices.
2. Stuff bell peppers with the mixture and bake until tender. Serve with avocado slices on top.

Afternoon Snack: Carrot and Hummus
Ingredients:

- Carrot sticks (fiber, vitamins)
- Hummus (plant-based protein, healthy fats)

Preparation:

1. Dip carrot sticks in hummus for a crunchy and nutritious snack.

Dinner: Grilled Tofu stir-fried with Brown Rice
Ingredients:

- Firm tofu (plant-based protein)
- Mixed vegetables (fiber, vitamins)
- Brown rice (complex carbohydrates, fiber)
- Soy sauce (low-sodium for flavor)
- Sesame oil (healthy fats)

- Ginger and garlic (flavor)

Preparation:

1. Stir-fry tofu and mixed vegetables in sesame oil with ginger and garlic.
2. Serve over cooked brown rice, drizzled with low-sodium soy sauce.

Dessert: Mango Sorbet with Mint
Ingredients:

- Frozen mango chunks (vitamin C)
- Fresh mint leaves (flavor)

Preparation:

1. Blend frozen mango chunks until smooth to create a refreshing mango sorbet.
2. Garnish with fresh mint leaves for a burst of flavor.

(I) Harmony and Nourish Balanced Meal Plan

Breakfast: Avocado and Tomato Toast with Poached Egg
Ingredients:

- Whole-grain bread (complex carbohydrates, fiber)
- Avocado slices (healthy fats, vitamins)
- Sliced tomatoes (vitamin C, antioxidants)
- Poached egg (protein)
- Sprinkle of black pepper and sea salt

Preparation:

1. Toast whole-grain bread and top with avocado slices and tomato.
2. Place a poached egg on top and season with black pepper and

sea salt.

Mid-Morning Snack: Greek Yogurt with Pomegranate Seeds and Walnuts

Ingredients:

- Greek yogurt (protein)
- Pomegranate seeds (antioxidants, vitamins)
- Walnuts (omega-3 fatty acids, protein)

Preparation:

1. Mix Greek yogurt with pomegranate seeds and top with crushed walnuts.

Lunch: Chickpea and Spinach Salad with Lemon-Tahini Dressing

Ingredients:

- Chickpeas (plant-based protein, fiber)
- Fresh spinach (fiber, vitamins)
- Cherry tomatoes (lycopene)
- Cucumber slices (hydration)
- Red onion slices
- Quinoa (complete protein, fiber)
- Lemon-tahini dressing (flavor, healthy fats)

Preparation:

1. Combine chickpeas, fresh spinach, cherry tomatoes, cucumber, red onion, and quinoa in a bowl.
2. Drizzle with lemon-tahini dressing for a satisfying salad.

Afternoon Snack: Sliced Apple and Almond Butter

Ingredients:

- Apple slices (fiber, vitamins)
- Almond butter (healthy fats, protein)

Preparation:

1. Spread almond butter on apple slices for a delicious and energizing snack.

Dinner: Baked Chicken Thighs with Sweet Potato and Broccoli
Ingredients:

- Chicken thighs (protein)
- Sweet potato wedges (vitamin A, fiber)
- Broccoli florets (fiber, vitamins)
- Olive oil, garlic, and rosemary (flavor, healthy fats)

Preparation:

1. Bake chicken thighs with sweet potato wedges and broccoli.
2. Drizzle with olive oil, minced garlic, and rosemary for added flavor.

Dessert: Dark Chocolate and Raspberry Yogurt Parfait
Ingredients:

- Dark chocolate squares (antioxidants)
- Fresh raspberries (antioxidants, vitamins)
- Greek yogurt (protein)

Preparation:

1. Layer Greek yogurt with dark chocolate squares and fresh raspberries for a delightful dessert.

(J) Flavorful Vitality Balanced Meal Plan

Breakfast: Spinach and Feta Breakfast Wrap

Ingredients:

- Whole-grain wrap (complex carbohydrates, fiber)
- Eggs (protein)
- Fresh spinach (fiber, vitamins)
- Feta cheese (calcium, protein)
- Salsa (flavor without excessive calories)
- Avocado slices (healthy fats)

Preparation:

1. Scramble eggs with fresh spinach and feta cheese.
2. Fill a whole-grain wrap with the egg mixture, top with salsa, and add avocado slices.

Mid-Morning Snack: Mixed Nuts and Dried Fruits
Ingredients:

- Mixed nuts (healthy fats, protein)
- Dried fruits (natural sweetness, vitamins)

Preparation:

1. Combine a variety of mixed nuts with dried fruits for a satisfying and nutritious snack.

Lunch: Turkey and Quinoa Stuffed Bell Peppers
Ingredients:

- Bell peppers (fiber, vitamins)
- Lean ground turkey (protein)
- Quinoa (complete protein, fiber)
- Black beans (plant-based protein, fiber)
- Diced tomatoes and onions

- Mexican spices (cumin, chili powder)
- Shredded cheddar cheese (calcium, protein)

Preparation:

1. Cook ground turkey with quinoa, black beans, diced tomatoes, onions, and spices.
2. Stuff bell peppers with the mixture, top with shredded cheddar cheese, and bake until the peppers are tender.

Afternoon Snack: Greek Yogurt with Sliced Strawberries and Honey

Ingredients:

- Greek yogurt (protein)
- Sliced strawberries (antioxidants, vitamins)
- Honey (natural sweetness)

Preparation:

1. Mix Greek yogurt with sliced strawberries and drizzle with honey.

Dinner: Salmon and Quinoa Salad with Lemon-Dill Dressing

Ingredients:

- Grilled salmon fillet (omega-3 fatty acids, protein)
- Cooked quinoa (complete protein, fiber)
- Mixed greens (fiber, vitamins)
- Cherry tomatoes (lycopene)
- Cucumber slices (hydration)
- Lemon-dill dressing (flavor, healthy fats)

Preparation:

1. Grill salmon with lemon and dill.

2. Combine cooked quinoa, mixed greens, cherry tomatoes, and cucumber. Top with the grilled salmon and drizzle with lemon-dill dressing.

Dessert: Mango and Coconut Smoothie
Ingredients:

- Fresh mango chunks (vitamin C)
- Coconut milk (healthy fats)
- Ice cubes

Preparation:

1. Blend fresh mango chunks with coconut milk and ice cubes for a refreshing and tropical smoothie.

Chapter Ten

Overcoming Challenges: Troubleshooting Your Weight Loss Journey

Embarking on a weight loss journey is undoubtedly challenging, but overcoming obstacles along the way is an integral part of the process. Recognizing that setbacks are natural and inevitable, you can proactively troubleshoot your weight loss journey by adopting a mindset of resilience and adaptability. Common challenges, such as plateaus or emotional eating, can be addressed through a multifaceted approach involving adjustments to diet, exercise routines, and mindfulness practices. Staying focused on realistic and sustainable goals, seeking support from a healthcare professional or a registered dietitian, and consistently reassessing and refining strategies are key components in navigating hurdles. By viewing challenges as opportunities for growth, you will not only overcome obstacles in your weight loss journey but also develop the skills and resilience needed for long-term success and a healthier lifestyle.

Addressing Common Obstacles and Setbacks in the Journey to a Healthier Weight

1. **Weight Loss Plateaus:**
    - **Challenge: After initial progress, weight loss may plateau, and individuals find it challenging to shed additional pounds.**
    - **Explanation: The body may adapt to changes in diet and exercise, slowing down the metabolism or retaining water. As a result, the scale may not reflect immediate progress despite sustained efforts.**
2. **Emotional Eating:**

- Challenge: Emotional stress, boredom, or other feelings may lead to overeating or choosing unhealthy comfort foods, hindering weight loss goals.
- Explanation: Emotional eating is often a coping mechanism, and it can be triggered by stress, anxiety, or even positive emotions. Recognizing these triggers and finding alternative ways to cope is essential.

3. Unrealistic Expectations:
   - Challenge: Setting overly ambitious weight loss goals or expecting rapid results can lead to frustration and a sense of failure.
   - Explanation: Healthy, sustainable weight loss is a gradual process. Unrealistic expectations can result in unsustainable practices, disappointment, and a higher likelihood of abandoning long-term healthy habits.
4. Social and Environmental Influences:
   - Challenge: Social events, peer pressure, and an obesogenic environment may contribute to unhealthy eating habits and hinder progress.
   - Explanation: Social situations often involve tempting, calorie-dense foods. Peer pressure or the availability of unhealthy food options can make it challenging to adhere to a healthy eating plan.
5. Lack of Consistent Support:
   - Challenge: Limited support from family, friends, or the community can impact motivation and

hinder progress.
    - Explanation: Having a supportive network is crucial for maintaining motivation. Lack of encouragement or understanding can make it more difficult to stay on track with healthy lifestyle changes.
6. Busy Lifestyle:
    - Challenge: Demanding work schedules, family responsibilities, and other time constraints can make it challenging to prioritize healthy eating and regular exercise.
    - Explanation: Finding time for meal preparation and physical activity can be difficult when faced with busy schedules. Prioritizing and planning are essential to overcome this obstacle.
7. Lack of Consistency:
    - Challenge: Inconsistent adherence to healthy habits, such as irregular exercise routines or frequent deviations from a balanced diet, can impede progress.
    - Explanation: Achieving and maintaining a healthy weight requires consistent effort. Inconsistency in diet and exercise can undermine the positive changes initiated.
8. Medical Factors:
    - Challenge: Certain medical conditions or medications may impact weight loss efforts.
    - Explanation: Conditions such as hypothyroidism or medications with weight-related side effects can make weight loss more challenging.

Consulting with healthcare professionals can help address these specific challenges.

1. **Inadequate Sleep:**
    - **Challenge: Poor sleep patterns or insufficient sleep can hinder weight loss efforts.**
    - **Explanation: Lack of sleep affects hormones that regulate hunger and satiety, leading to increased cravings for high-calorie foods. Additionally, fatigue may reduce the motivation to engage in physical activity, impacting overall energy expenditure.**
2. **Overreliance on Fad Diets:**
    - **Challenge: Adopting restrictive or unsustainable fad diets can lead to short-term weight loss but often result in long-term setbacks.**
    - **Explanation: Fad diets that drastically limit certain food groups or rely on extreme calorie deficits may lead to nutrient deficiencies, muscle loss, and a slowed metabolism. Once the diet is discontinued, individuals may regain the lost weight and face challenges in establishing healthy, balanced eating habits. Sustainable, well-rounded nutrition is key to long-term success.**

Understanding these obstacles and setbacks is crucial for developing strategies to overcome them. Tailoring approaches to individual circumstances, seeking support, and making sustainable lifestyle changes are key components of successfully navigating the journey to a healthier weight.

Strategies for Staying Motivated and Committed to Long-term Success

Staying motivated and committed to long-term weight loss success requires a combination of strategies that address physical, emotional, and behavioral aspects. Here are some effective strategies:

1. **Set Realistic Goals:**
    - Establish achievable, specific, and realistic goals. Break them into smaller milestones, making the overall journey more manageable and providing a sense of accomplishment along the way.
2. **Create a Support System:**
    - Surround yourself with a supportive network, whether it's friends, family, or a weight loss group. Having encouragement and understanding from others can significantly boost motivation.
3. **Celebrate Achievements:**
    - Acknowledge and celebrate your successes, regardless of their size. Recognizing and rewarding progress reinforces positive behaviors and helps maintain motivation.
4. **Focus on Non-Scale Victories:**
    - Shift the focus beyond the scale. Celebrate improvements in energy levels, better sleep, increased endurance, or changes in clothing fit. Non-scale victories motivate just the number on the scale.
5. **Incorporate Enjoyable Physical Activities:**
    - Choose exercises that you genuinely enjoy to make physical activity a sustainable part of your routine. Whether it's dancing, hiking, or playing a sport,

finding joy in movement makes it more likely to be maintained.

6. **Practice Mindful Eating:**
   - Develop mindful eating habits by paying attention to hunger and fullness cues. Savoring each bite and being present during meals can lead to a healthier relationship with food.
7. **Keep a Food and Exercise Journal:**
   - Track your daily food intake and exercise. This provides awareness, helps identify patterns, and can be a valuable tool for making informed choices and adjustments.
8. **Diversify Your Meals:**
   - Experiment with new recipes and foods to keep your meals interesting and flavorful. A varied and tasty diet is more likely to be sustainable in the long run.
9. **Prioritize Sleep:**
   - Ensure you get an adequate amount of quality sleep. Lack of sleep can negatively impact hormones related to hunger and stress, affecting your ability to make healthy choices.
10. **Manage Stress:**
    - Incorporate stress-reducing activities into your routine, such as meditation, yoga, or deep breathing exercises. Stress management is essential for preventing emotional eating and maintaining overall well-being.
11. **Plan:**
    - Plan meals and snacks to avoid impulsive, unhealthy choices. Having a structured meal plan makes it easier to stick to a balanced diet.
12. **Reassess and Adjust:**

- Regularly reassess your goals and strategies. If something isn't working, be open to adjusting your approach. Flexibility and adaptability are crucial for long-term success.

13. **Educate Yourself:**
    - Learn about nutrition, exercise, and healthy lifestyle habits. Understanding the benefits of your choices can reinforce your commitment to long-term well-being.
14. **Seek Professional Guidance:**
    - Consult with healthcare professionals, such as a registered dietitian or a fitness trainer, for personalized advice. Their expertise can provide tailored strategies for your unique circumstances.
15. **Visualize Your Success:**
    - Create a mental image of your long-term success. Visualization can enhance motivation and serve as a powerful reminder of the positive outcomes you're working towards.

Remember that long-term weight loss success is a journey that involves continuous effort, adaptation, and self-compassion. Integrating these strategies into your routine can contribute to sustainable progress and overall well-being.

Milton Keynes UK
Ingram Content Group UK Ltd.
UKHW022032301123
433552UK00015B/592

CW00642356

Workers at the Allen-Brown Violet Nursery at Henfield in 1912, with Decima Allen standing in the background. Courtesy of the Henfield Museum.

Published by Little Toller Books in 2023

Typeset in Garamond by Little Toller Books

Printed in Cornwall, UK by TJ Books Limited

All papers used by Little Toller Books are natural, recyclable products made from wood grown in sustainable, well-managed forests

A catalogue record for this book is available from the British Library

ISBN 978-1-915068-21-7

AN ALMOST IMPOSSIBLE THING

The Radical Lives of Britain's Pioneering Women Gardeners

FIONA DAVISON

LITTLE TOLLER

For the lady gardeners –
my mother Ann, Ange and Jo

CONTENTS

INTRODUCTION

> How can you be content to be in the World like Tulips in a Garden, to make a fine show and be good for nothing?
>
> Mary Astell, *A Serious Proposal to the Ladies*, 1694

In March 1906 Sir Joseph Dalton Hooker, retired Director of the Royal Botanic Gardens at Kew, and one of the greatest figures in British botany, received a letter from a Miss Symonds enquiring about the prospects for women in professional horticulture. His reply could not have been clearer: 'Gardening taken up as a hobby when all the laborious work can be done by a man is delightful, but as a life's work [for a woman] it is almost an impossible thing.'[1]

Joseph Dalton Hooker's response certainly chimes with the image we have today of Edwardian women and gardening. Period dramas have made it easy to conjure up an image of a woman wearing an elegant dress and large hat, languidly dead-heading old English roses. The real female gardeners we know best from this period are amateur or semi-amateur and decidedly not 'hands-on'. The wealthy heiress and gardener Ellen Willmott spent enormous sums and employed huge teams of skilled male gardeners to create her impressive gardens in England, France and Italy. Gertrude Jekyll was, and is, hugely influential as a writer and designer, but her commercial activity was deliberately low-key. She described herself as a 'working amateur' and did not charge for her designs, but instead sold her clients plants which were raised by her gardeners. Both women were independently well off (indeed in Willmott's case, until she spent all her inheritance, positively wealthy). Neither needed to work to earn a living. In both cases, whilst they were committed, creative and knowledgeable horticulturists, the laborious work of garden-making and maintenance was done for them by professional male gardeners.

The Edwardian Arts and Crafts-inspired gardens associated with Gertrude Jekyll in particular continue to entrance us. The fact that these beautiful gardens immediately pre-date the horrors of the First World War tinges them with melancholy but also somehow burnishes them, so that they glow with a golden perfection. The carefully crafted stone paths, wooden pergolas and overflowing herbaceous borders seem like a private oasis and a world away from conflict. But for many women of the era, gardening was much more than a delightful pastime and the idealised Edwardian garden, far from being a refuge from the world, was an arena where some of the most contentious issues of the day played out, a setting for symbolic and sometimes even destructive acts of protest. Not least of those issues was the question of whether women could lead independent lives, have access to the vote and make a meaningful difference to the world. Our image of feminist campaigners of this era, whether suffragettes, suffragists or social reformers, is firmly urban, but the surprising truth is that many saw horticulture as the key to a better life for themselves and a better world for all. These women experimented with new ways of living in the green settings of new garden suburbs and the countryside. Some aimed to use gardening to tackle problems of gender inequality, poverty, health, rural decline and environmental degradation. Others believed women horticulturists could play a key role in the future strength of the British Empire.

This book will follow the lives of six women, each from very different backgrounds, and with very different outlooks and values, who used their ability to nurture and grow plants to free themselves from the confined lives that conventional society had prescribed for them. In doing so, they had to battle derision, prejudice and hostility. Sir Joseph Hooker was right, making a life in gardening was almost an impossible thing, but that 'almost' left enough of a gap for some determined women to scramble through.

Women workers at the Royal Botanic Gardens, Kew, in November 1916.
Courtesy of the Royal Botanic Gardens, Kew.

1
NEW WOMEN

> There is an enormous and increasing number of single women in the nation, a number quite disproportionate and quite abnormal.
>
> W. R. Greg, *Why are Women Redundant?*, 1869

In March 1910 readers of *The Daily Mail* were confronted with an advertisement which read, 'Ten Thousand Englishwomen could be ranged in a line and shot. No one would be sorry. Everyone would be glad. There isn't any place for them.'[2] This was pretty strong stuff, but it was just an extreme example of a widely held belief: that the country was burdened with 'surplus women'. In 1854 author and social campaigner Harriet Martineau estimated that there were over 500,00 more women than men in Great Britain; by 1891, the number had risen to over 900,000. The chief reason given at the time was the high level of emigration amongst young men seeking opportunities across the British Empire. Every young man signing up to be a colonist, a member of the armed forces, a civil servant or a trader in the British colonies was one less for the women left at home to woo and catch. There was real anxiety that as a result there were 'surplus women' who would not find a husband to take care of them after their fathers died. The 'surplus' or 'redundant' women that bothered commentators most were middle- and upper-class women. Single working-class women were not viewed as surplus; they could go into paid occupations deemed suitable to their station, such as domestic service or in factories. For 'respectable' women higher up the social scale, however, conventional society offered very few options.

For many commentators, the solution to the excess supply of unsupported spinsters was obvious: the wholesale shipment of single women to the colonies where the marriageable men were. *The Daily Mail* advertisement quoted earlier was actually placed by the Canadian Pacific Railway as part of a campaign to encourage female emigration to Canada. However, many women were not content to admit that marriage and motherhood were the only viable and valuable roles they could play in society. Nowadays we rightly remember and celebrate the pioneers who broke through into male professions and public life and politics. But the role that gardening and horticulture played in facilitating female emancipation and self-expression has been relatively overlooked. Yet there was a time when many single women, who felt that society had no role or place for them, made a place of their own in the garden. In a relatively short period of twenty-one years, between 1893 and 1914, and starting from a point where the gardening profession was almost exclusively male, more than 630 women sat the RHS National Examination in Horticulture, making up around 15 per cent of the total number of entrants in that period. This is probably an underestimate, as it is based only on the entrants that I could categorically prove were female (a task made harder when from 1903 onwards the RHS stopped publishing first names of candidates). Many more women never took examinations, but still made a serious effort to build a career in gardening. This book will focus on six of them, with the hope that their experiences will illuminate a wider story that has been largely ignored or forgotten. None of the six we will follow enjoyed the distinction of being the very first woman to achieve what they did. The exceptional women who blazed a trail are exactly that: exceptional. I am more interested in the more ordinary people who follow immediately behind, the ones equipped with a more relatable set of talents, circumstances and ambitions. Their achievements may not have won them prizes in posterity – no blue plaques or statues for them – but by normalising new ways of living, they were every bit as influential in creating social change. The six women I have chosen ranged in age, education, political outlook and, to a degree, social class; but they all managed to make a living through horticulture. These particular women are also interesting because their choice of gardening as a career was not just a way to earn a living for themselves (itself a relatively radical act); horticulture offered them the opportunity to live a lifestyle that chimed with their beliefs and make a real contribution to improving the world around them. In their different ways, the women in this book had strong ideals, and training as gardeners gave them a set of skills that empowered them to make a difference.

We start our story in 1891, just before serious horticultural training for women became a realistic possibility. It is also a convenient date to begin our story because 1891 was a census year, so we can gain an accurate picture of what the six women, who ranged in age from 15 to 35, were up to before they entered the gardening profession. At this point Ada Brown, Isobel Turner, Edith Bradley, Olive Cockerell, Madeline Agar and Gertrude Cope had little idea that their future lives would be dedicated to a career in horticulture. Even just nine years shy of the twentieth century, a career in gardening was still an unlikely prospect for a woman. Progression as a professional gardener generally depended on serving a long apprenticeship whilst living in an all-male barracks known as a 'bothy', effectively making gardening as a serious career inaccessible to women. While working-class women had been doing paid work in gardens for centuries, they were restricted to the very simplest tasks, requiring no horticultural education or training and worked for a low day rate, often on a casual or seasonal basis. The six women we shall follow all came from middle- or lower-middle-class backgrounds and this type of menial, physical labour was simply out of the question for them. They were raised in a world that had very narrow and rigid definitions of respectability for women of their social class. The conventional genteel lady was destined by God and nature to be man's helpmate, nurture his children and protect the sanctity of his home. Indeed, many people argued that women's largely ornamental role, freed from the need to work for subsistence, was a sign of a 'higher civilisation'. Over the course of the nineteenth century, the increasing wealth of the middle classes had enabled them to hand over domestic chores to servants and the care of children to governesses and nurses. Thus the homely eighteenth-century housewife had turned into a lady of leisure and the idea had gained currency that paid work for women was demeaning. Passive and delicate, such a woman had supposedly neither the strength nor inclination to undertake strenuous physical activity. In 1864 the influential writer and art critic John Ruskin gave his famous lecture 'Of Queens' Gardens' in which he declared, 'The man, in his rough open world, must encounter all peril and trial ... But he guards the woman from this; within his house, as ruled by her, unless she herself has sought it, need enter no danger ... This is the true nature of the home – it is the place of peace.'[3] In truth the idea of 'separate spheres', with women at home and men monopolising the world of work, was never universally applied – there were always exceptional women who broke through – yet it was nonetheless a powerful social norm that shaped the world in which our six women grew up.

All this does not mean that middle- and upper-class women could not do any gardening at all, far from it. Gardens were seen as part of the private, domestic sphere that was a woman's natural place. By the early 1890s, gardening had become firmly established as a respectable pastime for women, but only so long as they did not get their hands too dirty or exert too much physical effort. In the early days of Queen Victoria's reign, Louisa Johnson wrote in her book, *Every Lady Her Own Flower Gardener*, that 'Flower gardening has progressed rapidly, and the amusement of floriculture has become the dominant passion of the ladies of Great Britain. It is a passion most blessed in its effects, considered as an amusement or benefit. Nothing humanises and adorns the female mind more surely than a taste for ornamental gardening.'[4] This 'dominant passion' can be traced back to the eighteenth century, when it became fashionable for educated aristocratic women to study botany and collect exotic plants. As the prosperous middle class expanded, this fashion was eagerly adopted further down the social scale, and the garden became

Advert for Dr Tibbles Vi-Cocoa from *The Gardening World*, 1904. This advert shows the kind of unskilled, menial horticultural work available for working-class women. Courtesy of the RHS Lindley Collections.

a place where socially aspirational women could demonstrate their taste and education. Unlike frivolous pastimes such as novel-reading or playing cards, gardening – beautifying and improving the home and its surroundings – also had the benefit of being seen as a morally upright activity. In 1858 Ann Judith Perry, the married author of the evocatively titled *The Afternoon of Unmarried Life*, advised that it was a suitable hobby for single women: 'On the ground of self-preservation, it behoves every unmarried woman to find some harmless mode of doing active service ... especially if she is exposed to the pernicious influence of a very secluded life [which is] as certainly dangerous to spiritual health as the miasma of standing water [is] to health of the body.' Gardening, she argued, kept a single woman busy and was an innocuous antidote to 'that state of unbalanced religious excitement to which some spinsters were prone.'[5]

For women wealthy enough to own a large garden and employ staff, the garden could be a place where they could exert some control. As early as 1751, Catherine Talbot (1721–70), a 'Bluestocking', declared in a letter to a close friend, 'I have but three creatures in the world over whom I have a right to exercise any government, a foolish dog, a restive horse and a perverse gardener.'[6] Of course, there was no guarantee that the gardener would listen to a woman, any more than the restive horse or foolish dog. Nevertheless, wealthy women with access to large gardens and the resources to develop them could earn respect and a place as an amateur gardener in the horticultural elite, even becoming Fellows of the Royal Horticultural Society and winning horticultural prizes.

All of our six women grew up with at least some access to private gardens and the opportunity to garden as a pleasurable pastime. Ada Brown's family lived in Hartfield House, an Italianate mansion house set in substantial grounds just outside Liverpool. Isobel Sybil Turner was brought up in a large eighteenth-century farmhouse near Ulceby in Lincolnshire, where her father farmed an estate of over 1,500 acres. Her home, Ulceby Grange, had a large garden, a conservatory and glasshouses. It is likely, given the size of the properties that Ada and Isobel both lived in, that their families employed gardeners, and this may have given them some experience of supervising, or watching their parents supervise, a head gardener.

In contrast, Edith, Madeline, Gertrude and Olive all grew up in the suburbs of London, where space was much more compressed, and if any gardener were employed at all, it would have been of the visiting or 'jobbing' kind. Edith Bradley lived in a substantial Victorian villa in Beckenham, which, although well connected to London, still had a quiet, rural feel to it. Madeline Agar's family home was also a handsome house in leafy Wimbledon, with what today would be considered a large garden. Olive Cockerell spent her early childhood in a slightly more modest house on Sydenham Hill, which does not appear to have had much outdoor space. Gertrude Cope lived only around three miles away from Olive at 13 Pepys Road in Peckham. By this time, Peckham had already lost its status as a suburb and was becoming more firmly urban and heavily built up, as artisans and clerical staff working in the city moved in, attracted by the railways and horse-drawn trams. Garden writers bemoaned the impact London smog could have on precious garden plants, yet urban and suburban middle-class women were some of the keenest gardeners in the land.

Before they had access to formal horticultural instruction, women gardeners were reliant on books and magazines to provide the information they needed. By the 1890s, female amateur gardeners represented an important market and a publishing boom was in full swing. Beautifully bound and illustrated gardening books, written by women for women, came onto the market to satisfy the need for accessible horticultural advice. Garden literature aimed at women repeatedly extolled the benefit of having one's own garden and being actively involved in its design and management. Many of the titles have a strongly possessive element – Louisa Johnson followed up her *Every Lady Her Own Flower Gardener* with *Every Lady's Guide to Her Own Greenhouse and Conservatory*. At a time when women enjoyed very restricted property rights and very little autonomy, an opportunity to possess, control and shape a physical space was precious. Within strict boundaries, some light physical activity in the garden was seen as socially acceptable. Jane Loudon, the pioneer female gardening author, felt that 'A lady, with a light spade may, by repeatedly digging over the same line, and taking out only a little earth at a time, succeed in doing all the digging that can be required in a small garden.'[7] Although this was still light, ladylike and definitely amateur gardening, instructive books did build a sense of community and raise ambitions about what could be achieved. The writers shared their experiences of success and failure and reassured women readers that they, too, could make the journey from ignorant beginner to confident gardener.

However, this leisurely life of gardening for pleasure relied on having an income to support it, which for most middle-class women meant either inheriting or marrying money. The three older women in our group of six, Ada Brown, Isobel Turner and Edith

Bradley, were all mature single women in their thirties by 1891 – past the conventional marrying age and liable to be labelled with the dreaded name 'spinster' or 'old maid'. Then there was the question of financial security; young women and their families often assumed that they would marry right up until it was too late to seek skilled training that might equip them to do anything else. Developing the capacity to live an independent life was considered an unnecessary measure for young ladies because their single state was intended to be temporary – they would soon be married – and to admit otherwise was to admit failure in the marriage market for themselves and their family. Jane Austen articulated this attitude very effectively in *Pride and Prejudice* when she wrote of her character Charlotte Lucas opting to marry the irritating Mr Collins: 'Without thinking highly either of men or of matrimony, marriage had always been her object; it was the only honourable provision for well-educated young women of small fortune, and however uncertain of giving happiness, must be their pleasantest preservative from want.'[8] It was widely believed that almost any marriage was better than life as an old maid. The respectable unmarried lady, educated for an elusive marriage but forced by her father's death or ruin to fend for herself, became an object of morbid curiosity and a mainstay in Victorian fiction.

Faced with the need to earn a living, a genteel but impoverished woman generally had a choice of three underpaid and overcrowded occupations – governess, ladies' companion or seamstress. The first two involved a socially awkward and constrained position as a live-in employee in a household, carefully holding oneself apart from the servants, but never on equal footing with the family. Seamstresses worked long hours for very little money indeed, with no prospect of saving for the day when eyesight and health failed and work became impossible. We do not know whether Ada's, Isobel's and Edith's single status was voluntary or not; whether there were no suitors or a long line of rejected Mr Collinses. Either way, although their situations were not quite as dire as the spinsters of Victorian fiction, crafting a life as a single woman was not without its challenges. Whilst their fathers' salaries and profits made for a comfortable upbringing, their long-term security was not guaranteed. Professional men like their fathers frequently did not make adequate provision for their death, disability or business failure. Without land or going concerns to inherit, single middle-class women could see a sharp drop in living standards when their fathers hit hard times or died. Living on the interest from a fixed capital sum or dividend from stock could involve a lifetime of careful economising.

Ada Eugenie Brown, the oldest woman of our group of six, was born in 1856 in Liverpool, one of the six children of Aaron and Lydia Brown. Aaron Brown was a 'provision merchant' – selling food and equipment to ships sailing out of Liverpool, with business premises in Chapel Street. Their large mansion in the affluent suburb of Allerton boasted a tower which gave good views of the ships coming into dock on the Mersey. The family employed five live-in servants, including a butler and a footman. Ada received a genteel education in London at the Champion Hill Ladies School in Dulwich. When Aaron Brown died in 1883, when Ada was 27, he left a substantial fortune of over £22,000 (which can be calculated as roughly the equivalent of £2.2m today). I have not been able to track down Aaron Brown's will, but it is likely that once this sum was shared with his widow and five other children, Ada would have been left with a comfortable amount of capital to live off, but not an enormous inheritance to last the rest of her life. By 1891 Ada Brown owned a house on Legh Road in the village of Knutsford Superior, employing just a single housekeeper. Whilst the days of butlers and footmen were over, Legh Road was a tree-lined road developed with large villas designed for wealthy Manchester industrialists and still a very desirable area to live. Ada was not the only unmarried daughter in the family, so, unlike many single women, she did not have to stay and care for her elderly mother, that job being undertaken by her sister Emma. Ada could probably have lived out her days in comfort, tending her own garden and, if the inclination took her, perhaps getting involved in charitable work of some description. With enough money, a 'respectable' single life was possible, if not necessarily an exciting or stimulating one.

Unlike Ada Brown, Isobel Turner's father was still alive in 1891. John S. Turner was a famous sheep and cattle breeder whose breeding stock was exported across the globe. At its peak, her father's Ulceby Grange farm in Lincolnshire employed thirty-seven men and eight boys. As the daughters of a large landowner, Isobel and her two younger sisters might have expected a financially secure future. However, by 1891 John Turner's business had been in decline for some time. In 1884 he had sold his herd of pure-bred shorthorn cattle that he had spent fourteen years building up and in 1886 he sold his flock of Ulceby Grange Rams in a sale that attracted a crowd of over two hundred people.[9] Since the 1870s, the combination of a string of poor summers and competition from cheap food imports had led to a nationwide agricultural depression, exacerbated in Lincolnshire by a severe outbreak of foot and mouth disease in 1883. With no son to inherit the farm, John Turner was winding down his stock-breeding business. This must have been a sad and worrying time for Isobel Turner. By 1891 her sisters had married, but 32-year-old Isobel was still living at home with her parents. She was a short, stocky and active woman who loved the outdoor country life. Looking back in later life, she described how she was 'for several years her father's assistant',[10] frequently accompanying him to agricultural meetings and shows. She bred prize sheepdogs, often the only woman competing in country dog shows. Had she been an eldest son rather than an eldest daughter, Isobel Turner, with her hands-on experience of the family business, would have automatically expected to inherit. It was not unheard of for widows and daughters to take on and manage farms. Nevertheless, it does not look as if Isobel Turner's father ever envisaged this as a possibility, despite her clear interest and inclination.

Edith Bradley was the only one of the three older women already earning a living in 1891. She was the daughter of an East India merchant, Thomas William Bradley, and had grown up in Beckenham in Kent. Her father's business links to India meant that the family home, White Post Cottage on Albemarle Road, was crammed with exotic souvenirs of his travels, from heavily carved teak furniture to tiger skin rugs. However, in 1874, when Edith was only fourteen, Thomas Bradley died without leaving any substantial inheritance for his widow and four children. Whilst her two brothers were able to take on careers as a solicitor and a tea planter, Edith and her older sister Florence had more limited options. Edith was a keen reader with a particular interest in history and, together with Florence, she became a teacher at a girls' school in Beckenham, just around the corner from the family home. It is possible that both Florence and Edith had themselves been pupils at the Broad Lea School for Ladies on Westgate Road and made the transition from pupil to pupil-teacher (where older students supervised younger pupils) before becoming full-time teachers at the same institution. Although the teaching profession was overcrowded and pay was low, by the late nineteenth century teaching in a school offered a more structured career path than becoming a private governess. Edith was passionate about education and extremely hard-working and by 1891, at the age of 31, she was the School Principal. She had reason to throw herself into her career, as by then she was not just supporting herself. Her older sister Florence suffered from mental illness and was subject to bouts of acute mania with extreme restlessness and spent nearly a year in the Bethlem Hospital in 1885. Hospitals like the Bethlem charged for room, board and treatments, so Florence's illness would have been a drain on the family finances. In 1887 the Broad Lea Ladies School was advertised in a local trade directory as being run by 'The Misses Bradley assisted by masters and mistresses',[11] but by the time of the 1891 census, Florence was listed as having 'no occupation'. Sadly, Florence was never to make a full recovery and ended her life in 1911 as an inmate at the Holloway Sanatorium in Egham. It was not just financial necessity that drove Edith to make a career in teaching. She was one of a generation of headmistresses determined to transform the quality of secondary education for girls. Although the Education Acts passed after the 1870s provided free mandatory schooling for both sexes, girls were not only educated differently from boys, but they had to fight for schooling beyond secondary level. The advertisements that Edith placed for her Broad Lea School announced that the school aimed 'to educate on Improved Scholastic Principles. Pupils prepared for University, Royal College of Preceptors Examinations.' Giving pupils a broad-based education that equipped them to sit examinations for university and teacher-training college was a big step forward from the type of education that had previously been deemed suitable for girls. Earlier in the century, if middle-class girls went to school at all, they were sent to small boarding schools that were often in overcrowded and ill-equipped converted private houses. As classes consisted of different ages and abilities, it was hard to organise a well-structured education and many schools did not try. They concentrated on equipping their pupils with 'accomplishments' such as drawing, dancing and a polite smattering of French. There was little motivation to study, and pupils seldom took exams for fear that the element of competition would be 'too masculine'. As Edith herself later wrote, 'The education of the average woman made her a useless being, except to grace the circle of society in which she moved; and very restricted in circumference most of those circles were!'[12] However, by the 1880s a new type of secondary school was emerging that had higher ambitions for its pupils and Edith Bradley was part of that movement.

This transformation in education was one of the main reasons that by 1891, the three younger women in our group already had a far wider range of opportunities available to them. Even though the word 'feminist' was not to be used for another four years, women like Edith Bradley attempted to redefine the problem of surplus women, not as an excess of women, but a paucity of educational and employment opportunities to enable them to live independently. Victorian campaigners for women's rights viewed education as critical to women's efforts to live life under their own control. Their argument was that as long as women remained ignorant, they would not realise their inferior position and would be ill-equipped to change it. Useful, well-paid work was the goal, and a wide-ranging and rigorous education was the first essential step to equip young women to find it.

Madeline Agar was sixteen in 1891 and just coming to the end of

Photograph taken while Madeline Agar (sitting second from the left) was a pupil at Wimbledon High School. Courtesy of Wimbledon High School Archive.

her time as a pupil at Wimbledon High School. The school offered a wider curriculum than most girls' schools of the time and had links with several Oxford Colleges. Like Edith Bradley's Broad Lea School, which boasted a gymnasium, Wimbledon High School also took the physical fitness of its pupils seriously. The school offered Swedish Drill – a demure form of physical fitness training. Madeline came from a very 'sporty' family; her father, Edward Larpent Agar was one of the principal founders of the modern sport of hockey, chairing the meeting that established the Hockey Association of Great Britain which formalised the rules of the game. Luckily for Madeline, Wimbledon High School was the type of progressive school that offered opportunities for girls to participate in competitive sport. As a rule, playing fields in girls' schools were rare, but at Wimbledon High School girls were taught the new sport of netball and even issued a tennis challenge to a neighbouring boys' school. Madeline was a keen tennis player, but she was also artistic and, in the summer of 1891 when she sat her examinations, she achieved a Distinction in Drawing.

Gertrude Cope was aged 15 in 1891 and her schooling was much less prestigious. She came from a lower social and economic level than the other women. Her father appears to have bounced from one career to another, not lasting very long in any of them. The census of 1881 listed his occupation as Baptist Minister, but by 1891 he gave his occupation simply as 'clerk' and by the mid-1890s he was described as a journalist. In 1891, Gertrude appeared to have finished her education and was helping her sister run a boarding house in Hastings and prospects for her future did not look promising.

Access to good secondary education was not the only way to broaden horizons. The final member of our group of six, Olive Cockerell, had a limited level of formal schooling in a small girls' school in Margate but she came from a bohemian, progressive family with a strong interest in the arts and natural history. In 1891 Olive was twenty-two and the census described her as an art student living with her widowed mother on Fairfax Road in Chiswick, close to the Bedford Park area. Bedford Park was a suburb aimed at the artistically inclined who could not afford to live in Chelsea, with houses designed in line with the principles of the aesthetic movement. The area attracted artists, writers and general free thinkers. Olive's father, Sydney John Cockerell, a coal merchant, had died in 1877 when she was just eight years old. Following his early death, lack of money was to be an issue for the family for many years. However, restricted income did not hinder their intellectual interests and strong beliefs. Sydney Cockerell had been a man of strong principles, with an interest in social reform and all five Cockerell children inherited their father's social conscience and radical politics. Olive's older brother Sydney Carlyle Cockerell, although forced to forego a university career to work in the family coal business, was interested in art and literature and harboured a desire to become a museum curator. He became friends with William Morris after attending his Sunday evening lectures at Morris's London home, the nearby Kelmscott House. Olive's second brother, Theodore Cockerell, developed a passion for natural history as a child, filling the house with specimens collected on his travels. In 1891 he was working in the British Museum, having just returned from three years in Colorado where he and his younger brother Leslie had been sent to recover from a bout of tuberculosis. Leslie stayed on in America to become a successful mining engineer. Their younger sister Una was to become an actress, working with Sir Herbert Beerbohm Tree's theatre company. Olive was regarded as the quiet one in the family and suffered from poor physical health from a young age, but she, too, took an interest in the latest ideas about art and society. I have not been able to find out where Olive studied art, but her studies were intended as a serious step towards making a living as an artist or illustrator.

Even in a bohemian household like this one, however, as a single young woman living at home, there were restrictions on Olive's freedom. Her brother Theo was scandalised when he learnt that as an art student, 'Olive has been acting as a model to a young woman who smokes cigarettes and offered her one!'[13] Like most unmarried women, Olive's first duty was still expected to be her family. Without the responsibilities of a family of her own, a single middle-class woman was expected to devote herself to caring for others. Olive's mother was an invalid who suffered from various ill-defined nervous complaints and the main duty of care fell on her. She was also the one that the family turned to when her maternal grandmother required nursing through the last distressing stages of terminal cancer in 1889, when Olive was just twenty years old. Four years later, in June 1893, she travelled to New Mexico to stay with Theo, who had recently obtained a post as State Entomologist for the New Mexico and Arizona State territories, and whose young wife Annie was expecting their first child. Olive was expected to put her art career on hold to help with childcare, a common role for a spinster sister. Tragically, Annie died just five days after the birth and suddenly twenty-four-year-old Olive was the main carer for a new-born baby boy named Martin. This was an isolated and demanding life, in a place where the only person she knew was her brother, who was utterly absorbed in his new career and his ambition to make his name as a scientist. Olive managed to maintain some artistic activity by illustrating the specimens that her brother collected, chiefly funghi, but she was lonely and unhappy. After two years, Olive wrote to her brother, Sydney, saying 'I'm not going to break down … I'm not ill at all … The chief trouble for me is Theo – please don't tell the following to anyone: I hate grumbling – but you know he never thinks of me in anything: never helps me in anything … I never get a word of encouragement or affection … He's wonderfully clever, and has splendid theories – and a grand character, but oh! He's hard to live with!'[14]

In many ways Olive was more fortunate than many single women, in that she had an influential advocate. Her father had been a close friend of and assistant to the housing reformer and co-founder of the National Trust, Octavia Hill, who was Olive's godmother. A strong advocate and role model for women leading an active life outside the home, Octavia Hill was acutely aware of the sacrifice Olive was making. When she learnt of Olive's predicament she wrote to Sydney and Theo saying, 'I cannot help feeling as if the strain would be really too much, so reserved a person means more than she says, not less, and the loneliness and absence from all art… surely, she has put up bravely for Theo's sake now long enough and he ought to think of her.'[15] However, even after Octavia Hill's intervention, it was to be a further three years before a professional nurse was found for her nephew and Olive was able to return home and resume her own artistic work. Her godmother was delighted and relieved.

Octavia Hill was the personification of a new vision of service for single women, one that went beyond caring for infant, old or sick family members and extended into the public sphere. Often described as the grandmother of modern social work, Octavia Hill managed fifteen housing schemes with over three thousand tenants across London. She set up a system of social housing which involved taking on and improving poor-quality housing stock and then renting it at affordable rates to poor families. By the early 1890s, Octavia Hill was a major public figure managing an enormous workload and sitting on a plethora of different committees. She was one of many single and married women who gave their time and energy to a vast array of volunteer associations, societies, leagues, guilds and alliances that aimed to make a difference to society. For some women a commitment to practical philanthropy involved active participation in local government, educational and poor relief boards. Octavia Hill herself was not a supporter of female suffrage yet work like hers nonetheless highlighted the case for giving women the vote. If women's intelligence, energy and drive could work on public and charitable projects that tackled some of the most pressing social problems of the day, why could they not have a say in how society was organised?

Even though Victorian social conventions were still strong and support for full female suffrage was still a minority view, the world was changing. By 1891 women were already starting to benefit from half a century of agitation, work and education that had positively changed conditions for women, with reform to laws around divorce and property rights after marriage. Some women even went to university, trained as doctors, and undertook social work. New technology was creating new opportunities. Mechanical typewriters and the new telephone system paved the way for a boom in white-collar jobs which offered opportunities for women to take up semi-skilled occupations as typists and telephone operators. Improved public transport meant women could travel across large cities without the need for a chaperone. *The Lady* magazine published a series in 1891 entitled 'London Locomotion' which proclaimed that not only was it now respectable for women to travel around London by omnibus, but that 'the fair sex' had ousted the 'sterner sex' from the top deck of the bus, forcing them to take refuge downstairs.[16] In the 1880s the invention of an affordable safety bicycle kick-started a craze for cycling amongst young women that had a significant impact on their lives, bringing a freedom to travel cheaply and independently. Although the term 'New Woman' was not to be coined for another three years, by 1891 the concept was already becoming a reality. The modern 'New Woman' that dominated the headlines of the 1890s rode a bicycle, worked in an office and even smoked cigarettes.

The question is, given these other opportunities, why did these six women, along with many others like them, decide that the ancient craft of gardening was the career they wanted to pursue? In the late 1800s the horticultural profession was traditional, hierarchical and male. Yet within a few short years, there were real hopes (and fears) that women would come to dominate and transform British horticulture by overturning the conventional image of a gardener and the way gardeners were trained and developed. In their different ways, our six women were to be at the heart of this transformation. How did this happen?

2

IF EVE HAD A SPADE

> If Eve had had a spade in Paradise and known what to do with it, we should not have had all that sad business of the apple.
>
> Elizabeth von Arnim,
> *Elizabeth and her German Garden*, 1896

In May 1891 several newspapers reported the opening of a new small business on Lower Sloane Street in Chelsea, which went under the name of The London Women's Gardening Association (LWGA). The Association advertised its services as 'the care of suburban gardens, conservatories, valuable plants in rooms and window boxes' all conducted by women gardeners. The newspaper reports spoke of ladies employed by the Association keeping plants tidy and alive while owners were away. Their services also included looking after 'graves in cemeteries, keeping them bright and in good order' (this was, apparently, 'one of those missions for which gentlewomen are decidedly suited'). Contemporary accounts were keen to stress that the ladies did not undertake 'digging, conveying soil, laying gravel and other details for which a man is required'.[17] It was hardly horticulture on a grand scale, but it was a start.

Within a couple of weeks of opening, however, the Association's premises were the venue for a meeting that paved the way for a much more significant female incursion into the male world of horticulture, when the redoutable Miss Emma Cons persuaded the LWGA's founder, Mrs Edith Laxon Chamberlain, to become involved in a plan to create places for female students at the Swanley Horticultural College in Hextable in Kent. Today, Emma Cons, a long-time friend and colleague of Octavia Hill and one of her first lady rent collectors and proto-social workers, is best known for taking over the Royal Victoria Hall (the Old Vic) to provide inexpensive teetotal entertainment for the poor and for founding the Morley Memorial College for Working Men and Women. But she was also a longstanding supporter of women's rights and was particularly interested in proving that women could undertake a wide variety of skilled work. She was not afraid to use herself as a guinea pig: in her younger days she had apprenticed herself to a watch engraver to challenge the notion that only men could perform such work. She became London's first lady alderman in 1889 and it was a conversation with a fellow alderman who had a nephew training at the recently opened Swanley Horticultural College that alerted her to the possibilities of horticultural training for women.

Swanley Horticultural College had opened in 1889 as a private residential college devoted to training male students in the scientific principles of horticulture. The founder and managing director was a businessman named Arthur Harper Bond who had purchased the freehold of a forty-three-acre country estate in Hextable, close to the town of Swanley in Kent. The estate included a large house which had originally belonged to Sir Edward James Reed, a ship designer. The building's chief distinguishing feature was its billiard room, all the fittings of which had come from the cross-channel ferry the *S.S. Bessemer*, designed by Reed. When the mansion house was converted to a horticultural college, the Bessemer saloon became the assembly hall and library. The college was part of a national expansion in formalised technical education aimed at improving standards in agriculture and horticulture. In a world of increasingly rapid scientific and technical innovation the old ways of learning 'on the job' were no longer sufficient. High-quality training combining theoretical and practical instruction was required if British growers were to hold their own against cheap imported food. Concerned that the country was falling behind more forward-looking competitors abroad, the government provided funding to local authorities to set up colleges and pay bursaries to students. Swanley's prospectus proclaimed, 'Here every facility is given to young men to acquire thorough and practical knowledge of the latest and most scientific, and in consequence, most profitable system of Horticulture.'[18] The scientific courses offered included zoology, natural history, botany, chemistry, geology, meteorology, hydrostatics, hydrodynamics, surveying and engineering – all designed to give students a comprehensive understanding of the principles underlying the most effective and efficient means of propagating and cultivating plants. There were hands-on practical classes in horticulture, dairy-work, book-keeping, and beekeeping. The students were expected to work on ornamental and productive plots in the college grounds. This was a technocratic and modern alternative to the old apprentice system of horticultural training.

The idea of women studying at Swanley was raised within just a month of the college's opening. A lady correspondent had politely enquired, 'Will you favour me with a prospectus of the Horticultural College & kindly state whether ladies are admitted to its benefits either as residents or non-residents?'[19] Her request went unanswered, however; it took Emma Cons, Edith Chamberlain and a number of other determined campaigners to force the doors open three years later. Just as she had decades earlier with watchmaking, Emma Cons decided that the best way of proving that women were capable of coping with the intellectual and physical rigours of horticultural training was to do it herself. So, in the autumn of 1890, together with her partner Ethel Gertrude Everest, she attended the college for several weeks. What the young male students made of two middle-aged women sitting in on their classes was not recorded. A later history of the college described the women as 'two energetic spirits', so it seems that Emma Cons and Ethel Everest threw themselves into the experience wholeheartedly.[20] Those few weeks at Swanley convinced Emma Cons that a college-based education in horticulture would be an entirely beneficial and achievable goal for women. In May 1891 she persuaded Edith Chamberlain to

Portrait of Mrs Edith Chamberlain, member of the board of the Swanley Women's Branch and founder of the London Women's Gardening Association. From her *Book of Gardening*. Courtesy of the RHS Lindley Collections.

host the first meeting of the 'Swanley Women's Branch Managing Committee' and to become its Honorary Secretary.

The aim of the first meeting was to draw up a prospectus and outline how some of the practical difficulties of introducing female students to an all-male residential college could be overcome. Wisely Emma Cons had recruited to the committee women with both a commitment to female emancipation and some practical knowledge of gardening. Along with Edith Chamberlain, the invited guests included Miss Fanny Rollo Wilkinson, regarded as the first professional female landscape architect. It is interesting that Emma Cons does not appear to have recruited the most famous female gardener of the time, Gertrude Jekyll, to the cause, but this may have been because she did not have a personal connection to draw upon. Edith Chamberlain and Fanny Wilkinson were both part of the network of social campaigners, feminists and suffragists that lived and worked in Central London, a tight social group that also included Elizabeth Garrett Anderson, Millicent Fawcett and other prominent figures in the nineteenth-century women's movement. Gertrude Jekyll was never part of this metropolitan set. The group that sat down in the Lower Sloane Street shop, surrounded by 'pretty tables, brilliant in crystal and china and floral decoration'[21], drew up a prospectus that met with the approval of the trustees of Swanley College. They also solved the accommodation problem, confirming arrangements with Mrs Elizabeth Watson, a local widowed woman of impeccable respectability, to open a hostel near the college and serve as its Lady Superintendent.

There were a number of reasons why these campaigners seized so eagerly on the opportunity to open Swanley Horticultural College to women students. An article in *The Examiner* as early as 1879 had suggested that gardening was 'upon reflection, entirely reasonable' as an area of paid work for women – especially those who had not had access to sufficient education to prepare them for professions such as law or medicine, or who lacked the natural talents for more artistic pursuits ... It is but a small minority who will ever be able to embrace the learned professions, should those professions be thrown open to them, and only those can become artists who are specially gifted.' But for the role to remain ladylike, as befitted middle-class women, it was essential it was not pursued at the level of manual labour. 'Let not our readers picture to themselves a strong-minded, able-bodied female, with garments inelegantly kilted, either trundling a barrow or wielding a spade,' the anonymous author stressed. 'Such is not by any means the writer's ideal ... The lady gardener should confine herself to the higher walks of horticulture, in which science is needed ... Let the classes at Kew and Chiswick be opened to women, lectures be given to them at South Kensington and opportunities offered to them of practical instruction under the gardeners at parks.' But how likely were Kew or the RHS to open their gardens to women trainees? Perhaps recognising that the possibility was remote, the article ended, 'It rests very much with women themselves to take the matter up and bring it to a successful issue.'[22]

Swanley, as a private college which needed paying students to thrive, was a much easier prospect for determined women to 'take the matter up with', as they could persuade the college authorities that women offered a lucrative new market. The hope was that a college-based course could equip female students for higher and more cerebral horticultural roles, relieving them of the need to compete with male gardeners in the more hands-on physical gardening tasks.

With the permission to admit women to Swanley in place, the Swanley Women's Branch began actively promoting the opportunity to potential students and, just as importantly, to their families. It was important that horticultural training be seen as a respectable undertaking that did not completely overturn conventional ideas of femininity. In 1892 Edith Chamberlain published a book entitled *The Gentlewoman's Book of Gardening*. Most of the book was given over to practical horticultural advice but the final chapter covered the prospects for middle-class women of making a living from gardening. 'The papers are full of distressed gentlewomen and her only resources so far seem to be "art", needlework… and "decorative" painting,' she wrote. Surely women who had been brought up in a middle-class house 'could easily qualify themselves for starting as lady-gardeners and so continue the pleasant country life they have been accustomed to.'[23] Aside from the question of respectability, the other barrier was the widely held view that women were unfit for physically demanding work (despite the very evident proof to the contrary in the form of thousands of working-class women toiling in fields, factories and sculleries up and down the land). Conscious of this argument, the proponents of the new Swanley Women's Branch stressed the health of its female students and publicised expert medical testimonies from Sir Edward Henry Sieveking and Mrs Elizabeth Garrett Anderson, who were both co-opted as members of Swanley's council. Sieveking was physician in ordinary to Queen Victoria and at the first annual meeting of the Swanley Women's Branch in 1893 he declared:

> A study of the prospectus of the College, as well as a personal inspection of the Women's Branch at Swanley, justified my saying that there is a large field for suitable development for female taste

> and female energy, in gardens, in greenhouses, in the management of trees, of flowers, in the poultry-yard, in book-keeping, without entailing undue physical exhaustion or making demand upon their bodily strength, exceeding what may be fairly demanded of a healthy young woman … I believe that the development of Swanley College may prove largely instrumental in promoting one of the most healthful occupations for women, healthful in body and mind.[24]

This type of reassurance was constantly needed. In an article in *The Scottish Review* on 'The Redundancy of Spinster Gentlewomen' the author T. P. W. claimed, 'The very exercise of muscular achievements suitable only for men has the effect of hardening and roughening the feminine exterior; while it is too often associated with a strident voice, a self-assertive manner, a brusque and abrupt address to malekind, and a general lapse of attractiveness. All of which attributes tend to damp a man's matrimonial intents.'[25] Even fifteen years after Swanley admitted female students, proponents of horticultural training for women still reported having to contend with parental misgivings. The father who worried that his daughter would be 'constantly weeding and digging amongst plants … returning home at night physically exhausted' and the mother who thought that 'rough exposure to all weathers will play havoc with a good complexion' and had 'visions of a brown, sunburnt face, or a wrinkled parchment one, knotted fingers, stiff joints, uneven shoulders'[26] still needed persuading to allow their daughter to study gardening.

Parental caution notwithstanding, this modern professional gardening, based on new scientific principles, and relying on brain more than brawn, seemed to occupy a uniquely promising position as a career for women. As outdoor work, it satisfied the ambitions of more radical feminists to demonstrate women's potential to break free from the old restrictive stereotypes of weak and passive femininity. On the other hand, gardening, if conducted at a more supervisory level, was sufficiently associated with domesticity to be an unthreatening occupation for more conservatively minded women. Indeed, one principal of a gardening school sought to reassure parents that horticultural training would not lessen a chance of a young woman finding a husband – far from it. She wrote, 'A somewhat mistaken idea is sometimes held that women who are obliged to follow a definite career are less likely to marry than their sisters who remain at home in quiet surroundings. It is often found however, that of daughters say of a country clergyman, it is those out in the world as secretaries, companions or gardeners who do marry ... They should too be better helpmates to men leading active lives.'[27] Gaining horticultural skills could easily be seen as a useful preparation for married life. As one writer for *The Leeds Mercury* wrote, 'There is one thing to be said of a training for women in gardening, especially, which cannot be stated in reference to many other careers for women, namely that, even if the student marries, the value of her training will not be lost, as is so often the case in other branches of industry. It is often said, with truth, that when a father goes to great expense in training his daughter for a profession or business, the outlay may be almost or entirely thrown away in the event of her marrying. But, unless a woman is to pass her life in the heart of a crowded town, training in horticulture will be valuable and a source of delight to her, however much married she may be.'[28]

The first female student at Swanley was in fact a married woman named Mrs Benison, who entered the college as early as June 13, 1891, just around a month after the prospectus was issued. The selection of a married woman (who did not intend to garden professionally) was a relatively 'safe' and 'respectable' beginning for the training of women at Swanley. Within a few months, four more women students arrived. Progress stalled in the following year when no women applied but things picked up in 1893 when ten women enrolled. One possible reason for the uptick in interest after 1893 was the decision by the Royal Horticultural Society to introduce a national public examination in horticulture. The RHS had experimented with creating formal qualifications for trainee gardeners in the past, but the General Examination in Horticulture was a much more serious project to create a national qualification with a rigorous examination that any student could sit. Although there is absolutely no evidence at all that the RHS had women in mind when they introduced the exam, the effect was profound. For the first time students of any gender had an opportunity to attain an objective external endorsement of their skills which could be shown to any potential employer. As a written examination which focused on theory that could be taught in a classroom, the RHS examination was a clear alternative to the traditional system of verbal or written references from head gardeners or employers. Horticulture was modernising and with access to the right training, perhaps at last the time was right for women to enter the industry on a more equal footing.

Madeline Agar, the sporty ex-schoolgirl from Wimbledon, was an early student at Swanley Horticultural College. A petite, almost elfin-looking girl, she enrolled on February 5, 1894, aged just 19, and paid a fee of £80 for a year's tuition, room and board. In the year between leaving Wimbledon High School and enrolling at Swanley, Madeline had worked as an assistant teacher at a small private girls' school called York High School for Girls, right in the centre of York. It may be that her experience at York High School was not to her taste, or that she had concluded that she would have better job prospects if she was able to demonstrate that she had training to teach gardening and nature studies in addition to core academic subjects, but whatever her motivation, it was a big step. Even acquiring all the items on the long uniform list issued by the college was no mean feat. The list included: a coat and tunic of Swanley tweed (obtained from Messrs Egerton Burnett of Wellington, Somerset), a blazer with monogram for second-year students, a Boy Scout's belt from Messrs Gammages' department store in London, blouses with turn-down collars, a jersey or sweater in white or the surely more practical brown, and knickers (home-made to a regulation pattern). In addition, a silk handkerchief, brown felt hat, two pairs of extra strong boots or shoes, a Mackintosh, one pair of clogs or gumboots, a blue serge apron and one pair of strong gardening gloves completed the trousseau needed for the first term. For the summer months, the list included tunics in green fabric from Harrods, a straw hat to prevent sunburn and, to cover the legs, 'The Swanley Stocking', a summer-weight stocking, extra-long from the London Glove Co. on Bond Street. As well as all this clothing, each student was required to bring '2 pairs of sheets, 2 pillowcases, 4 towels and 4 dinner napkins; all … must be distinctly marked with name in full.' [29]

Whilst neither the college fee nor the shopping list presented a problem for Madeline, who presumably had help from her family on top of any money she had accumulated as an assistant teacher, they would have been an issue for someone of more humble background and income, such as Gertrude Cope. Even in 1891 the new Women's Branch Committee saw that the college's high costs would be a barrier to 'ladies of small means' unless scholarships or bursaries were available. At first many counties like Kent explicitly restricted educational bursaries to male students. Swanley obtained some private donations for female students, but they saw that the only way to solve this problem long-term was to lobby county councils to provide bursaries and scholarships to women, too. A petition was mounted requesting that Kent County Council fund two scholarships to support women students at Swanley. The council finally endowed one scholarship for a female student at Swanley in August 1893 and a handful of other councils, including Essex, followed.

Essex County Council permitted women to study short subsidised courses at its Chelmsford Technical College (then known as the Central Laboratory, Chelmsford) and by 1894 Gertrude Cope, another of our six, had moved from her sister's boarding house in Hastings to 15 Duke Street in Chelmsford to take a short course there. At some point in 1894, Gertrude sat an exam for a scholarship held at the City and Guilds Technical College in Finsbury. She achieved high marks and was awarded a £40 scholarship towards the cost of a one-year course at Swanley Horticultural College. Ironically for the daughter of an ex-Baptist minister, both the Chelmsford College and the Swanley scholarship were funded through the Local Taxation (Custom and Excise) Bill. This was a bill designed to reduce the drinking of hard liquor by raising taxes on the importation and manufacture of spirits. Despite teetotalists' hopes, the bill did not have much effect on levels of alcohol consumption and large amounts of money were

A typical student room at Swanley Horticultural College, taken from a college syllabus pamphlet. Courtesy of the RHS Lindsey Collections.

collected. The resulting funds, nicknamed 'whiskey money,' were passed onto local councils like Essex to support teenage boys and girls to study a range of technical subjects including horticulture. With the support of her 'whiskey money' scholarship, Gertrude Cope enrolled at Swanley on January 15, 1895.

As some of the earliest female students at Swanley, Madeline and Gertrude were taught alongside, but kept rather separate, from the male students. The young women lived in a red-brick building called South Bank, well away from the male student accommodation called North Bank. The young women were very much the minority; they were tightly chaperoned and made to sit at the back of the class to avoid distracting the male students. House rules in South Bank were strict. Students had to be in their bedrooms by 10 and lights were out by 10.30 pm. In an article reporting on this new development, the Kew Gardens staff magazine gently teased that facilities included 'pleasant drawing and dining rooms in a refined and comfortable home, with a lady superintendent to see them all in bed by a quarter past ten', implicitly contrasting with the more basic accommodation traditionally offered to young gardeners.[30] Female students were not allowed out alone after dusk and although they were allowed to ride bicycles, they were only permitted to do so on college grounds. At first the female students were excluded from some of the heavier manual tasks taught on the course, but a report in *The Queen* magazine proudly declared that, as well as distinguishing themselves in theoretical work, 'they are equally active in practical work, and may be seen hoeing or carting, besides attending to the bees, the chickens, the dairy and carrying out all the multitudinous processes of the gardener.'[31]

By 1895 there were thirty-four female students studying at Swanley. Madeline's and Gertrude's fellow students included Annie Gulvin, a policeman's daughter from Maidstone, and Alice Hutchings, a dairyman's daughter from Deal, both of whom like Gertrude came to Swanley with a scholarship. Other students were from much wealthier backgrounds. They included Constance Hay-Currie, daughter of Archibald Hay-Currie, the British Consul in Nice. The opportunity to study and socialise with people from very different social backgrounds was very unusual for the time and one of the unspoken benefits of the Swanley experience. A commentary published in 1899 on the College's performance noted sniffily that 'To be boarded and lodged free with a pleasant outdoor life for two years may possibly have served as special incentive to perseverance in the case of those holding County Council scholarships.'[32] It is true that out of only thirty-six who remained for two years (the prescribed period of study) twenty were holders of scholarships but it may simply have been the case that, without the backstop of family money, women from more modest backgrounds worked harder to prepare themselves to earn an income.

Despite this social mixing, it seems the Women's Branch of the College rapidly adopted the atmosphere of a private girls' boarding school. Just as at Wimbledon High School, competitive sport was popular. Madeline beat Annie Gulvin in the College Tennis Singles Championship, and both also participated in the annual Christmas show, singing 'When Love is Kind' to great acclaim. Formal College photographs show the women students smartly dressed and artfully arranged on the steps of the veranda at the front of the main house, for all the world like guests at an Edwardian country-house party. But the academic side of College life was taken seriously, and all the girls worked hard. As Jessie Smith, one of the very first group of women to train at Swanley, put it, 'It was the beginning of women gardeners and all those anxious to start this work for women were watching with some anxiety to see if we were going to be any good at it.'[33] Writing a little later in 1903, a visitor to the College gave an account of the female students that gives an idea of their attitude and work ethic. In a letter to *The Gardening World*, Arthur Dean wrote:

> I could not for one moment mistake their intensity, their determination, their industry. How many youths would like to do as those girls did during the strawberry season, turn out at 4 a.m. to gather the fruit for that morning's market, or be up at 6 a.m. for outdoor work? As a rule, even when their ordinary day's work was over, I saw them at 6 p.m. come out onto their own plots, carrying cans of water, hoeing, digging, tying up and doing all sorts of work with gusto. Our youths would have made wry faces and would have been off to cricket or tennis. Many of these Swanley girls have been tenderly brought up also and have rich parents. But they detest the useless, aimless lives that custom would force upon them, and live for work and usefulness. Really, they mean business.[34]

The students' hard work paid off. When the RHS examinations came round in May 1895, Annie Gulvin caused a sensation by achieving the highest marks in the entire country, with 260 marks out of a possible 300, winning her a silver-gilt medal from the RHS. Madeline Agar and Alice Hutchings also gained first-class awards with 215 marks each. This was a ringing endorsement of the College's decision to admit women and was widely covered in the horticultural press and in newspapers inclined to be supportive of women's rights. The college prize-giving day on June 20, 1895, was a splendid occasion. After students and VIP guests enjoyed a tea featuring 'excellent specimens of fruit culture in the shape of very fine strawberries grown in the College grounds' they gathered in the opulent Bessemer saloon to hear speeches from the Chairs of Kent and Essex County Council congratulating Annie Gulvin on her 'brilliant achievement'.[35]

Annie was not the only female student to receive applause. Students from the Women's Branch outperformed the male students in the list of internal college prize winners too. Madeline Agar won the prize for best student in Practical Horticulture and was the only student to obtain a first-class pass in Advanced Theoretical Chemistry, whilst other female students won the Principles of Horticulture prize, Practical Chemistry prize, and all the prizes for Botany. Proudly looking on as prizes were awarded were Emma Cons and Fanny Wilkinson. In the following year's RHS examination, Gertrude Cope maintained the high standards when she also achieved a first-class pass, one of four women to do so. This meant that in 1896, out of a national entry of 152 candidates, whilst women made up only 1 per cent of the national entry, they made up 25 per cent of the top-marked candidates. This success did not go unnoticed in the press and there was enormous optimism for the prospects of the new 'lady gardeners'. In the intake of new students for that year, for the first time, the number of female applicants to study horticulture at Swanley outnumbered male applicants.

It seemed that the garden was becoming an increasingly 'feminine space'. On March 7, 1896, whilst Gertrude was still at Swanley, influential amateur gardener Mrs Theresa Earle visited the College to see the work of the female students. She published an account of the visit a year later in her bestselling book, *Pot Pourri from a Surrey Garden*, saying, 'It immediately struck me as quite possible that a new employment may be developed for women of small means out of the modern increased taste for gardening.'[36] Her book, an enormously popular mix of anecdotes and advice on a wide range of domestic and gardening topics, was part of a new wave of gardening books by female authors. They were different in tone and content from the earlier, more didactic gardening books. Female writers were writing about gardening as much more than a respectable and edifying pastime, now it was a creative and empowering activity, both physically and mentally. By the time Madeline and Gertrude graduated from Swanley, arguably the most influential gardener in the land was a woman. Gertrude Jekyll's own garden at Munstead Woods was acknowledged as a dazzling success, demonstrating her innovative approach to colour, founded in her training as a fine and decorative artist at the School of Art, Kensington. Working together with Edward Lutyens, she was commissioned to design gardens and borders across the country. She wrote prolifically for William Robinson's *The Garden* and *Country Life* and in 1899 she published her first book, *Wood and Garden*. In this she asserted that gardening was an artform: 'For planting ground is painting a landscape with living things, and as I hold that good gardening ranks within the bounds of the fine arts, so I hold that to plant well needs an artist of no mean capacity.'[37] Other writers in this new wave took a more personal tone, and their books mapped their emotional and spiritual development alongside the development of their gardens. Elizabeth von Arnim was an Australian-born heiress who married a rather stern German count, and she wrote about her growing obsession with the gardens of his estate at Nassenheide, Pomerania, in Eastern Germany in her bestselling book titled *Elizabeth and Her German Garden*, published in 1898. She wrote, 'I sometimes literally ache with envy as I watch the men going about their pleasant work in the sunshine, turning up the luscious damp earth, raking, weeding, watering, planting, cutting the grass, pruning the trees – not a thing that they do, from the first uncovering of the roses in the spring to the November bonfires, but fills my soul with longing to be up and doing too.'[38] She confessed that on occasion, she went out to do some surreptitious digging while the servants were asleep. The way these authors wrote about their gardening emphasised a loose, exuberant approach to planting that highlighted the aesthetic creativity involved in garden-making rather than just the technical aspects of cultivation. Eleanor Vere Boyles' *Days and Houses in a Garden* described her garden at Huntercombe Manor in Buckinghamshire as the place where 'all my most favourite flowers grow in wild profusion'.[39]

When this artist-gardener approach combined with horticultural knowledge and high social status, as with Ellen Willmott or Gertrude Jekyll, the horticultural establishment was welcoming. Gertrude Jekyll was universally admired, and Ellen Willmott's knowledge of roses was well acknowledged. The RHS awarded them its highest accolade in 1897 when it gave them both a Victoria Medal of Honour, a new award created to mark Queen Victoria's Diamond Jubilee. However, the male horticultural establishment sometimes had little time for other female gardening authors. In 1901 the *Journal of the Kew Guild* included a short satirical poem entitled 'The Lady Gardener'. It went:

Once our literary daughters, when the writing impulse spake,
Spent their fancies on romances – hearts that ache and hearts that break;
But a change has come upon them and today they bend their mind,
To the fashion for a passion of a vegetable kind.
Since a book now needs within it, ere to favour it can win,
Gardens shady, with a lady babbling daintily within.
Mary, Mary literary, How does your garden grow?
With lines from Keats, and cooking receipts,
And publishers all in a row![40]

The staff at Kew might scoff, but gardening books written by and for women were enormously popular. *Elizabeth and Her German Garden* earned over £10,000 in the first year of publication, with eleven reprints during 1898, and by May 1899 it had been reprinted twenty-one times. These books promoted gardening to women as an opportunity for artistry, self-expression and even therapy, a way of handling the psychological toll of their restricted and dutifully conformist lives.

The increased profile of gardening for women and the success of the Swanley students in the RHS examinations created a high demand for horticultural training for women. Across the country, private gardening schools for women, many run by women, sprang up to meet this need. Many of the places offering to train female gardeners were primarily market-garden or nursery businesses that offered to teach skills to women as they worked. Others were schools first and foremost and any produce grown in the school gardens subsidised the training. Some sound very small indeed, such as 'Mrs Richmond's private establishment at Lustleigh' which in 1904 advertised that it took 'a very limited number of students' for instruction in theoretical and practical horticulture and, rather more idiosyncratically, 'photography chiefly dealing with flowers'.[41] Schools like this were too small and short-lived to leave good records of their students. The six hundred plus women I have tracked who entered the RHS National Horticultural Examination between its launch and the outbreak of the First World War were only the tip of the iceberg in terms of the number of women who received horticultural training in this period. In the years running up to the First World War, there were at least nineteen private gardening schools operating across the country and, though many did not enter pupils for the RHS examination, they still aimed to prepare their students for horticultural careers.

One well-known private school was run by the formidable – and through her own book, *Gardening for Women,* influential – Frances Wolseley. She was the daughter of Viscount Garnet Wolseley, the commander-in-chief of the British army. If her father was reportedly the inspiration for Gilbert and Sullivan's 'Model of a Modern Major General', Frances was very much her father's daughter, resembling him in her short stature, smart dress and brisk military manner. In her youth, Frances endured the normal aristocratic rituals associated with 'coming out' but she was much more comfortable in the countryside and by 1899, at the age of 27, both she and her family seem to have accepted that she would not marry. She occupied herself gardening at the new family home near the village of Glynde in Sussex. In 1902, despite lacking any formal horticultural training herself, she decided to set up a gardening school, taking over the Dower House on the estate for the purposes. At first the school was limited to ten pupils with just one paid teacher. *The Gardening World* described it as 'an excellent scheme which enables ladies wishing to take up gardening as a profession or a pastime to go through a course of indefinite duration, according to requirements, offering pupils the privilege of working in Lady Wolseley's gardens at the Farm House, Glynde. This seems a capital way of helping ladies anxious to learn practical gardening and the plan might commend itself to other philanthropic owners of country places.'[42] Although smaller schools like Glynde could not offer the professional tuition or facilities of a college like Swanley, they had two advantages for many prospective students of horticulture. Firstly, they were a great deal cheaper. For example, Frances Wolseley only charged her pupils £10 a year, compared to the £80 Swanley charged. Secondly, being smaller, they could claim to offer a more intimate, family atmosphere, which was less intimidating for young women, most of whom would never have been away from home on their own before. Frances Wolseley made much of the fact that she interviewed all her pupils personally before admittance and made no bones about the fact that she only taught 'ladies'. This social exclusivity was reassuring for families wanting to be sure that their daughters would not mix outside their social class. Learning to garden, with its association with working-class manual labour, was already outré enough for many families, without the risk of living with and studying alongside working-class girls.

In addition to the private gardening schools, many small horticultural businesses took in female pupils, offering hands-on experience and training. However, where the main purpose of the enterprise was running a market garden or nursery, pupils could be taken on primarily as cheap labour, and the quality of horticultural training was questionable. One disillusioned pupil wrote to the Suffragist newspaper, *The Common Cause*:

> Though my experience of gardening extends only over a period of two years, I have seen quite enough of it to make sure that it holds – whatever it may do for others – no future for me. I have been to two small gardening schools and have worked for several months on a gentleman's private estate. The schools, I believe, were originally intended for market gardens. Lack of funds or the expenses of hired labour must have suggested the idea of pupils. So the market gardens became, in name, schools – in fact, still remained market gardens. The crops still remained the chief object – the interests of the pupils being often forgotten. A was strong, so A trenched. B was clever

> with her fingers, B pruned. C was neither, so washed pots or swept leaves. A, B and C might stay at the school two or three years and entirely miss out some portion of a gardener's training. It was not my experience that A, B and C did stay two or three years. I did not.[43]

Cautionary tales like this did not dampen women's enthusiasm for horticultural training. Back at Swanley, the number of female students entering the College consistently outnumbered the male entrants. There were some internal misgivings; at the International Women's Congress of 1899 a Mr Propert 'from Swanley Horticultural College' claimed that the physical work in the course was having a deleterious effect on the female students; 'the physical alteration that took place was not a good thing', he said. The shape of the arm altered, women lost their proper shape, they developed broad shoulders like a man. He even claimed to have seen women with masculine neck muscles.[44] Fortunately, Mr Propert's misgivings about muscular necks were ignored – by 1902 the college authorities saw the way the wind was blowing and chose to make the college single-sex again, but this time as a women-only college. Training was one thing, however. The real challenge for Madeline, Gertrude and all the other female students emerging from college courses and private gardening schools was to find paid work.

Photograph of Gertrude Cope (centre) with Eleanor Morland (left) and Alice Hutchings (right) in their working uniform at the Royal Botanic Gardens, Kew, *c.*1898. Courtesy of the Royal Botanic Gardens, Kew.

3

GARDEN 'BOYS'

> No matter how good an education you may give to a young woman up to the age of twenty-two or twenty-four, she will not, without many years of hard apprenticeship and very hard practical labour ... be able to take the post which is given to professional gardeners.
>
> Hugh Macan, *Progress in Women's Education in the British Empire*, 1898

The boom in female gardening schools and the examination success of Madeline Agar, Gertrude Cope and the other Swanley girls was not greeted with universal delight in the horticultural world. The letters pages in horticultural magazines contained numerous complaints that passing exams was all very well, but that real competence as a gardener could still only be gained by experience. The fact that young women could gain high marks in horticultural examinations was seen by some as proof in itself that paper qualifications could not be relied upon as evidence of gardening ability. There was also a strong feeling that the Swanley students were at an unfair advantage if examinations were to become the criteria for judging gardeners. Pampered college students had much better conditions to study in than the average apprentice or under-gardener trying to study by candlelight in a cramped bothy after a long day labouring in a garden. This letter published in *The Journal of Horticulture*, signed 'A Novice,' is typical in tone: 'I should like to know a little about these institutions (Swanley and Central Laboratory Chelmsford). I wonder if these students could compete with us in actual work, such as digging, mowing, wheeling, stoking, fumigating and all other duties which the young gardener has to fulfil? What would the ladies think of us if we were to go in for examinations in dairying, dressmaking, or cookery, although I am sure the latter would be very useful to many of us. I think there is very great credit due to those young gardeners who do pass when they have such rivals to compete with.'[45] The sense of alarm that women were outperforming men in the RHS examination results reached a peak in 1907 when the four top marks all went to female entrants. *The Journal of Horticulture* wailed 'What are all the men doing to let the first four places be filled by women? The assumption that the latter are more clever than men hardly deserves consideration, since in all branches of mental activity, the best men can beat the best women. Probably the men apply their powers less seriously, or in other directions.' The *Journal* consoled its male readers with the fact that 'The RHS first-class certificate does not command first-class consideration from gardeners engaging assistants' but admitted 'its possession is an enviable card of recommendation, and the days are rapidly passing away when a gardener will look askance at the holder of such a certificate as "no good as a worker"'.[46]

The success of the 'Swanley Misses' was also noticed by their male counterparts at the Royal Botanic Gardens at Kew. Kew offered a rigorous training to male apprentices, with a mixture of practical and theoretical training similar to that at Swanley. The 1894 issue of the staff and student magazine, *The Journal of the Kew Guild*, noted wryly that they had 'rivals in the field'. However, the tone of the article did not suggest that the writers took the Swanley students very seriously. The article included the suggestion: 'Cannot some arrangement be made whereby a Kewite and a Swanley Miss can join their forces and thus be a source of strength to each other? We might then have gardeners offering their services for the outdoor department, wife to take charge of the orchids and fruit, or a woman gardener might undertake to manage a large garden, her husband to act as foreman. Kew and Swanley should certainly have a special attraction for each other. Double-barrelled gardeners would be an advantage and their offspring would be born gardeners; but alas! Gardeners as a rule are forbidden to have offspring.'[47] The statement that gardeners were not allowed to have children was a reference to the low wages of most professional gardeners and the impossibility of raising a family on a young gardener's income. The gap between the high fees charged at Swanley and the average gardener's wage was one of the reasons why many in the horticultural world saw Swanley students as wealthy dilletantes, just dabbling in gardening. The £80 fee for a year's study at Swanley was more than most professional gardeners could earn in a year, so the sceptics had a point.

Attitudes like these meant that, however good their paper qualifications, Madeline, Gertrude and their fellow Swanley students still had a mountain to climb if they wanted to craft a real career in the horticultural world. Two years of technical training in a college was simply not sufficient to qualify for this type of post and it was widely felt that extensive, hands-on experience was needed before anyone could hope to effectively supervise other gardeners. Even staff at the College itself saw the limitations of purely academic training – for both sexes. Ada Goodrich Freer, Honorary Secretary of the Women's Branch, admitted, 'At the end of the two years' training he (the term is used generically) having passed, let us suppose, the Royal Horticultural Society examinations, and gained the College diploma, looks about for employment. He has probably not the years, and most certainly not the experience, to enable him to take command of others, and except in some villa garden which will add little to his knowledge or experience, he has no choice but to become an under-gardener at a few shillings a week.'[48] But female graduates of Swanley had the additional barrier of widespread scepticism that they were physically up to some of the heavy labour that horticulture involved, so they were unlikely to find even an under-gardener post where they could gain more practical experience and get a foot on the career ladder towards a head gardener position. This is borne out by the fact that the many female graduates of horticultural schools and colleges had to settle for short-term temporary posts after they finished training. This would often involve being employed for a limited period to lay out a garden or 'put it in order' before leaving the owner to manage it on their own. Frances M. Broade, who studied at Swanley and attained a first-class mark in the RHS examination in 1897, went down this route. She took a temporary post in Bristol in 1900 'attempting to put a very barren garden into order' and reported back via a letter to the Swanley student magazine, with some helpful advice to other students thinking of doing the same:

> Now I hope you will not mind a few words of warning to you who are hoping to be professionals. Never go to a temporary post without having down in black and white: 1. Your working hours, 2. Time allowed for meals, 3. Pay and any other items you may find necessary (such as sharing a room or not etc.) You never know where you may be sent and with unprincipled people it saves no end of bother to have a hard and fast rule. I wish we could also have a fixed scale of wages. It would be so much more satisfactory.[49]

The following year she had moved on, this time to be a gardener to three spinster sisters in Lyme Regis. Elsie Ford was another gardener who moved rapidly between temporary placements in smaller gardens. In her letter to the Swanley student magazine she explained,

> Since I left Swanley the line I have followed has been that of taking temporary work for periods varying from a week to three months in duration. I have been to three or four during the past year. I spent a week in Cambridge last Autumn, renovating a small herbaceous border and planting a large quantity of bulbs. In January I went to a convalescent home at Hale to take Miss Prior's work for a few weeks while she was away. Then in June I went to Germany, to a German family in the Black Forest at their Summer residence, at the same time giving lessons in gardening to their two little girls.[50]

Sometimes the duration of work on offer was extremely short, such as the post advertised in *The Common Cause* in 1913: 'Wanted October, Lady Gardener to visit for a fortnight, help rearrange small garden near Liverpool, moderate terms. S. Penmaen, RSO Glamorgan.'[51] This peripatetic life did not suit everyone. Apart from the frequent movements, income was sporadic and uncertain.

Elsie Ford put a brave face on things when she spoke at the Annual Meeting of the Society for Promoting Employment of Women in May 1900, remarking that, 'The salary that a woman would earn as a gardener might be actually less than a teacher; but it compared very favourably when one considered how much less expensive a gardener's life entails in the matter of clothes and keeping up appearances,'[52] but in practical terms, this kind of working life made it impossible to earn enough to live independently. Census and college records show that many 'lady gardeners' returned to live with their parents. Women who did not want to settle for this life of occasional work and had ambitions to craft a lifelong horticultural career with prospects needed to find work in more prestigious settings to develop their CVs.

Arguably the two most prestigious gardens in the country for an aspiring young gardener to work in were the Royal Horticultural Society's garden at Chiswick and the Royal Botanic Gardens at Kew. The RHS Chiswick Garden was barred to women – even those who had excelled in the RHS's very own examination. This was proved categorically in 1898 when Swanley student Olive Harrisson achieved the highest mark in the country in that year's RHS exam. In 1898, in addition to awarding a silver gilt medal, the RHS had announced that the top student would be eligible for a scholarship to fund training at its Chiswick Garden. Even though a woman, Swanley student Annie Gulvin, had come top just three years earlier, it still seems to have shocked the RHS when Olive Harrisson wrote asking to take up her scholarship. Reverend Wilks, the Secretary of the RHS, wrote back saying that this was out of the question and that the reason that the rules had not explicitly ruled this out was that, 'Only males being allowed at Chiswick, it was never contemplated that a female might claim the scholarship.'[53]

On the face of things, Kew looked no more likely to employ female Swanley graduates than the RHS. In 1895 the Director of the Garden, William Thistleton Dyer, declared, 'We treat our young men as men … We wish them to be manly, self-respecting and strenuous.'[54] However, within a year, he had changed his tone and agreed to let high-performing Swanley graduates work at Kew. On January 13, 1896, Gertrude's and Madeline's classmates, Annie Gulvin and Alice Hutchings, signed the register of employment at Kew. The reasons for Thistelton Dyer's change of heart are not clear. A descendant of Annie Gulvin recounts a family tale that Victoria's daughter Princess Louise lobbied Thistelton Dyer to give her a chance. Certainly, Princess Louise was a supporter of women's rights and expressed an interest in horticultural education for women, but unfortunately no documentary evidence survives to back this up. Perhaps Mr Thistelton Dyer was convinced by what he saw on a visit to Swanley that he reportedly made in 1895.[55] Whatever the reason, in 1896 he decided that Swanley graduates could train at Kew. The whole scheme was a small-scale trial with very limited numbers.

A year later, in January 1897, Gertrude Cope joined Annie and Alice at Kew, along with fellow 'Swanleyite' Eleanor Morland. The four girls were not taken on as full employees, as that required over five years' work experience, nor could they be classed as labourers who performed all the heavy work. That only left them the positions of 'boys' or 'improvers' who were taken into the garden to learn skills whilst earning the lowly wage of just ten shillings a week. These four were followed by a few other Swanley students in subsequent years, but numbers were always restricted. The news that Kew had taken on a handful of female gardeners would have been of niche horticultural interest if it had not been for one odd stipulation. In order to take up the places on offer Kew insisted that they had to wear exactly the same uniform as the male gardeners. They wore peaked caps, shirt and tie, woollen jackets and waistcoats and most shockingly of all, trousers. It is hard to understand now just how transgressive this was; it spoke volumes for the determination of Gertrude and her colleagues that they agreed. The type of trouser they wore was tightly gathered below the knee, tucked into thick woollen socks and leather gaiters. Known as knickerbockers, they were a style of trouser that was also being adopted by some of the more daring 'New Women' in order to undertake sports like cycling, mountain-climbing and skiing in more safety and comfort than voluminous skirts. The reasons given for the uniform were many and varied – from protecting precious plants from damage by long skirts to not distracting male gardeners and allowing the female gardeners to blend in from a distance, so as not to alarm visitors. If the last point was the reason, it backfired spectacularly. The press and public could not get enough of the 'girl garden boys'.

Endless articles in newspapers up and down the land described the new phenomenon, always focusing in breathless detail on their unusual outfits. This report in *The Gardening World*, written in 1903, gives a feel for the slightly prurient tone that the women had to endure:

> Working like a Trojan amid the green grasses and spring blossoms of Kew Gardens may be seen just now a lady in man's attire who is employed as a 'boy' gardener at a salary of 10s per week. Her name is Miss Smith and she is there by permission of the Director, who allows ladies on the gardening staff on condition that they work in male costume. Very attractive and comfortable she looked when seen seated on the edge of the cucumber frame digging weeds out of flowerpots. She was clad in a grey flannel shirt with a turn-down collar and green bow tie, a dark waistcoat, blue serge knickerbockers fastened just below the knee, dark-blue stockings and heavy garden boots. Her coat was lying in a shed nearby, and her sleeves were rolled up above the elbow. She wore, somewhat rakishly tilted forward, a workman's blue cap, while a wealth of light chestnut hair was done up in a knot behind. [56]

Some misgivings were voiced about the physical labour that would be expected of these young women if they were to work alongside men – 'Is it physiologically wise to submit their frames at the most critical period of their growth to the toil necessarily involved in these duties?' asked *The Yorkshire Post* in February 1896, when Annie Gulvin's and Alice Hutchings' employment was announced – but this was a minority worry.[57] Most newspapers fixated much more on the novelty and impropriety of their dress. Part of the fascination seems to be the assumption that, in dressing like young men, Gertrude and her colleagues would automatically adopt masculine behaviours and attitudes. The rise of the 'New Woman' had provoked a rash of cartoons suggesting that newly assertive women were metaphorically wearing the trousers and now that in Kew they literally were, the press had a field day. *The Bognor Regis Observer* felt the need to reassure its readers that 'as the trousers are only worn when at work, the question of New Womanity does not arise.'[58] *The Daily Gazette for Middlesbrough* reported that the girls now 'literally wear the breeks as they pursue their outdoor avocations and jingle their weekly wages of 10s in their trouser pockets, just like men.' The reporter suggested that it would be better if the women could wear a short skirt over their trousers just as Lancashire pit girls did, as 'a more comely, decent, sensible-looking set of healthy, strong-limbed, rosy-faced women it would be difficult to match anywhere.'[59] The suggestion was not taken up and the girls continued to attract attention, even many months later. In October 1897, *The Northern Echo* reported that 'A good many curious persons have been making pilgrimages to Kew to see the new gardeners, but they work in that portion of the garden marked off as "private" and the visitors are disappointed.'[60] There were even music-hall songs written about them:

> A rumour went forth, and the town was aglow,
> From Greenwich to Richmond, from Peckham to Bow,
> And the man in the street made a fine how-de-do,
> When he heard of the ladies who gardened at Kew.
>
> They gardened in bloomers the newspapers said,
> So, to Kew without waiting all Londoners sped,
> From the roofs of the 'buses they had a fine view,
> Of the ladies in bloomers who gardened at Kew.
>
> The orchids were slighted, the lilies were scorned,
> The dahlias were flouted, till botanists mourned,
> But the Londoners shouted, 'What-ho the, Go to –
> Who wants to see blooms now you've bloomers at Kew?'[61]

One of the girls, Ena Powell, wrote honestly about the experience for the Swanley student magazine in 1900. She admitted, 'Since I came here, I have learnt to sympathise sincerely with the animals in the zoo! I can just imagine how the poor things feel when they are stared at for five minutes at a time and remarked upon. I cannot say that I exactly enjoyed that part of a Kew "boy's" life at first, but now I am quite used to it.'[62]

The girls took lodgings in homes close to the garden and newspaper reports differed as to whether they travelled to work in their uniform, hiding their legs under a long coat, or whether they changed into their unusual uniform once safely at work.[63] A much-reproduced photograph of 1898 captures Gertrude Cope standing between Alice Hutchings and Eleanor Morland. They look comfortable and confident with hands in their trouser pockets and long hair carefully crammed into their flat caps. The outfit looks much more practical than long, heavy skirts, not to mention petticoats and corsets. However, the most important detail in the photograph is what Gertrude Cope clutches in her left hand – a small notebook for writing down details of the rare plants in the Botanic Garden. The opportunity to learn practical horticulture amongst one of the finest collections of plants in the world was worth every moment of being described, dressed and paid as a boy. The starting point for all new recruits at Kew was the propagation pits, where they learnt how to strike cuttings and pot on new plants. Looking back after leaving Kew in 1900, Alice Hutchings spoke for all her colleagues when she wrote, 'One gets a love for plants, and everything connected with their well-being and well-doing, not gained anywhere else, certainly not at College.' She concluded, 'The advantages outweigh the disadvantages of dress, long hours (very trying at first) and everything else.'[64]

It is likely that the 'everything else' included not only the media coverage and public fuss, but also the reaction of their colleagues in the garden. There are indications that at first the reception was, at best, lukewarm. In 1896, just after Annie Gulvin and Alice Hutchings started at Kew, the staff magazine, the *Journal of the Kew Guild*, included an editorial which grudgingly conceded, 'The dignity of labour applies, we suppose, equally to women as to men. Given fair play and no favour, we do not object to anyone competing in the field of horticulture, be it prince or peer, retired army officer or young lady.' However, the article also returned to the old chestnut of the physicality of garden work: 'Some of the work seems to be too laborious for them, but that is their affair. They can scarcely hope to become all-round gardeners capable of managing a garden single-handed, but the work of certain departments in large establishments can no doubt be done as well by women as by men.'[65] This was hardly a warm welcome and Gertrude Cope must have been glad of the company and support of her Swanley friends and colleagues. Looking back on her time at Kew, Alice Hutchings reflected that whilst the management at Kew was 'without one exception, I think just and fair … prejudice there was and is, or why should the remark have fallen, "If you had been a young man …" I will not finish – I shall be accused of egotism.'[66] It was not egotism to suggest that if they had been male, the female Kew trainees would have had an easier path. Alice was clearly very capable, and on March 1, 1897, she was promoted to the rank of 'Gardener', with responsibility for 'certain houses and frames'[67] and an increase in wages to 21 shillings a week. Just over a year later, she was promoted to sub-foreman of the herb department, giving her responsibility for supervising men and boys. Meanwhile Gertrude and Eleanor Morland were posted to the herbaceous department, a department in Kew that offered some of the best opportunities to develop skills and knowledge about plants that would be relevant to a broad range of private gardens.

The Swanley girls were proving themselves in the most prestigious botanical garden in the country and other botanical gardens followed suit in offering trainee places for women. The Director of the Glasnevin Botanic Garden in Dublin agreed that women could come to train at the garden, but they would not be paid. Mary Graves, sister of the poet Robert Graves, had attended Swanley and was one of the first women accepted for training at Glasnevin in 1898. Just as Gertrude Cope and the other girls at Kew experienced, numerous visitors asked about the women gardeners, but all requests to meet the girls were refused, Frederick Moore, the Director, saying categorically that they were not there on show. The Royal Botanic Gardens in Edinburgh also accepted female trainees, described as 'probationers'. Constance Hay-Currie, who had been at Swanley at the same time as Gertrude Cope and Madeline Agar, enrolled as a probationer in 1897. She was dismissed by the Regius Keeper, Sir Isaac Bayley Balfour, however, for refusing to wear the uniform of boy's knickerbockers – but not out of any feminine modesty about showing her legs. In Balfour's memorandum of her dismissal, he recorded that she wanted to wear skirts because 'she considered it an advantage to show she was a woman, in order to encourage women to take up gardening.'[68] The independent-minded Miss Hay-Currie was wealthy and able to suit herself, she did not need to worry about finishing her training or receiving a good reference to help secure a job. In 1900 she wrote to the Swanley student magazine recounting how she had purchased a cottage and five acres of land in Swallowfield, near Reading in Berkshire 'in order to have a garden of my very own, and it is certainly delightful to feel that I can do exactly as I like in the way of alteration and improvement.'[69] Two other RGBE probationers, Lina Baker and Annie Morrison, donned the knickerbockers without complaint.[70]

The influence of the Kew experiment spread beyond the world of botanical gardens. The famous orchid grower, Frederick Sander, visited Kew and noted the excellent work carried out by Gertrude and her colleagues. Apparently, this convinced him to employ women at his nursery at Bruges, though for unexplained reasons he felt that 'women cannot easily be employed or circumstances adjusted' in his extensive orchid houses in St Albans.[71] Perhaps he was worried that women might faint in the extreme heat of the orchid house, or worse, see men working shirtless. This was one of the reasons that Joseph Dalton Hooker, Thistleton Dyer's father-in-law and predecessor as Director of Kew, had given for why it was inadvisable for women to be employed at Kew. In addition to the 'digging, manuring and all the disagreeable parts of gardening' they would have to work in hothouses where 'the men, I believe, work simply in their trousers, and how could a lady work with them!'[72] If Gertrude Cope ever worked alongside shirtless male gardeners, she survived the shock and successfully completed her time as a Kew 'garden boy' in November 1898.

Even with the benefit of a year's training at Kew, employers willing to take a chance on giving a post to a female gardener were thin on the ground. Fortunately for aspiring female gardeners, there were some potential employers who saw their gender as an advantage rather than a hindrance. After leaving Kew in the winter of 1898, Gertrude Cope found employment as a gardener for an all-female college. This was the Anstey Physical Training College at Leasowes, Halesowen, near Dudley. It was only the second college in the country to train women as physical education teachers. The college had been established a year earlier by Rhoda Anstey with just three students. Students were instructed in education and medical gymnastics, massage, anatomy, physiology, hygiene, artistic and folk dancing, voice culture and teaching practice. They were also taught how to play outdoor games including cricket, lacrosse, netball and tennis and this of course necessitated extensive playing fields. Gertrude Cope was more than a sports groundskeeper, however. In taking on the sixteen-acre gardens at Leasowes, she was taking on one of the most significant gardens in the country, albeit one that had seen hard times. In the eighteenth century the parkland at Leasowes was internationally famous for its design and natural beauty as a *ferme ornée* or ornamental farm, integrating farmland and ornamental park. The creation of the poet William Shenstone, it had once attracted famous visitors, including William Pitt, Benjamin Franklin and Thomas Jefferson. However, after William Shenstone's death in 1763, Leasowes Park passed through several hands and fell into neglect. By the time Gertrude Cope took charge, the grounds had 'gone wild' as one ex-student later remembered, but they were 'glorious' and no one would 'ever fail to remember the beauty of it all.'[73] Photographs survive in the Birmingham City Archives of students in gymslips disporting themselves in a range of impressive poses with the house in the background. The house is bedecked with window-boxes, hanging baskets and pots, presumably all Gertrude's work.

By the standards of the time, life at Anstey Physical Training College was unconventional to say the least. Gertrude's employer Rhoda Anstey was an intense and eccentric woman who dressed in sandals and an Arab-style djibbah. She was a vegetarian, temperance campaigner and theosophist. Theosophy was a religious system which was drawn from Buddhist and Hindu thought and emphasised the oneness of all life and brotherhood of all people. Its supporters believed in clairvoyance, telepathy and the potential for travel on the astral plain. Theosophy was particularly popular among women at the turn of the century, as the Theosophical Society offered women opportunities for leadership denied them in the conventional religious organisations. Rhoda Anstey had a profound commitment to feminism, and she drew a clear parallel between bodily strength and self-determination for women. With only a handful of students, the college was a tight-knit community, and staff and students all ate together in the communal dining hall. Vegetarianism was actively encouraged, and everyone was sent to their rooms to rest for an hour after lunch. It was a much more unconventional setting than strait-laced Swanley or Kew, and Gertrude would have come into contact with a wide range of new ideas and attitudes. One student recalled, 'College was not hide-bound or narrow in its outlook … and one remembers the diversity of gifts held by visitors to the college: the readings in Miss Anstey's own sitting room, the following of the Boer War in the newspapers after dinner. We had a good deal of freedom.'[74]

Gertrude's fellow Swanleyite, Madeline Agar, also found her best opportunity to start a gardening career was as a school gardener. She already had some teaching experience – her year at York High School for Girls – before joining Swanley and she may well have undertaken the Swanley course with the intention of going back into the education sector as a teacher of gardening and nature study. Nature study had become a fashionable subject to teach children both at home and school from the middle of the nineteenth century, albeit with reservations in some quarters about the inclusion of the sexual aspects of botany. In a way that feels very familiar to modern parents anxious about their children's addiction to their smartphones, there was concern that, thanks to increased industrialisation, children were becoming detached from nature and its health-giving benefits. A steady stream of educational books recommended children should be given a patch of ground to tend as an ideal environment to learn natural science, gain an appreciation of nature's beauty and develop habits of hard work and self-reliance. Queen Victoria added the royal seal of approval when she had gardens created for each of her children at Osborne House. The royal children were expected to keep these up with minimum assistance from the gardeners and they each had their own set of miniature tools. Long absences from the Isle of Wight must have made the royal children's input intermittent, but it was the thought that counted and where the royal household led, others followed. Teachers who could demonstrate that they had expertise in this area could potentially command better positions and higher wages. Supporters of careers for women spotted this opening and promoted it. The suffrage-supporting newspaper, *The Common Cause*, noted 'Many girls' secondary schools have a woman gardener who is well able to look after the garden – which has no glass – and to teach the girls. If she has board and lodgings in addition to her salary, it is a desirable and pleasant post. If school gardening in elementary schools should become general, the County Councils will require inspectors and probably lecturers, and these are suitable posts for women.'[75]

Madeline Agar was an early example of a woman gardener based in a school. Her first paid gardening post after leaving Swanley in 1896 was at Wycombe Abbey School in Buckinghamshire. This girls' private school opened in September 1896, and it is likely that Madeline was one of the first teachers there. The school founder was Miss Jane Dove. A committed suffragist, Miss Dove felt that it was vital that girls were given an education that prepared them to be active citizens, capable of making a positive difference to society. Wycombe Abbey School was established with the explicit aim of providing girls with the equivalent quality of education that boys received at the prestigious public schools. To achieve this, pupils were treated to strict discipline, with daily cold baths and unheated classrooms. In addition to the usual academic subjects, competitive sports were encouraged as well as more unconventional subjects like carpentry and gardening. Madeline Agar oversaw the school gardens, a set of terraced gardens laid out when the school moved into the

Gardens at Wycombe Abbey School created by Madeline Agar. From *A Primer of School Gardening*, 1909. Courtesy of the RHS Lindley Collections.

Gothic-style Loakes Manor and surrounding buildings. Like lots of gardeners dealing with gardens handed over by builders, she found 'The beds just round the houses were done in true contractor's style – about six inches of very fine soil laid on the raw chalk and neatly raked.' However, with the assistance of 'an additional man for the purpose', she soon improved the soil and enjoyed laying out the new borders. Most of her time was spent instructing the pupils in tending their own garden plots. In 1900 the gardens were well established, and she wrote an enthusiastic account for the Swanley magazine. 'Excellent roses and sweet peas have been notable products. Our flower show in June was a success. There were 244 entries which shows keenness from a school of 220 and the prize roses were quite good. How lovely sweet peas are now! We grow mostly named kinds and have become quite learned in the sorts ... Alpine strawberries have become a feature with us. They fruit continuously from June to October not largely at any time, but so that two or three times a week one can have a few to eat or present to friends.' She gave her pupils a lot of autonomy in running their plots and they chose and bought their own seeds, often from the local seedsman Ryder

& Son (later sponsor of the famous Ryder Cup golf tournament), because 'He puts up everything in penny packets and for a shilling one can stock a garden. A penny is not a great venture, and the girls will often try something new to make up the shillingsworth.' Not much older than her pupils, and certainly not much taller, Madeline Agar comes across as an approachable teacher who communicated her enthusiasm for plants and gardens. Although the school was not equipped with greenhouses or hot beds, she encouraged the girls to be ambitious in their gardens, boasting, 'This year we have successfully reared zonal geraniums from seed and several others, amongst them being Japanese chrysanthemums. In fact, I am beginning to think anything is possible. Last February after I had distributed the seeds, an ardent gardener went in the afternoon to her garden and sowed every packet. Imagine my dismay when she told me, for they were chiefly half-hardies, and the frost was on the ground. Of course, I prophesied failure, but cosmea and several Japanese chrysanthemums came and grew rampant.'[76]

Later, Madeline Agar wrote a book on school gardening which was packed with practical advice for teachers wishing to set up a school garden. Her writing suggests that she had a clear-eyed, unromantic view of children in gardens. She wrote, 'The teacher should bear in mind that tools will not last forever, and a certain amount of breakage is unblameable … The children should be encouraged to report loose handles, leaking cans and other deficiencies, which they certainly will not do if all damage is a heinous offence. At the same time, the young are mostly rough and reckless and need constant reminders not to dump heavy cans of water on stony paths, not to stand on rakes and hoes and generally to avoid all ingenious misuse to which a child will subject tools.'[77] She took a similarly straightforward line on pest control: 'As a rule quite young children have no objection to collecting any creatures, and when a child shows repugnance to handling things, he should be helped to overcome it. Of course, handling is altogether different from killing, and it is but proper to have an objection to that. But killing must be done only too often, and the children should be taught to do it quickly and not impose a lingering death merely to save their own feelings.'[78] However, she did acknowledge that since 'Insecticides for attacking creatures through poisoning their food generally contain arsenic in some form', it was probably 'not advisable to keep them about where children are. Finger and thumb and soapy water should be substituted.' Sometimes the pests were larger and soap and water would not suffice: 'Occasionally a mole may be caught while working. The movement of the soil betrays its presence, and if a fork is thrust into the moving part, the mole may be thrown out. They are easily killed by a blow on the snout.'[79] This was a world away from the ladylike tone of Louisa Johnson and *Every Lady Her Own Flower Gardener.*

Schools were not the only single-sex institutions happy to employ female gardeners. The Edwardian era saw a revolution in the care of chronically sick and disabled people, with more emphasis on providing care in a pleasant environment than the large forbidding institutions of earlier generations. Many of these institutions were deliberately set in large and beautiful grounds. Someone was needed to care for these gardens and support the inmates or patients to garden. Jessie Smith, along with her sister Mildred, was one of the first female students at Swanley in 1891, and by 1896 she was employed as gardener at the Duxhurst Farm Colony for Female Inebriates. The Colony, set in 180 acres of land between Reigate and Horley was the brainchild of social reformer and temperance campaigner Lady Isabella Somerset. After a close friend of hers committed suicide under the influence of alcohol, the deeply religious Lady Somerset became determined to tackle the devastating effects alcoholism could have on women of all classes. Whilst poor women turned to drink to find temporary relief from their hard lives, women higher up the social scale, frustrated by the tedium of their lives or trapped in unhappy marriages, could also become lonely victims of alcoholism. Like many social reformers, Lady Somerset was convinced that the countryside offered a better environment for recovery than the temptation-filled city. Advised by the US-trained female medic, Dr Sarah Anderson-Brown, she also felt that the passive indoor occupations offered to women in hospitals, reformatories and prisons were not enough to foster the physical and moral transformation that these women needed. At a meeting to raise funds for the home, 'Dr Miss Anderson-Brown' explained that alcoholism was one of the 'most curious diseases that ever a physician had to treat, because it was not only broken-down physical health, but broken-down moral health and broken-down souls ... With outdoor employment, and plenty of it, and proper food – there would be a great deal of vegetable food and fruit in the diet – they hoped very soon to be able to restore a great many of the patients to their homes and friends, where they had friends, and to place upon their feet those who had none.'[80] The Duxhurst Colony focused heavily on outdoor activity in isolated and tranquil surroundings and gardening was a key part of everyday life. The Colony was equipped with a large greenhouse where chrysanthemums were grown for sale and patients were also trained by Jessie Smith to work in extensive fields growing sweet peas, sunflowers and lavender. The Colony was exclusively for women, apart from the dependent children of the patients who stayed in a special building called The Nest, and Lady Somerset, who was a supporter of women's suffrage, was keen to employ a female gardener to oversee all the gardening activity. In the British Women's Temperance Association's Annual Report of 1896, Lady Somerset noted proudly that Miss Smith had been able to 'introduce among the patients a spirit of emulation in the gardening work that could never have been brought about if we had the services of a "mere man".'[81]

Institutions like Anstey Physical Training College, Duxhurst Colony and progressive girls' schools, which were set up by women with a vision for a more compassionate and just society, provided opportunities for female gardeners at a time when other employers were hard to find. Attractive gardens and healthy locally grown seasonal food and the experience of growing it were valuable elements of the regime that these institutions offered their pupils, inmates and patients. This must have added a real sense of purpose to the work of the women who cared for these gardens. However, these were relatively closed worlds and the gardens that they created for these institutions were unlikely to make a splash in horticultural circles. Moreover, although they were doing important work, these new institutions were reliant on fees or charitable donations and were often working on very tight budgets. They simply did not have the resources for spectacular horticultural features. Women gardeners like Madeline Agar and Gertrude Cope were doing rewarding work, but they were still firmly on the bottom rungs of the horticultural career ladder. Whatever the benefits of gardening for an institution, the pinnacle of the horticultural profession was still the post of head gardener in a prestigious private or public garden, managing multiple specialist departments and a large garden staff. But who would trust a woman with such a large undertaking?

Ada Brown and Decima Allen loading plants from the Allen-Brown Violet Nursery before setting off by horse and cart to Henfield Station, 1912. Courtesy of Henfield Museum.

4
WOMEN TAKE CHARGE

Why should we not have our female Paxtons and Kents?

'Horticulture as a Profession for Ladies',
The Garden, September 7, 1873

In 1900 the garden historian Alicia Amherst wrote to Reverend Wilks, the Secretary of the Royal Horticultural Society, to ask if he could recommend a female head gardener for her to employ. His reply was unequivocal: 'I am afraid I cannot help you. I know of no woman gardener who has what you want and all-round knowledge, so as to be able to direct the foremen of the departments. I do not believe such a person exists. Miss Jekyll herself would not be able to take such a post – she could not direct melon-growing or early grape-forcing and so on.'[82] Reverend Wilks was far from alone. Almost to prove his point, Gertrude Jekyll herself, although she was a patron of Frances Wolseley's Glynde College for Lady Gardeners, never employed women in her own garden. The influential author and editor of *The Garden* magazine, William Robinson, was also a supporter of Frances Wolseley's school but he did not employ any female gardeners at his garden at Gravetye either. Ellen Willmot went even further, famously writing that a woman would be 'utterly hopeless and unsafe in the borders'.[83] In 1901 a female journalist itemised all the objections to female head gardeners that she had heard raised by the 'scoffers' whom she said, 'maintain women gardeners cannot organise the amount of labour which is necessary in a large garden and that their skirts knock everything down, that all gardening spells hard work, and this in turn leads to rough hands, coarse skins, large feet and ugly figures, lastly that they are taking the bread out of men's mouths.'[84]

To obtain a head gardener position in this environment, a woman would need to be either very lucky or prepared to make compromises. Even Swanley's star pupil, a graduate of Kew, had to accept a less than ideal post in order to manage a garden. This was Annie Gulvin, who had studied at Swanley alongside Madeline Agar and Gertrude Cope and achieved the remarkable feat of scoring the highest marks in the country in the RHS examination. Like Gertrude, Annie Gulvin was from a relatively humble background. She came to Swanley on a scholarship from Kent County Council, and after she joined Kew as a 'garden boy' just a short while before Gertrude Cope. On leaving Kew in January 1897, Annie Gulvin took the post of head gardener to Mr James Brogden of Iscoed Mansion, Ferryside, in Carmarthenshire. The *Journal of the Kew Guild* proudly reported, 'Miss Gulvin has the distinction of being the first woman to take sole charge of a garden on exactly the same terms as a man.'[85] She would be living in the gardener's cottage and take full responsibility for the management of all areas of the garden and a team of four men. On the surface, it appeared that Annie was taking on a substantial post, exactly the kind of position Reverend Wilks has predicted it was impossible for a woman to attain. Iscoed Mansion was a large eighteenth-century house set in extensive parkland. The Brogden family were local industrialists, heavily involved in the development of Porthcawl. Ordnance Survey maps of the time show that the garden included ornamental gardens, an orchard, a large walled kitchen garden and a comprehensive set of greenhouses. But Iscoed was also something of a poisoned chalice, a neglected garden belonging to a family that no longer had the funds to sustain it. The Brogden family business had gone into liquidation in 1884 after an unsuccessful venture in railway construction in New Zealand. Annie wrote, 'On my arrival I was piloted round the garden by an "old hand" who gave me discouraging accounts of my predecessors' troubles. The condition of the place too was disheartening.'[86] Whilst her first impression of her new garden was pleasure at its setting, 'surrounded by some of the prettiest scenery of South Wales', she also confessed,

> Unfortunately, this delightful impression did not stay with me when viewing my special charge, the garden, for the former head gardener had left a few months before, and the place had been neglected in consequence. The old age of the garden was easily seen in the ancient pear trees and dilapidated walls, and the black topsoil over-rich with plentiful supplies of manure and the absence of the correcting influence of lime. The four vineries, orchard-house (containing about thirty peach trees and vines), and the cucumber frames also date back to the early days of culture under glass, being heated by hot-air flues. Insect pests of all kinds abounded, and to these troubles were added rats, mice and birds – starlings especially, which took away whole berries at a time, and did not hesitate to break lights in their efforts.[87]

Undaunted, Annie set to work and applied her energy to tackling the long list of problems. One of the worst areas of the garden was the large vinery where the grape crop was riddled with mildew. She pinpointed that the problem lay with the border which 'consisted of about 16" of topsoil with no drainage material (except for the skeleton of a horse!) over a layer of concrete', so overhauled it. Next she tackled two smaller vineries which she cleared of their aged vines and converted to new uses – 'one was planted with peach trees in a mixture of soil similar to that used in the vine border, and the other was fitted with hot-water pipes and prepared for tomatoes etc.' The conservatory blew down in a heavy gale, but Annie was not downhearted or defeated by this setback; she recycled the glazing for cold frames, philosophically describing the incident as 'an ill wind that supplied us with a number of frames' and got on with erecting a new conservatory. Then in spring, she reported, 'The flower garden was turfed and laid out anew, new beds cut and filled with rose trees, yuccas, cannas, pampas grass etc. In the front of the house the beds were planted with *Rhododendron nobleanum* and Azaleas with a border of variegated Euonymus. A narrow border round part of the house took about 300 Euonymus, with a

Portrait of Annie Gulvin, who came top in the RHS examination of 1895 and secured a post as head gardener at Iscoed in South Wales. Courtesy of the RHS Lindley Collections.

background of *Mahonia aquifolium*.' As if this was not enough to prove Reverend Wilks was wrong in assuming that a woman could not manage a large and complex garden, Annie Gulvin also took in hand the five-acre kitchen garden to produce surplus produce which she sold to local hotels, along with baskets of flowers such as arums, geraniums, sweet peas and chrysanthemums. She described how 'a large portion of the ground is planted with strawberries of which during the season from 18 to 20 lbs were sent off by 7am every morning, the early supplies realising 1s per lb. This good result and ready sale induced the planting of 3,000 runners late in July, which have already made good plants ... The care of the fruit trees is a large item. Every available wall supports a fruit tree of some kind, and besides two grass orchards there are many pyramid and bush fruit trees.' Even with this workload, Annie found time to maintain her interest in the science of horticulture, continuing the habits of close observation she had learnt at Swanley and Kew. She noted, 'Some of the buds (on redcurrant bushes) were attacked with a mite which under the microscope tallied exactly in all points with the blackcurrant mite (*Phytoptus ribis*).'[88]

Within a year of her appointment Annie Gulvin was able to write back to her Kew colleagues that 'We are gradually getting things ship-shape ... From what I have seen of the gardens of the neighbourhood, I do not think we shall have occasion to fear comparison with the best of them. If Kew were only nearer, I should feel perfectly happy.' In the same letter Annie was careful to reassure her ex-colleagues that 'My men are all that I could wish, no cause for anxiety in that quarter.'[89] Annie Gulvin was still a very young woman; she was only twenty-one when she took charge of the gardens at Iscoed. Although her academic qualifications and time at Kew will have given her confidence in her horticultural abilities, managing a team of four men must have been intimidating to begin with. Certainly, her colleagues at Kew felt she should be congratulated. The editor of the *Journal of the Kew Guild* wrote, 'Her success has been a source of satisfaction to all who know the nature of her undertaking, and clever though she is, many will be surprised that one of her sex so young should have conquered all the difficulties of a first situation which was evidently not of the apple-pie order.'[90]

In 1898 Annie's success was rewarded with a £10 a year pay rise and she was able to appoint an assistant. She chose another 'lady gardener', a Miss Groome. This was possibly Dora Groome who later went on to manage a nursery near Petersfield. Annie Gulvin wrote proudly, 'Our garden is a source of interest to the craft, and we have many callers, evidently curious to know what a woman gardener can do. My staff is now quite contented to be controlled by one of the 'weaker' sex. I think that when men see that our intentions are serious and that we are not afraid to work, they respect our efforts to find employment outside the very restricted boundary within which till recently women's work was confined. Altogether my situation is a most agreeable one. Miss Groome and I occasionally go for a long tramp into the country.'[91]

Gertrude Cope, another Kew 'boy', will have followed Annie Gulvin's progress with keen interest, and it was not long before she had an opportunity to supervise staff and manage a garden herself. After around a year working at the Anstey Physical Training College at Leasowes, she was on the move to a new job. Again, the *Journal of the Kew Guild* kept a close eye on its female alumni, reporting in the 1899 issue that Gertrude had been 'engaged by G. Cadbury Esq, The Manor House, Northfield, near Birmingham, as foreman, her special charge being herbaceous and alpine plants. She is to receive 30s a week with furnished cottage. Her assistant is another lady gardener from Swanley, who will occupy the cottage with her. Miss Cope has been succeeded at the Leasowes by another lady gardener.'[92] Annie Gulvin had been forced to compromise to get a head gardener post by diving in at the deep end with a garden in a poor condition. Gertrude Cope was in many respects more fortunate. She had found a 'foreman' role in charge of a department in a large garden, so she was going to gain management experience in a more gradual, less pressurised way, which was more in line with the way most men progressed through the profession. Her assistant was Olive Harrisson, the fellow Swanley student who the previous year had come top in the RHS examination and had had the temerity to ask for her Chiswick scholarship. Turned down by the RHS, she now had the consolation of a job with Gertrude Cope at Northfield.

Their employer, George Cadbury, was the co-owner with his brother Richard of Cadbury Brothers, the famous cocoa and chocolate makers. In 1879 the brothers had opened a new chocolate factory in a wooded valley just four miles outside Birmingham. As a Quaker and philanthropist, George Cadbury was intensely interested in the wellbeing of his workforce and in 1895 he began constructing a model village for his workers which he named Bourneville. Unlike many industrialists, George Cadbury chose to live close to his factory and workers' homes. In 1894 he had purchased Northfield Manor House and moved his large family there. The house was refurbished in a Mock Tudor style by architect George Gadd, who had designed some of the early factory buildings at Bourneville. By

1899 when Gertrude Cope started work at Northfield, the family consisted of ten children, five from George Cadbury's first marriage and five from his second marriage to Elizabeth Cadbury, née Taylor.

It is perhaps to Elizabeth Cadbury that Gertrude owed her opportunity. Like her husband, Elizabeth Cadbury was a Quaker and Christian Socialist, but she was also a committed supporter of women's rights. In 1898 she founded the Birmingham Union of Girls' Clubs and was active in the YWCA and in the National Council for Women. She was also Vice President of the Electrical Association for Women, an organisation which sought to alleviate women's domestic drudgery by promoting the benefits of electricity in the home. These interests and beliefs help explain why the couple were open to the idea of employing female gardeners. In 1899 Ada Goodrich Freer, the Honorary Secretary of the Women's Branch at Swanley, reported 'Nine-tenths, at least, of would-be employers who have applied to me for women gardeners are themselves women, and in very many cases they have offered as a reason that they thought it right to promote a new opening for women's work.' Elizabeth Garrett Anderson, the first woman in Britain to qualify as a physician, employed a string of Swanley graduates to care for the garden of her home in Suffolk. This backing was not always entirely selfless, as Ada Goodrich Freer also pointed out, 'I am bound to add that many of these withdrew on finding that women's work is not to be had cheap, and that a woman who has devoted two years to an expensive training does not propose to accept less than the wages of the ordinary under-gardener.'[93] With wages of 30 shillings a week and free housing, the Cadburys were paying the going rate for a foreman, so it is safe to say their incentive in giving Gertrude an opportunity was not to save money. There was also a connection between the Cadbury family and the Anstey Physical Training College that might additionally explain how Gertrude Cope came to the attention of her new employers. In 1899 Margaret Cadbury, George Cadbury's niece, joined Anstey College as a student. The Cadbury family were later very unhappy that Margaret came under 'the influence of theosophy and one of the many cults of mental healing'[94] whilst at Anstey and they eventually intervened to persuade her to abandon these beliefs but it is possible that Margaret recommended Gertrude Cope as a gardener to her uncle during her time there. It seems that Gertrude Cope had not picked up too many unconventional ideas or habits at Anstey College to deter the Quaker Cadbury family from employing her.

When Gertrude Cope and Olive Harrisson arrived at Northfield, Bourneville Village was still under construction, but gardens and open spaces were already at the heart of the Cadbury vision for the welfare of their workforce. Bourneville famously had no public houses but was well supplied with green space. In addition to gardens around the houses, there were public parks, allotments and playing fields. The factory itself also sat within landscaped grounds for open-air refreshment and exercise for the workers. The Cadburys went to very great lengths to maintain their gardens and parks; by the 1930s there were fifty gardeners and groundsmen working at Bourneville. The garden staff were expected to be horticultural mentors for their neighbourhood, offering classes in gardening, donating seeds and selling plants and flowers from the company greenhouses to Bourneville residents. Although Gertrude Cope worked in the private gardens of the Cadbury family home at Northfield, this fifty-acre estate was also seen as one of the resources that the family used to support the health and wellbeing of the local community. For the Cadburys it was important that their own private gardens were models of good cultivation for their workers to aspire to and they opened them up as spaces for their employees to learn from and enjoy and for other social projects outside their business life. The garden was frequently the setting for garden parties for poor families from Birmingham, with hundreds of children treated to tea and games in the grounds. In 1894 a special wooden barn was built in the gardens to host picnic parties for local groups. The Cadbury company magazine regularly reported on house parties and outdoor events such as garden parties or picnics for the workforce and Gertrude will have been expected to ensure that the gardens were an attractive and appealing setting for these events.

At first Gertrude was working under another ex-Kew gardener, J. Dyfry-Jones, who was in charge of both the gardens at Northfield and the development of the Bourneville village parks and gardens. However, by 1904 the development and maintenance work for the Bourneville estate had grown to the extent that Mr Dyfry-Jones dedicated all his time to the public gardens and Gertrude Cope was promoted to the position of head gardener at Northfield. Unlike Annie Gulvin, who had had to accept a position in a dilapidated and neglected garden, Gertrude was working for an employer who took a keen interest in the garden. Northfield was a lovely setting, with ornamental gardens, woodland and a man-made lake. The Cadbury children could be a handful; family letters recount that the children frequently got into trouble with the garden staff for trampling on flower beds and climbing trees. Gertrude and Olive shared a gardener's cottage and received visits from old college friends. In 1900 C. F. Fellows, another ex-Swanley student living in Stratford-upon-Avon wrote that she and her sister had been to visit Miss Cope and Miss Harrison 'in their pretty little cottage at Northfield, and were shown the beautiful grounds where they work, especially admiring the well-wooded drive to the house and the bright and sunny flower garden.'[95] Olive Harrisson gave a glowing account of their work at the end of that year: 'The last year has been an extremely busy one for Miss Cope and I. We have had such a tremendous lot of new plants and shrubs to put in, one lot of the Alpine plants for the rockery were very interesting indeed; we hope the rabbits will have mercy on them ... We put a good number of hardy Chrysanthemums out in the borders, but the rabbits ate them all off, so we shall grow them in the walled garden in future ... One afternoon we had a most exciting time, punting about on the lake, trying to reach a small island, on which we wanted to plant *Primula japonica*. After wandering about for some time, we managed to anchor safely on the island, did our planting and got back to the boat house in grand style.' It was not all work; on their days off they visited flower shows and Olive described visiting the Midland Chrysanthemum Show and the Worcester Fruit Show which they 'enjoyed immensely'.[96]

It was not a luxurious existence; shared accommodation in a gardener's cottage was comfortable but basic. Gertrude and Olive would work long hours while keeping themselves fed and their house tidy without the aid of a servant in the days before any labour-saving devices. It is possible to get a feel for the female gardener's lifestyle from *Gardening for Women*, a book of advice to potential female gardeners that Frances Wolseley wrote in 1908. She cautioned, 'It should be remembered that lady gardeners usually must brush their skirts and possibly have to clean their own boots. A small cottage does not afford much space, so nothing should be bought which is not absolutely necessary.'[97] At the same time, a female head gardener could not afford to let standards slip when it came to her own appearance. To maintain the respect of her team and her employers, it was important that she always looked like a lady. Whilst they were students, a shirt with a turn-down collar and tie was acceptable, but when they reached the status of head gardener, Frances Wolseley advised that they should make more effort: 'A stand-up linen collar will give a neat appearance.' Practicality was still the main concern when it came to clothes, however. 'It should be seen that the tailor gives two comfortable deep pockets' to any coat, she advised.[98] Frances Wolseley also stressed the importance of making an effort to eat properly: 'Women living alone are very apt, from laziness, to fall into a habit of drinking tea and eating only bread and butter. Work certainly cannot be done on this, solid food is absolutely necessary.' Not all her housekeeping tips were as helpful. Another tip was: 'Asbestos mats for placing under saucepans on a closed stove cost only 4d each and prevent contents burning.'[99] It seems that Gertrude Cope managed to juggle all these responsibilities – perhaps her experience as a teenager helping to run her sister's boarding house helped. In 1900 J. Dyfry-Jones reported back to Kew that the Cadburys 'appear to be well satisfied with their lady gardeners.'[100] A woman running a large garden was still a rarity and Gertrude Cope would have been relieved that a positive account of her work was sent back to Kew.

As head gardeners, the women had a degree of freedom to shape the look and feel of the gardens in their care. The women who emerged from the horticultural schools tended to be early devotees of 'the wild garden', a new style of garden design associated with a romantic appreciation of natural forms, traditional crafts and vernacular architecture, as exemplified in the Arts and Crafts movement. In her letter to the Swanley student magazine in 1900, Olive Harrisson wrote that she and Gertrude Cope had been busy 'wild gardening down the drive' at Bourneville and described how they planted one bank with '*Fritillaria meleagris* and another with Chionodoxas, also mounds of wild daffodils and snowdrops and scillas.'[101] Lilian Deane (another ex-Swanley student), while working as an assistant at Burstall, went on a visit to see the gardens at Hintlesham Hall where she saw 'an avenue of umbrella-topped thorns of various kinds, backed by a great bank of clipped laurel' which she described as 'quaint' but 'all extremely artificial and un-Robinsonian.'[102] This was a reference to the garden writer and friend of Gertrude Jekyll, William Robinson, who championed this new, more naturalistic, style of garden design.

In May 1900 Gertrude Cope returned to Kew for the inaugural Kew Guild Dinner. This event was an opportunity for past and present garden staff and students to get together for a convivial meal and catch up on each other's news and careers. Gertrude met up with her fellow 'garden boys', Alice Hutchings and Eleanor Morland. While Alice Hutchings was still at Kew and had been promoted to Sub-Foreman of the Alpine Pits, a position with some supervisory responsibilities, Eleanor's experience also confirmed the impression that the most promising horticultural career opportunities were to be had working for employers who had a strong personal belief in the women's movement. After leaving Kew, Eleanor Morland had spent a year back at Swanley teaching and looking after the grounds. She had then returned to the family home in Gloucestershire to oversee the design of her father's and uncle's gardens. She had only one other paid position – a short period overseeing an orchard in Market Rasen belonging to Jessie Boucherett, a campaigner for women's rights who had helped to set up the Society for Promoting the Employment of Women in 1859. By the time of the dinner, news would have reached them that Annie Gulvin, too, had also found new work with a sympathetic female employer. After just under two years at Iscoed, Annie Gulvin became head gardener to Lilian Cranfield at her home in Burstall in Suffolk. Lilian Cranfield came from a family of supporters of women's suffrage. Her mother had chaired the first Ipswich Women's Suffrage Society as early as 1871 and the family were related by marriage to Elizabeth Garrett Anderson and her sister Millicent Fawcett. At Burstall, Annie Gulvin had a team of men to manage alongside her assistant, Lilian Deane.

As they sat around the table for the Kew Dinner, the women doubtless compared notes. It would be surprising indeed if, between themselves at least, these young women did not discuss the barriers and difficulties they faced as they climbed the career ladder to manage male garden staff. Although Gertrude Cope did not leave any written account of her experiences at Bourneville and Annie Gulvin seemed determined to put a positive spin on her experiences, the wider attitudes displayed in the horticultural press of the time makes it hard to believe they would not have had some horror stories to share. One gardener named Albert R. Gould felt moved to write to the *Journal of Horticulture* that women taking head gardener posts was 'an awful state of affairs; they will be placing us in a very humiliating position; we shall only be allowed to wash pots and crocks and do the stoking. It is useless to tell them that wearing men's clothes and doing men's work is out of their sphere … But it is the question as to whether many will occupy head gardener's or foreman's positions very long, as mere men, especially the horticultural type, detest having a woman in command.'[103] Condescension, while not outright rejection, was also a frustratingly common attitude. The tone taken by the gardening journalist F. W. Burbidge, gives us a clear idea of the patronising welcome young female head gardeners could face: 'Given a becoming costume and robust health, the bonnie lasses are quite welcome to come and play in the garden. We are all glad to see them; they are, God bless'em, as welcome as was Eve in Paradise – as welcome as are the flowers in May. But the tall and braw lads in the bothy will pity their struggles with the spade and hasten to assist them.'[104]

Annie Gulvin had been keen to make clear in her letters to the Kew Guild that she had no problem from her male employees, after they saw that 'our intentions are serious and that we are not afraid to work'. Lilian Deane, however, was not so confident, and confessed that she was relieved to return to work at Swanley after seven months at Burstall since she 'enjoyed the greater freedom given by the absence of "the men". I was always in such great awe of the Burstall men!'[105]

One way to avoid the intimidating male gardeners was to work in a garden which only employed women. Ada Cassidy, daughter of a prominent Donegal family, studied at Swanley and passed her RHS examination in 1898. By 1900 she was head gardener at Bignor Park in Sussex, supervising a team of three female gardeners, Frances St Barbe, Frances Meadmore and Emily Boorman, all ex-Swanley pupils. Ada Cassidy was known affectionately by her team as 'The Missus' and all four seem to have enjoyed themselves enormously working at a garden that had once been horticulturally very significant. It had been created by famous garden designer William Sawrey Gilpin and originally owned by John Hawkins, the man who published *Flora Graeca*, one of the great botanical books. Like Iscoed, the garden had seen better days, but the four sent a very jolly account of their work to the Swanley student magazine in 1900: 'The work here is mostly out of doors, there being only five houses of rather ancient order, stoking is constant and accomplished under many difficulties. The wet days keep us fairly busy moving plants from place to place to avoid the drips.' They worked hard but the impression is that they had fun. They describe contending with 'more than the usual pests' in the form of 'twenty-seven fat little pigs' whose grunts

> rouse the first unwilling riser who flies after them regardless of appearance. Between her yells and the pigs, the others turn up just in time to see the last curly tail disappearing through the gate ... The peacocks disport themselves on the seed beds and have proved excellent judges of the choicest fruits, as also the rats wished to do in the fruit rooms. To complete the Zoo, we have a most intelligent Donkey, whose one idea is to open the numerous gates by which

> he lets himself and his two constant companions, the ponies, into whatever part of the ground they wish to go … We are living a true gardener's life, inhabiting a small cottage in the gardens. The 'joys' of living in the country are fully appreciated (?) here.[106]

Yet all-female gardens, like Bignor Park, were few and far between.

*

The truth was that if a woman aspired to be a head gardener, she must expect to manage a team of gardeners that was mostly made up of men and boys. But how was she to command their respect? Gertrude Cope and Annie Gulvin could draw authority from the knowledge, expertise and qualifications they had gained at Swanley and Kew but they were to be almost uniquely privileged in that regard. The offer of placements at Kew for women turned out to be a sadly short-lived experiment. By 1902 there were no female 'improvers' left at Kew and only a handful of women were given the opportunity of extending their horticultural education in this way. The women who followed into the profession had to rely on their own personal leadership qualities, backed only by the training they could gain at colleges like Swanley or the Glynde College for Lady Gardeners, or even shorter courses at smaller private garden schools.

It was not impossible, but it involved an impressive degree of assertive self-confidence. One woman who had such confidence was Isobel Turner, the Lincolnshire farmer's daughter. In 1891 she was accompanying her father as he wound down the last of his substantial stock-breeding business, but after her father died in 1893, the farm, the house and its contents were all sold off at auction and Isobel Turner and her stepmother moved from Ulceby Grange. From about this time Isobel started referring to herself as Miss J. S. Turner. Perhaps this was in honour of her father, John Turner, or perhaps she had another first name or nickname she preferred to use over Isobel, but unfortunately there is no record to tell us. All correspondence and publications for the rest of her life were signed or addressed J. S. Turner. She briefly went into partnership with a local nurseryman named John Smith selling flowers close to Ulceby Junction before somewhat unexpectedly turning up as the head gardener on a large private estate in Scotland.

In the 1901 census lists, a Miss J. S. Turner, aged 42, is identified as head gardener at Dochfour Gardens in Inverness. This was a remarkable transformation, particularly as there is no record of a J. S. or Isobel Turner attending any of the horticultural colleges of the day or sitting the RHS examination. Her employers were Colonel James Evan Bruce Baillie and his wife Nellie Lisa Baillie, the daughter of Baron Burton, owner of Burton's Brewery. Neither of her employers was an obvious supporter of female emancipation and I can find no family or social connection between the Turners and the Baillies to account for her appointment. Her father had been active in Conservative and Unionist politics and Colonel Baillie was a Conservative Unionist MP, so it is possible that this was their connection, but unfortunately there is no surviving documentation to prove this theory.

Dochfour had been the home of the Baillie family for over five hundred years. Most of the fifteen-acre formal gardens that surrounded the house were laid out in the 1830s and 40s by Evan Baillie, who had made a fortune as a slave trader and plantation owner in the West Indies. By the time J. S. Turner arrived the gardens featured Italianate terraces, walled gardens, a water garden, rose gardens, yew topiary, kitchen gardens, and orchards extending down to the edge of Loch Ness. Her address in the census was recorded as 'Dochfour Gardens' so she probably lived in the Gardener's Cottage which was built in 1875 and attached to the exterior wall of the kitchen garden. Dochfour had a large and well-equipped garden and employed a team of around sixteen gardeners. The garden had been expanded in 1881 to include glasshouses, producing a variety of exotic fruit and vegetables including bananas in a Banana House. As head gardener, J. S. Turner was a significant figure in the local community. The local paper, *The Inverness Courier*, carried several reports in 1901 of Miss J. S. Turner providing 'tasteful decorations' from the gardens at Dochfour for local events such as the Dochgarroch School Concert.

J. S. Turner did not stay long at Dochfour, however. We next locate her, after positions as a horticultural lecturer, at the Glynde College for Lady Gardeners. In 1905 she became Frances Wolseley's head gardener and main instructor. It is highly likely that it was J. S. Turner who gave Frances Wolseley the detailed insights into the practicalities of being a head gardener that feature in her book, *Gardening for Women*. Certainly, for someone who had never personally been employed as a head gardener herself, Frances Wolseley wrote very confidently about what women needed to do to succeed as head gardeners. The tone taken in the book suggests that both Frances Wolseley and J. S. Turner relied to a large degree on the confidence to supervise the lower classes that they had acquired through their own upper-class upbringing. The two women certainly come across as redoubtable, with no time for self-doubt of any kind. For instance, it was important, Frances Wolseley declared, that female head gardeners should assert their authority as quickly as possible. 'Arrangements should be made also for power to dismiss any subordinate who is lazy or misbehaves and this should be acted on without hesitation upon the first proof of neglect …' the book advised, adding, 'There is no doubt that a lady, with superior education, tact and taste should succeed where many men have failed. It must be borne in mind that the employer's pleasure has to be studied, and that the men will have to be managed with firmness and strict fairness.'[107] In fact, Frances Wolseley believed that *only* women with the advantages of a higher social status should aspire to management roles in horticulture. She wrote, 'I see indeed a vast outlook of work and happiness for educated women, the daughters of professional men, but for the maidservant or secondary school girl it would seem the farm and not garden life holds out far more suitable prospects … the men under-gardeners who must of necessity be employed, too, for hard work, would not welcome in their profession young women of their own sphere of life. They would resent the cooperation of one of their women friends although they would gladly allow a lady to direct their work.'[108]

In fact, the experience of Swanley's most successful female graduates refutes this. The irony is that it was arguably the students from relatively lowly social backgrounds, those who came to the college on a scholarship, who were the most successful in head gardener roles. Of the four women initially taken on at Kew, only Eleanor Morland, the daughter of a factory owner and Justice of the Peace, paid the full course fees. Gertrude Cope, Alice Hutchings and Annie Gulvin all relied on scholarships, as their families were far from wealthy. Whilst Eleanor Morland did some unpaid work after Kew, designing gardens for members of her family, it was the girls from more humble backgrounds who took on the challenge of developing serious careers in horticulture.

Yet, whatever a female gardener's background, character or abilities, there remained one barrier that ambitious women faced that men simply did not. If a woman were to have a career in horticulture long enough to give her time to develop a reputation and rise to head up a large garden, she would have to remain single. It was taken as read by people of all political persuasions that a woman could not combine a career with the duties of a wife and mother. Whilst society could tolerate single women working and even aspiring to a professional career, it was nearly universally expected they would give it up as soon as they married. Even the progressive Cadbury family dismissed female factory workers who married, giving them a 'marriage gift' of a bible and a carnation when they left. Male gardeners generally had to wait a long time to marry, at least until promotion earned them high enough wages or they had access to tied accommodation large enough for a family, but, since they did not have to contend with a biological clock, this wait did not rule out a family life altogether. This reality lay behind the widespread complacency in parts of the horticultural establishment that, whatever the success of a few individual women, the profession would remain overwhelmingly male.

The experience of many of Gertrude Cope's peers bears this out. Within a year of starting work at Burstall, Annie Gulvin, the pioneering Swanley graduate, had met and married a solicitor twenty years her senior named Alan Turner. Again, the *Journal of the Kew Guild* shared the news, writing of her career that she 'ended it by taking to herself a husband'. The editor smugly noted that he 'had always held that there was no fear of the profession being overcrowded by the addition of ladies to its ranks ... we can wish no better finish to a lady gardener's career than that accepted by Miss Gulvin.'[109] Annie Gulvin, once the poster girl for lady gardeners, became Mrs Turner, housewife and mother. She wrote a slightly plaintive letter to the *Kew Journal* in 1903, in which she said, 'I feel like an old war horse when I receive anything related to the horticultural world.'[110] Annie's successor at Burstall, Alice Hutchings, did not last much longer. She returned to Swanley to take up a post as an Assistant Teacher and met back up with an ex-colleague from Kew, William Patterson, now also an instructor at the college. In January 1903, *The Gardening World* carried the announcement: 'Miss Alice Hutchings who was Mr Patterson's colleague at Swanley, has joined him at Reading, but it is no secret that she has joined him for life. Thus, it happens that lady gardeners finish up their careers in the old-fashioned way.'[111]

Not everyone followed this well-trodden path. Gertrude Cope continued her life as a single woman, remaining head gardener at Northfield Manor for twenty years until 1921. After only three years as Gertrude Cope's assistant at Northfield, Olive Harrisson left to get married and was succeeded by several other female assistants who came and went, while Gertrude stayed on. The conventional view at the time was that even a high-achieving career was a poor second best when compared to the rewards of married life and motherhood. Gertrude's life at Bourneville was a quiet one; she did not go in for horticultural prizes and the garden she developed and cared for never attained a high profile. However, she stayed for a long time and there were other rewards. The pleasure that the garden gave to the wider community as a backdrop to picnics and other events run by the Cadburys must have been rewarding to Gertrude, who took community service very seriously throughout her life. Gertrude Cope was not given to self-publicity; she did not write articles for the gardening press and no memoir or diary has survived to give us any clues to her reflections on her career. However, others in her shoes did and in an article entitled 'The Work of a Woman Gardener', published in *Votes for Women* in 1910, we can perhaps gain a picture of the life of a woman gardener in charge of a large garden. A Miss Cadby wrote about her experience as a head gardener on a country estate, explaining that,

> Occupation is bound to influence character. The girl gardener will not be quite like her indoor sisters. She lives practically in the open, and her interests have to do with Nature and growing things. She has little time for accomplishments, and her fingers would be too stiff for musical instruments and too rough for fine needlework; but she has time for reading, and while working in her garden has plenty of opportunities for thinking things out. She stands aloof from the rush and complications of life. Her nerves are not fretted with modern restlessness. She is calm and confident that what she is doing is well worth while, and very certain that she, at least, is not mistaking the shadow for the substance. [112]

The world might still have to wait for a female head gardener to match Joseph Paxton, but women like Gertrude Cope had proved beyond doubt that they could rise to the challenge of being a head gardener, managing considerable resources quietly and competently in order to steer and develop their gardens year after year.

THE WOMAN'S

AGRICULTURAL TIMES,

THE OFFICIAL MONTHLY ORGAN OF THE

AGRICULTURAL ASSOCIATION FOR WOMEN.

Edited by the COUNTESS OF WARWICK.

Vol. I.—No 1. JULY, 1899.

"THE NEW WOMEN AND THE OLD ACRES."

BY THE EDITOR.

It is with many high hopes that this little paper goes out to the world, a tiny fledgling now, but with a mission and a purpose to fulfil when the time for the growing of wings comes, and the subject of women in relation to agriculture waxes sound and strong and is an established force. Out of the opinions and discussions that may arise in these columns, points of weakness may be strengthened, but the main object is to attract to the organisation many who see in these proposals, not indeed the method by which great numbers of women can find a happy and profitable occupation—for that were too much to expect—but that here and there will, without doubt, be discovered and selected women, who are strong, energetic, and adapted to the work; and to the lives of these (even now a considerable number) may be brought a competence earned amongst those country surroundings which they have loved and lost.

During the past two or three years, since it became known that I was trying to elaborate a project of Agricultural Settlements for Women, I have received great numbers of letters, for the most part written on the same lines. 'We are,' the writers say, 'the daughters of professional men, or of farmers, brought up in the country; our parents are dead; we have £500 in funds; we have been forced by poverty into lodgings in big cities, where we are eking out the sad span of life on £15 a year, recognising in the dreary seclusion of our tiny city tenement that there is a green world beyond the gates, with woods and streams, from which we are shut out for want of opportunity.'

No doubt there are these women, waiting to be mustered, women who would give their whole hearts to country work, and who, could they but earn by their personal services a further £30 a year, would enjoy all the days that remain to them. I admit, of course, that almost everything depends upon the careful selection of the colonists; that many more women are unsuited than suitable for such a life. But the difficulty attending a careful and rigid selection is not at all insuperable.

It seems to me that, while hardly recognised thus far, the entire drift of things of late years favours the scheme of Agricultural Settlements for Women. In place of the old 'hard labour for life' system of farming large areas, with heavy machinery and much harnessing of horses, and driving of carts long distances to the railway over bad roads, there is to-day

The most casual traveller in the United Kingdom, as I pointed out a short time ago in *The Outlook*, cannot fail to be struck with the extreme emptiness of the country and the extreme fulness of the towns, and these extremes become more marked year by year. Should the "casual traveller" fail, however, to see what is so apparent, the newspapers and magazines dilate on this serious matter with a gravity befitting the subject. But the young men still flock into the towns, and the young women are not far behind. What does this mean? National trouble of a grave nature. As has been well said, an army and navy which draw their recruits from slums is not likely to be irresistible. To British people this should be an all-impelling argument. What, then, can be done? What remedies tried? Obviously the country must be made more attractive, by new interests, new outlets for industry, revivals of buried handicrafts, and a general influx of fresh vitality. Where men's hearts are, there are also their treasures. If only village homes could be made more attractive, and wages raised to enable men and women to have a little leisure to enjoy their lives and the great gifts of Nature with which they are surrounded, although familiarity therewith has shut their eyes to the fact! In these days of rapid and easy travelling and general locomotion there should not be that lack of social and human interest which engenders monotony. Monotony! that crime of the country which drives people to towns!

Of course, it may be argued that the above platitudes are well worn, and that it is useless to try to dam the stream which is flowing so fast to the sea; it is too late. But at this stage fortunately the national dogged obstinacy steps in, and the apathetic Briton rouses himself with a sort of shake, and says "Something really must be done, or the Germans will beat us all to pieces."

Now, curiously enough, side by side with this question of rural depopulation comes the other equally difficult problem of the "surplus million of women," and how to dispose of them? Our sons have gone abroad to distant parts of the Empire to carry on the work of Empire-building, after first having had large sums of money expended on their education, which was probably meant to fit them for a profession in England. Our daughters meanwhile have grown up without any definite purpose in life, except perhaps to get married; their education has fitted them for no career, and thus many find themselves between the ages of twenty and thirty face to face with the problem of existence. Limited means, or entire absence of means, makes it necessary that they should make an income somehow. In towns every profession is overcrowded; a bare subsistence can only be obtained for

The Woman's Agricultural Times – although Countess of Warwick was credited with editorship in early editions, it was Edith Bradley who edited and wrote most of the articles. Courtesy of the Museum of English Rural Life.

5

NEW WOMEN FOR OLD ACRES

> If the wider spread of a congenial and profitable career for educated women can be coupled with a renewed appreciation of the beauties and possibilities of a simple country life, two very urgent economic problems will be on the road to a happy solution.
>
> 'Horticulture as a Career for Women', *The Times*, December 26, 1907

By 1897 the success of Swanley's students and the general enthusiasm for gardening as a potential career for women had attracted the attention of Edith Bradley. In 1891 Edith was the headmistress of a small girls' school in Beckenham, but in the years that followed, her interests expanded into opening routes to higher education and more interesting careers for women, and this led her, via a long and winding route, to horticulture.

In the 1890s opportunities for tertiary education for women were still very limited. The University of London was unique in admitting women on the same footing as men. The new women-only colleges at Oxford and Cambridge offered opportunities for small numbers of women to study at a high level but could not award degrees. These were exclusive and expensive courses, requiring prospective students to already have a high level of education, so they were well beyond the reach of most young women. Edith Bradley felt something needed to be done and, in 1892, with remarkable self-confidence, she wrote a letter to *The Times* to let the world know about her 'entirely novel' idea to open up 'quite a new field of congenial work for highly educated women.'[113] Edith had been involved in administering the Beckenham branch of the University Extension Movement, a campaign established in the 1870s to offer higher education to those unable to attend the elite universities of Oxford and Cambridge, and had noticed that the programme of lectures and summer schools on offer were at too high a level for most middle-class girls and working-class men. She spotted an opening for female lecturers who could bridge the gap with more accessible lectures, and in the process develop a viable and rewarding career for themselves.

To this end, between 1892 and 1896 Edith Bradley established the Association of Women Lecturers, with offices at 4 Caroline Place, Mecklenburgh Street in London and herself as the Managing Director. Edith worked tirelessly to promote the Association and encourage organisations to commission lecture programmes, organising countless musical events and 'drawing room' meetings where well-connected and sympathetic women gathered to hear her speak about the Association. She quickly realised that aristocratic and elite patronage was valuable in attracting both backers and column inches in the press and she recruited the Duchess of Sutherland, the Earl of Stamford and Mrs Frederick Beer, wife of the proprietor of the *Sunday Observer* as patrons. However, as she admitted in an interview in *The Queen* magazine, 'in her enthusiasm she somewhat rashly started the scheme without any funds'[114] and by March 1896, Edith was forced to admit that, although the scheme had recruited forty women lecturers and enabled over one thousand lectures to be delivered across the country, financially it was a failure. She had been working without taking a wage or reclaiming her considerable travel expenses and had made herself ill with overwork and stress. At the fourth annual meeting of the Association Edith read a report which 'unfortunately showed anything but a satisfactory financial state of affairs… Miss Bradley regretted that in consequence of her state of health, she would be obliged to make rather a long voyage… During her absence, an honorary secretary will keep the Association alive, and on the return of its originator, it will either be started again on fresh lines, or abolished altogether.' The Earl of Stamford spoke warmly of her efforts to keep the Association going, and 'likened her to a solider wounded in a gallant fight, which he trusted she would resume with increased vigour when her health was fully restored.'[115] It is not clear whether Edith Bradley ever did undertake her planned trip to New Zealand but by the end of 1896 she had left the Association of Women Lecturers behind and taken a new job, that of 'Confidential Secretary' to Frances Evelyn, Countess of Warwick. In this role she did return to the 'gallant fight' with 'increased vigour', but this time the battlefield was to be the garden rather than the lecture hall.

The two thirty-seven-year-old women could hardly have been more different. Edith had worked for a living from a young age. She was an earnest, hardworking and serious-minded woman. Her personal appearance was neat, unassuming; she had a pleasant but unremarkable face and a 'slow, well-modulated' voice;[116] her taste in clothes was plain, verging on the dowdy. In contrast, Frances Greville was enormously wealthy, having inherited her grandfather's estate and become one of the country's richest heiresses at the age of just three. She was chosen by Queen Victoria to marry Leopold, her youngest son, but at an early stage of the courtship, Frances, known to close friends and family as Daisy, decided instead to marry his equerry, Lord Brooke, heir to the earldom of Warwick. Lady Warwick, as she became, was a famous society beauty, whose trendsetting dress and hairstyles were reported in breathless detail by the press. She was also the personification of the 'Naughty Nineties', notorious for her extravagant lifestyle and her numerous lovers and admirers. At the time she met Edith Bradley, she was in the process of gently ending her most famous affair, with the Prince of Wales, chiefly because she was pregnant with the child of another lover, Joe Laycock, a British army officer and Olympic sailor. As she said in her autobiography, 'My life was crammed full. I enjoyed every minute of it.'[117] Nevertheless, despite their contrasting backgrounds, lifestyles and appearances, the two women did share some interests. For one thing, they were both keen cyclists. Daisy Warwick was so well known as a cyclist that she is often cited as the inspiration for the song 'Daisy, Daisy' with her 'bicycle made for two'. Edith cycled for practical reasons, to enable her to travel independently and cheaply to her various meetings and lectures. More importantly, however, both women shared a commitment to social reform and a conviction that sitting back and doing nothing was not an option. By the time she employed Edith Bradley in late 1896, Lady Warwick had already begun to take an active interest in the education and training of young people to improve their prospects. Earlier that year she had founded Bigods School, where children aged 7 to 11 were taught basic academic subjects alongside agricultural and horticultural skills. She had also started a needlework school on her family estate in Essex where girls were apprenticed in dressmaking, millinery and embroidery, selling their wares at a shop in Bond Street.

It was not unusual for aristocratic women to get involved in philanthropic 'good works'. Where Daisy Warwick differed from other women of her background, however, was her espousal of radical and even socialist ideals. Her political conversion came about in a typically extravagant and idiosyncratic way. In February 1895 she had hosted a ball at Warwick Castle to celebrate her husband's succession to the title Earl of Warwick. This party, to which five hundred guests were invited wearing costumes from the court of Louis XVI, was opulent even by the high society standards of the day. Daisy came as Marie Antoinette in a dress embroidered in gold thread and diamond stars. The event, unsurprisingly, received critical coverage in the radical press and one story, by Robert Blatchford in the socialist paper *The Clarion*, was so scathing that it prompted Lady Warwick to storm into his office to demand an apology. Far from backing down, Robert Blatchford proceeded to lecture her for three hours on economic and political matters, stressing the unacceptable gulf between the excessive consumption of the wealthy and the hardship faced by the labouring poor. This conversation, together with friendships she struck up with the campaigning journalist W. T. Stead and the agricultural reformer and trade unionist Joseph Arch, appears to have had a deep and

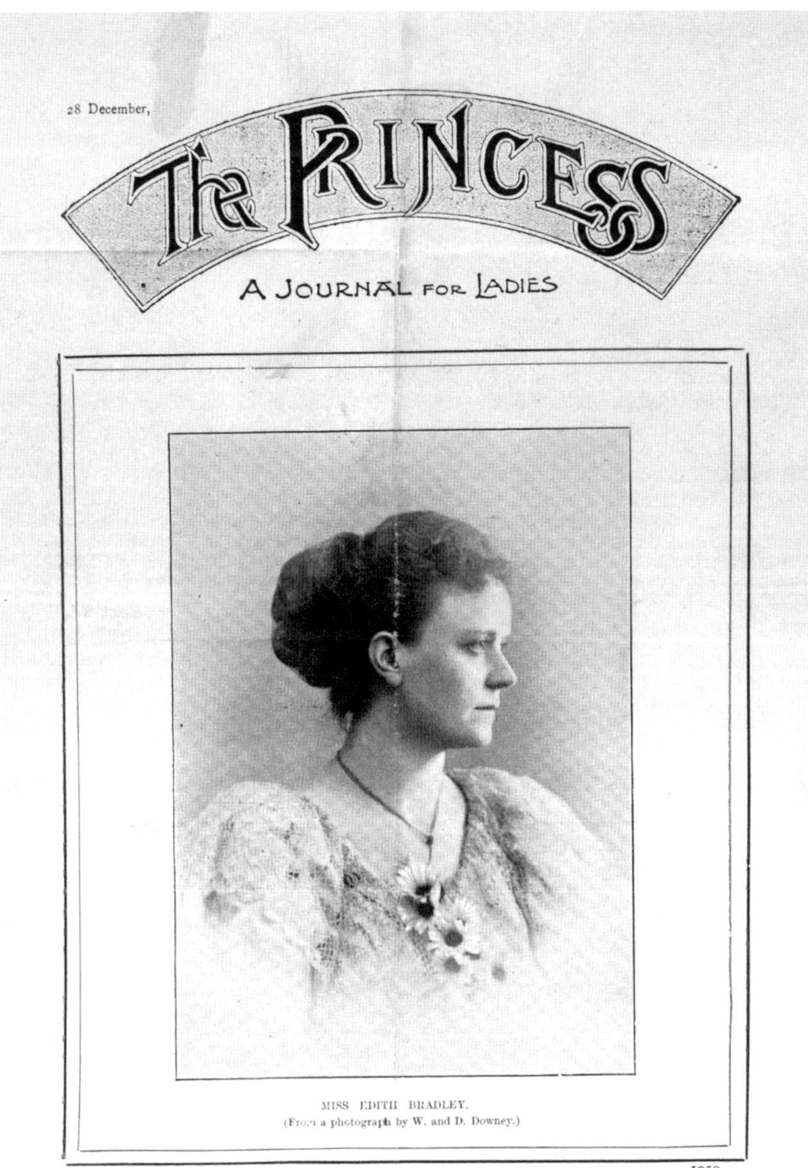

28 December,

THE PRINCESS

A JOURNAL FOR LADIES

MISS EDITH BRADLEY.
(From a photograph by W. and D. Downey.)

1059

Photograph of Edith Bradley from an article in *The Princess*, taken just before she began working for Lady Warwick. Courtesy of the Museum of English Rural Life.

Frances Evelyn 'Daisy' Greville, Countess of Warwick.
Courtesy of the National Portrait Gallery.

lasting influence on Lady Warwick. She threw herself into the field of rural reform to improve the lot of the rural poor. Our image of Victorian poverty is dominated by images of urban slums and appalling conditions in factories, but there was also real hardship and hunger in the British countryside at that time. For decades, British farmers had struggled to compete against cheap imports, particularly of grain, from Europe and North America. Agricultural depression had slashed rural wages, depleted rural populations and left the nation heavily reliant on imported food. There was also widespread worry that vital traditions were being lost and that British rural life was in terminal decline. The call for a rural revival, often under the slogan 'Back to the Land', originated in a desire to reverse the negative consequences of decades of industrialisation and urbanisation and was a movement that attracted many progressive thinkers – and Lady Warwick.

It is not clear how Edith Bradley obtained her new job with this unusual employer. One possible connection was an ex-patroness of the Association of Women Lecturers, the Duchess of Sutherland, who was half-sister to Lady Warwick. Perhaps she suggested to Lady Warwick that Edith Bradley, as an energetic organiser, might help her run her philanthropic campaigns smoothly. However it came about, Edith's meeting with and employment by Lady Warwick was pivotal to the future direction of her life.

In July 1897 Lady Warwick and Edith Bradley both attended the Victoria Era Exhibition at Earl's Court. This event, launched to celebrate Queen Victoria's Diamond Jubilee, was a strange mixture of patriotic tub-thumping and high-minded educational exhibits. Alongside marching bands, classical-music concerts, sculpture halls and displays of the latest scientific advances (such as incubators complete with real premature babies), the event featured a series of conferences on the key issues of the day. One conference focused on women's education. Thanks to her work establishing the school at Bigod's Hall, Lady Warwick was appointed chair of a sub-section of the conference entitled 'Agricultural Education for Women in Great Britain and the Colonies'. As Lady Warwick's Confidential

Secretary, Edith Bradley took on responsibility for taking notes on the sessions for future publication. The topic aroused such keen discussion that 'the session was prolonged far beyond the allotted time.'[118] Speakers included Lady Georgina Vernon who sold honey from her home at Hanbury Hall. She proposed that 'activities connected with agriculture' were the answer to the 'problem of how to obtain the most profitable and suitable employment for women of the upper classes.'[119]

It appears that during this conference, the concerns and causes of Edith Bradley and Daisy Warwick combined. Could educated women, trained in the latest horticultural techniques, bring modern, fresh ideas to reinvigorate the rural economy that Lady Warwick wanted to reform? Although she had left the Association of Women Lecturers behind, Edith Bradley was still determined to find arenas where women could pursue rewarding careers. Was it possible that the wide-open spaces of the countryside might be more welcoming than the crowded male-dominated cities? It seemed that applying female intellect and energy to the rural economy was a way of bringing new blood and ideas to the countryside at the same time as giving 'surplus' women new opportunities to live financially independent and rewarding lives. As Daisy Warwick wrote, 'Careful pondering over these matters has convinced me that the solution of these two perplexing problems will be found in the juxtaposition of both.'[120] Other women, too, were inspired by the conference. A group of women, many associated with the Women's Branch at Swanley, decided to create the Women's Agricultural and Horticultural International Union in order to enable them to keep in touch and take forward the idea of horticultural training for women. Edith and Daisy decided to go their own way rather than join the WAHIU. In many ways they were far more ambitious than their peers in their expectations of the difference women could make.

What really convinced the two women that combining the two issues of agricultural reform and 'surplus women' could work was the fact that one of the most popular suggested solutions to the revival of the rural economy seemed particularly accessible to women. Many agrarian reformers argued that the answer to the agricultural depression was to encourage a shift from large arable farms to smallholdings, a system of land tenure more commonly found in Continental Europe. Agriculture in Britain had changed dramatically in the eighteenth and nineteenth centuries with the consolidation of landholdings and the introduction of mechanisation, which had bought an end to the small-scale farming of cottagers in favour of larger-scale capitalist agriculture. By the late nineteenth-century, however, English farms relying on the monoculture of grain were being undercut by even larger-scale producers from Canada, the USA, Australia and New Zealand. And having largely neglected or abandoned local orchards and vegetable gardens in order to concentrate on grain, the country was now dependent on importation of grain from overseas, as well as fruit, herbs and vegetables. Local fresh fruits and vegetables were falling out of working people's diets as they turned to cheap processed and preserved imports. It was frequently said that smallholdings, intensively growing fruit and vegetables, combined with poultry and dairy farming, could be more profitable and yield higher wages for workers than mechanised arable farms. Social reformers saw the grip that large landowners had on the British countryside as both unfair and inefficient.

Daisy Warwick and Edith Bradley were both particularly excited that the 'lighter branches' of agriculture (market gardening, poultry-keeping, beekeeping, dairy management) at the heart of this vision of the future appeared to be particularly suited to adoption by women. Edith Bradley described these areas of agriculture and horticulture as 'all work on the land which requires skill rather than mere physical strength.'[121] While there were some exceptional women who managed large-scale arable or cattle farms, such as Katherine Courtauld, a member of the wealthy textile family, whose father gave her a 243-acre farm to manage as a twenty-first birthday present, or women who took over a large family farm after their father or spouse died, they were very unusual. In contrast, managing a smallholding felt much more accessible to women than large-scale arable farming or managing large herds of sheep or cattle.

This venture was a departure for Lady Warwick. Hitherto her philanthropic efforts had been directed to working-class girls and boys. This drive to introduce educated women into the countryside was a much more 'top down' initiative. Although smallholdings did not require as much capital to acquire and equip as larger-scale farms, they did need some money. Furthermore, running a modern, efficient and profitable smallholding required a high level of technical and scientific training. Both implied that these new businesses would be run by women from more well-to-do backgrounds who could afford the outlay on land rental and private training courses. It was even seen as socially advantageous to focus on middle- and upper-class women as being at the vanguard of this movement. In 1900 Mrs Chamberlain (founder of the London Women's Garden Association) gave a paper to the Women's Institute in London where she declared:

> Social movements spread from the top downwards. If presently girls and women of the less educated classes find a country life and work on farm or garden is not without charm for the more educated classes, they will not be so anxious to get away to towns and shops … When it is seen that ladies are healthy, happy and contented working on the land, the rustic damsel will begin to think it may be worthwhile to acquire knowledge of the primitive industries they so neglected.[122]

Articles in *Country Life* magazine, the voice of upper-class rural living, also noticed that as working-class rural women retreated from the land to take up factory work, middle-class townswomen were increasingly seeing the potential of life on the land. 'It may be taken as the tendency all over England for the woman of the soil to quit field labour as quickly as she can,' it argued, but this was counterbalanced by another equally significant social trend. As they put it: 'Exit the woman, enter the lady.'[123]

*

The traditional model for a smallholding was a farm or market garden large enough to support the cultivator and his family but small enough to be cultivated by their labour without substantial amounts of permanently hired labour. The smallholdings that Edith Bradley and Lady Warwick had in mind as being particularly suitable for women were even smaller allotments of half an acre or less. Even on smallholdings like this, it was assumed that women would not manage these as an individual endeavour. Instead, they envisaged settlements or colonies of women smallholders, thus addressing the issue of isolation in the country, as a gentlewoman needed companions of her own social class, otherwise she might 'sink' to the level of her neighbours. These settlements would be run on cooperative lines, with the women banding together to achieve economies of scale by buying supplies and equipment in bulk and marketing and transporting their produce together. Edith Bradley set out clearly the scope of their ambitions in an article she wrote in February 1898 in response to one published the previous year entitled 'The Monstrous Regiment of Women' which had criticised the women's movement. Her article, under the rousing title 'The Agricultural Brigade of the Monstrous Regiment of Women', proposed that women farmers could mitigate one of the most pressing national and social problems of the day: 'the wholesale desertion of the villages for the towns, or the emigration to foreign countries'. This army of women, once trained, would 'stay the depopulation of our villages' and 'keep some of the money in this country which is annually spent on foreign dairy, poultry and horticultural produce'. Women of the agricultural brigade would be 'bringing back country life to England, and so assist in strengthening, not only the national, but the Imperial life of our Empire'.[124] Stirring stuff, but words were not enough. In August 1898 a report in *The Times* gave details of the pair's plan of action saying, 'Lady Warwick's idea is that it should be useful to form settlements of women in different parts of the country for the cultivation of the land and thus enable them to add to their incomes by the sale of fruit, vegetables, poultry.' But, before these female agricultural settlements could be established, a rigorous course of instruction was needed, as 'Those women therefore who propose to embark seriously in such an enterprise must first qualify themselves for the work.'[125]

In the Christmas issue of *The Land* magazine for 1897, Lady Warwick published details of a scheme for training women in the lighter branches of agriculture. She proposed the opening of an Agricultural Training College for Women prior to the establishment of Women's Agricultural Settlements in different parts of the country, chiefly populated by women trained at the college. Whilst Lady Warwick, with her wealth and social status, was the main public face of this campaign, it was up to Edith Bradley to make the dream a reality. From the very beginning, a pattern was established whereby Lady Warwick was the figurehead, but it was Edith Bradley who did the hard work. She began by taking a short course in dairy work at the Nottingham Institute, as her upbringing in Beckenham had presumably given her limited experience of agricultural life and skills. Over the next few months Edith also began a busy campaign of letter-writing to individuals and institutions to test the possible response and support for the idea of an agricultural and horticultural training school for young ladies. In March 1898, she wrote to the University College Nottingham to ask if they would build cottages for 'an Agricultural Settlement for women in the neighbourhood of Nottingham' which could be occupied at a 'nominal rent'. She sent a letter to the Yorkshire College in Leeds asking about their Evening Continuation Schools for Allotment Gardeners and whether this course of study could be adapted to prepare women for careers in market gardening. She wrote to individuals for their support and to the Parliamentary Committee for Women's Suffrage. She even wrote to Madeline Agar's employer at Wycombe Abbey School, Miss Dore, to see if she had any pointers that could inform the scheme.

Having investigated several options, Edith Bradley and Lady Warwick finally settled on the University Extension College, Reading, as the partner organisation with whom they would work to take their scheme forward. The college had set up an agricultural department in 1893 and received a grant from the Board of

Agriculture and from several county councils. It offered courses that spanned both theory and practice, with residencies on farms. In November 1894 the college had piloted the inclusion of a month-long course on poultry farming, horticulture and beekeeping within the department's curriculum. From the outset these courses were technically open to both men and women, though in practice very few women participated. Reading also had the advantage that it was the base for the British Dairy Institute, the country's main centre for research and education in dairy work. There was plenty on offer here for the two determined women to build on.

The next step was to find suitable accommodation for female students on a larger scale. In July 1898 'dressed in green cycling suit and brown hat', Edith Bradley 'pedalled around Reading house-hunting.'[126] She found the perfect house on Bath Road, just twenty minutes' walk from the college and set in three acres of land which the students were permitted to cultivate for practical work. As well as the practicalities of setting up and running the student hostel, she persuaded Suttons, the nearby seed merchants, to give students use of their seed trial grounds. Kelway's peony nursery in Somerset and several other horticultural businesses also gave generously and wealthy local families such as the Huntley and Palmer biscuit manufacturers also contributed funding. From there things moved very quickly. By September 1898 a prospectus for the school was advertised in *Country Life* and 'The Lady Warwick Hostel' opened in October 1898 with twelve students. Naturally, Lady Warwick was President of the Hostel and Edith Bradley was Warden, her previous experience as a headmistress of a girl's school giving her excellent qualifications for running such an institution. The Hostel was an immediate success, thanks in no small part to Edith Bradley's hard work. A complement of teaching staff was created to provide practical instruction to supplement the lectures provided by the college. A letter published in *The Gardening World* described the set-up: 'At Reading, the head is Miss Edith Bradley, a warm-hearted, earnest lady, and she is ably seconded by Miss Crooke, a most practical-minded and able lady, with whom anyone who pooh-poohs the lady gardener student would do well to have a little straight talk ... Depend upon it, the woman gardener has become a permanent fact.'[127]

By June 1899 applications were pouring in, and Edith Bradley rented another house (Maynard House) and then another (Brooke House). Together, these houses provided accommodation for fifty students and ten teaching staff. In fewer than six months, the ambitious pair felt ready to start expanding their plans. In February 1899 Lady Warwick and Edith Bradley set up the Lady Warwick Agricultural Association for Women 'for the definite purpose of helping to organise and direct the extensive amount of work being carried out by women in agriculture, horticulture, dairy and poultry work, beekeeping and other outdoor occupations, as well as all rural industries.'[128] In a way that was very reminiscent of the Association of Women Lecturers this new association aimed to act as both an employment agency and an advocacy organisation with its own monthly newsletter, *The Woman's Agricultural Times*. There was a General Committee of around sixty distinguished members including principals of other colleges, professors, Sir Cecil Rhodes, Sir Winston Churchill, Mrs Asquith, Dr Elizabeth Garrett Anderson, A. W. Sutton and M. J. Sutton, along with various other aristocratic friends of Lady Warwick, all under the chairmanship of J. Marshall Dugdale. Again, although the organisation, like the hostel, bore Lady Warwick's name, it was Edith Bradley who was the driving force behind the Association, acting as its day-to-day manager and 'Organising Secretary'. All the work of managing the committee, running the recruitment agency, putting together the magazine and writing much of its content was done by Edith. In September 1900 an alumni group named 'The Guild of the Daughters of Ceres' was established so that students could keep in touch after they had left the college; it was yet another initiative for Edith Bradley to run. It seemed that she had learnt nothing from the experience of running the Association of Women Lecturers.

In contrast, Lady Warwick kept to her usual routine of spending her summers holidaying in Paris and in the South of France. On her return from her 1900 summer trip, she described herself as 'wildly busy with matters agricultural',[129] but it is hard to see how that was truly the case. At the very least some of her attention must have been taken up by being at the heart of a public scandal. As she later explained, 'In my circle there was a kind of freemasonry of conduct. We could be and do as we liked according to the code. The unforgiveable sin was to give away any member of the group … A scandal was a romance until it was found out.'[130] In 1900 she did come very close to committing the unforgivable sin of exposing the extramarital affairs of her contemporaries. Having found love letters written by her lover, Joe Laycock, to another woman, Kitty Downshire, Lady Warwick decided to send them to her rival's husband, the Marquess of Downshire, in a doomed attempt to bring an end to that relationship. The matter ended up in the divorce courts and the ensuing publicity even prompted the Prince of Wales to keep his distance from Daisy Warwick for a time.

Meanwhile, the Lady Warwick Hostel went from strength to strength, so much so that Edith and Lady Warwick began to see the arrangements at Reading as inadequate. The scattered grounds and split student accommodation were inconvenient and there were signs that the relationship with the Reading college was becoming strained. Writing sixteen years later, Lady Warwick recalled 'the girls had not been popular at Reading, where the college students thought they were intruders if they ventured beyond the dairy … I could not help thinking that if the idea was to grow, it must have room and a more congenial atmosphere for its development.'[131] In Edith Bradley's annual review of the year's work in 1901, she remarked, 'It is true that Reading still laughs in its sleeve at what it has been pleased to designate a "Rich woman's fad."'[132] Another possible source of discontent was a feeling that the courses provided at Reading were overly theoretical and too focused on mainstream agriculture. Virtually none of the Hostel's female students took the entire Reading Agricultural Diploma course; most took the shorter horticultural course, with smaller numbers taking poultry and dairy courses. Edith Bradley later wrote, 'It was desirable from every point of view to arrange the necessary theoretical side of the training with the least possible expenditure of time and also to teach only what is definitely required for the scientific side of the work'[133] in order to leave more time for practical learning. After only three years relying on Reading University Extension College for theoretical classes, the pair felt confident enough to 'go it alone' with their own prospectus and course of instruction, based at new, larger premises. In 1901 they launched an appeal to raise £30,000–50,000, with King Edward VII as patron. Lady Warwick addressed a meeting at the Mansion House and within two years sufficient funds had been accumulated to purchase Studley Castle in Warwickshire and 340 acres for £25,000.

Edith Bradley, her teaching staff and forty students moved to Studley Castle in late 1903. The estate and main building were badly neglected, but the grounds included a fine range of lean-to glasshouses and a one-acre kitchen garden. Two hundred-foot-long greenhouses were transported from Reading and re-erected by the students themselves. Living conditions at first were tough. Looking back a year later, Edith remembered 'the discomfort and difficulties of settling into a new place were very great … a household of between fifty and sixty people with unfinished baths and a necessarily inadequate hot-water supply was – to put it mildly – trying to the temper.'[134]

For the next two years the work for Edith was unrelenting. The Studley letter book survives in the archive of the Museum of English Rural Life, and it is crammed with letters written by her, giving a strong impression of the range of cares and concerns involved in her life as Warden. She was personally involved in everything: designing the uniform and college crest, chasing student fees, hiring and firing staff, and overseeing student discipline. Although the fees were lower than at Swanley, the Studley Castle Horticultural College tended to attract a more well-heeled set of students who were sometimes quite hard work to control. An Australian journalist, Margaret Harkness, who wrote reports of the London social scene for the Australian press, noted that the Lady Warwick Hostel 'has been a godsend to many girls in what are known as "the upper classes", and anyone who reads the College paper will see what these rather slangy and horsey young ladies are doing as gardeners and farmers all over the

United Kingdom. One meets them in trains, and they are already quite a type, although the Hostel was only established in 1898.'[135]

One letter to a Miss Hart, dated April 1905, gives a strong impression of the challenges Edith Bradley faced with some of her 'slangy and horsey' students: 'I am very annoyed with you, more than I like to write. On going through the rooms this morning, I saw that you left your cubicle in a most untidy state, and in spite of all I have said about tea leaves being thrown down the sink, there were great collections there, which I can only conclude were put down by you ... I cannot think why you are so tiresome and give such unnecessary trouble, besides annoyance, and if you are not going to do better, I really cannot help you.'[136] Or there was the equally vexing Miss Charlton. Edith Bradley wrote to her sister, plaintively asking, 'Do you think it would be possible to get her to do her hair in a less conspicuous manner and also to dress more neatly? I was particularly annoyed with her appearance the day she went to Birmingham with Miss Crooke when it was anything but subdued, and unless she is really prepared to fall in with the general tone of the College, I am afraid I shall have some difficulty with the Committee in getting them to sanction her return.'[137] Edith Bradley may have held relatively radical views on female emancipation, but she was socially conventional and enough of a realist to know that female horticultural students faced plenty of hurdles and prejudices without presenting themselves as anything other than respectable ladies.

On top of these day-to-day concerns there were financial worries. Although enough money had been raised to purchase Studley Castle, it fell short of the amount needed to create an endowment to support the running costs of the College and the wider aims of the Agricultural Association. Lady Warwick was both wealthy and generous, but she could not individually cover all the costs of the College. Edith Bradley worked hard to bring in money by selling produce and preserves from the garden. She invested in setting up a production line for preserving fruit and vegetables. The Minutes of the Executive Committee of Lady Warwick College recorded on March 16, 1904, that 969 lbs of marmalade were made at a cost of

£12 and while to date only 208lbs had been sold, '1200 lbs more will be made' and ''The premises adjoining the Dairy are required for jam-making and an American Evaporator No 3 to consume 10 to 15 bushels of apples per day is required' at a cost of over £26.[138] In the process of getting this business up and running, Edith Bradley developed a great deal of personal expertise in fruit preserving, even inventing a device she called the Mercia Patent Steriliser which won awards from the RHS.

Fruit preserving was never going to earn Studley College the amount of money needed, however. The real answer was to obtain some official recognition of the College and its training to unlock either central or local government funding and support. A report of a speech Edith Bradley gave at a conference held at Studley in July 1903 to celebrate five years of the College gives an idea of the frustrations she faced at being passed from pillar to post by different government departments. 'As we occupy a sort of position midway between both, Education says, "I can't deal directly with Agriculture" and Agriculture says "Education must help you, because all my official efforts are to benefit farmers and other *men*; if we enlarge our borders and take on women engaged in agriculture, especially the lighter branches, *where* shall we find ourselves?"'[139] Despite being faced by constant stone-walling, Edith kept up an energetic campaign to get Studley College recognised as a Technical Institute by the Board of Education, even going so far as to track down and collar a government minister at a public meeting and demand that he pay the College a visit.

*

Amid all this work, Edith did not forget the dream of setting up cooperative settlements for women. The first edition of the Association newsletter, *The Woman's Agricultural Times*, articulated Lady Warwick and Edith Bradley's vision of 'agricultural settlements where, for those who have small incomes, cottages will be built with land attached which the trained women will cultivate. It is proposed

Photograph from a brochure for Studley Castle, showing the luxurious bedrooms that the wealthier students could expect, *c.*1910. Courtesy of the RHS Lindley Collections.

that the cottages should be built in pairs, and that in each two women shall live as partners; six or eight of these cottages will form a settlement, presided over by a superintendent, who will advise about the crops and also market the produce of the settlement. Cooperative principles will prevail.'[140] In 1903 Edith Bradley wrote a book called *The Lighter Branches of Agriculture* which was both a manifesto for the settlement idea and a practical guide to the skills required to run a smallholding. With highly detailed chapters on market gardening, dairy work, beekeeping and marketing produce, the book also described how Women's Agricultural Settlements were the 'logical sequence' for women leaving training colleges such as the Lady Warwick Hostel. She acknowledged that 'The idea of Women's Settlements has been greatly ridiculed as being contrary to the regulations which govern society' but argued 'surely the settlements offer inducements and possibilities of a useful life leading to a definite end, which does not exist at present in many schemes for the Betterment of Women.'[141]

However, purchasing or leasing land to make this dream a reality required serious investment. In 1904 Edith Bradley proposed the establishment of a limited company called the Studley Castle Agricultural Society Ltd to take over the creation of settlements and the wider work of the Agricultural Association, with herself as Managing Director and Lady Warwick as President. This was agreed by the College's Executive Committee and an appeal was put out to attract shareholders. Six months later, in the Warden's Annual Report for 1904, Edith Bradley reported that she had issued shares in this company and that 'the number of shareholders is 84 and 468 shares have been taken up.' It was nowhere near enough. Even Edith admitted, 'I should like it to number 1,000 at least.'[142]

Lady Warwick, on the other hand, continued living her high society life, bouncing from drama to drama. In April 1904 she gave birth to a daughter, Mercy, later revealed to be the child of Joe Laycock, with whom she had kept up an on-off relationship, even though he had married her rival, Kitty Downshire. He finally abandoned Daisy that spring and after recovering from the birth, she decided to renounce romance forever and throw herself into international socialism instead. In August 1904 she attended the International Socialist Congress in Amsterdam where she had great fun eating in a 'slummy restaurant' and rubbing shoulders with revolutionaries, remarking blithely, 'I really find a pretty hat and a sweet smile opens the doors of even Socialist hearts.'[143] Whether that was true is another matter, but the fact remains that the drama and excitement of this new cause seemed to be all-absorbing for Lady Warwick herself. In autumn 1904 she began touring northern constituencies in her motor car, specially painted in socialist red, to speak in support of prospective parliamentary candidates for the new Labour Party. Following visits to Glasgow, Sunderland, Jarrow, Newcastle, Manchester, Burnley and Accrington, she retired to rest, in a very Daisy way, at a luxurious hotel in Aix-les-Bains and then Paris. It seemed that Lady Warwick, now dubbed 'Comrade Warwick' by Margot Asquith, had moved onto other causes, leaving the commitment to promoting horticultural and agricultural work for women behind.

Things reached a head in the summer of 1905 when Edith received more disappointing news. All her hard work lobbying for formal recognition and funding seemed to be falling on deaf ears. Despite determined lobbying by Edith, the Warwickshire County Council announced that they would not make a grant to support the college. Shortly afterwards, at a Founder's Day event at Studley in July, Lady Warwick apparently criticised some aspect of the management of the scheme. This appears to have been the last straw for Edith Bradley, who had given her all for the cause. For Lady Warwick to suddenly reappear, clearly with no appreciation of Edith's efforts and make critical comments was intolerable and Edith resigned on the spot. That Lady Warwick was being unreasonable was evidenced by the fact that virtually all the college staff resigned along with Edith.

At the following College Executive Committee meeting Lady Warwick referred vaguely to Miss Bradley's resignation, 'which in the interests of the College she had felt bound to accept' and quickly announced that she had found a successor in Miss Faithful, secretary to Miss Balfour, the Prime Minister's sister.[144] For her part, Edith Bradley took a well-earned break in Italy. But the experience clearly left her feeling hurt and bitter. In 1909 Dr Lillias Hamilton became the new Warden at Studley and got in touch with Edith Bradley to ask her advice. They were to develop a long and friendly correspondence but her initial reply to Dr Hamilton showed that, even after four years, she still felt wounded by her experience with Lady Warwick. 'You have my very deepest sympathy,' she wrote. 'I know that your task is beset with difficulties on every side, all the more subtle because your enemies are unseen (at least in my case they were) but all the greater will be your victory if you win, as I devoutly hope you may.'[145]

*

Edith may have broken with Lady Warwick and Studley but that did not mean that she gave up on the dream of placing women at the heart of a rural revival – far from it. Almost immediately after her resignation, *The Northern Whig* newspaper announced her intention 'to start again in the lighter branches, this time to develop the ultimate object of the scheme *viz* to form an agricultural settlement for those trained in the work. She will have the support her two sub-wardens, who have been connected with the work from the commencement and four or five other members of the staff, who have all resigned with her.'[146] Yet the way she went about this was surprising. It would be expected that, following her experience with Lady Warwick, Edith Bradley would have been wary of attaching herself to another eccentric, wealthy patroness, and yet that is exactly what she did. In fact, in allying herself with Victoria Woodhull Martin, it could be said that Edith Bradley had stepped from the frying pan into the fire.

Any summary of the biography of Victoria Woodhull Martin risks reading like a work of fiction. Her life story up until the point Edith Bradley met her had already included going from rags to riches twice, working as a travelling spiritualist, advocating for women's rights and free love, and becoming the first woman to campaign for President of the United States. Born in poverty in Ohio in 1838, but blessed with good looks and a commanding personal presence, Victoria Claflin married an alcoholic quack doctor called Canning Woodhull at the age of just 15 and had two children, named Byron and Zula Maud, by the age of 23. She initially made a living as a medium and 'spiritual physician' in St Louis. There she met Colonel James Harvey Blood, a 29-year-old Civil War veteran and believer in spiritualism. Victoria promptly fell into a trance and announced that his future destiny would be as her husband. Setting aside the inconvenient detail that they were both already married, they declared themselves betrothed by the 'powers of the air' and set off on a tour of the Midwest as 'Mr and Madame Harvey', telling fortunes. James Harvey Blood was a well-read political radical who introduced Victoria to the latest thinking on women's rights, 'free love' and socialism; she remained a vocal supporter of women's suffrage all her life.

By 1868 she and Blood had set up home in New York in an unconventional household which included her ex-husband and their two children, her parents, her sister Tennessee, and several other hangers-on. In New York she met Cornelius Vanderbilt, the railway and shipping magnate who was in an impressionable state having recently become widowed. Victoria gave him spiritual advice and healing sessions and in return he passed on lucrative Stock Exchange tips, enabling her to make $700,000 in just six weeks. Emboldened by this success, Victoria and Tennessee decided to prove that women could be a success on Wall Street, and in January 1869 set themselves up as the first women stockbrokers. In April 1870 Victoria went one further and announced she would stand for President in 1872, even though she did not have the backing of a political party and would be a year short of the minimum age set out in the Constitution. She began a newspaper, *Woodhull and Claflin's Weekly*, dedicated to her campaign, with the slogan 'Suffrage without distinction of sex'. Unfortunately, the publicity attracted the attention of the press to her domestic arrangements, and her opponents used her living with two husbands and her support for 'free love' against her. Victoria refused to back down, and indeed started a relationship with another man, Theodore Tilton. At a public meeting she boldly declared, 'I am a free lover. I have an inalienable constitutional and natural right to love whom I may; to love as long or short a period as I can; to change that love everyday if I please.'[147] The remark was quoted widely in ostensibly moralistic but titillating press coverage, and cartoons appeared characterising her as 'Mrs Satan', a nickname which stuck.

Victoria's nomination for President was ratified by the Equal Rights Party in June 1872, but amid bad publicity supporters such as Vanderbilt began to desert her and her financial and personal situation deteriorated rapidly. She also faced court cases for libel and obscenity. Her presidential campaign collapsed and although she avoided prison, she was left with crippling legal bills. But in 1877 Victoria had a stroke of good luck. Cornelius Vanderbilt died and to prevent news of his links with spiritualism and Victoria leaking out, his son reputedly paid Victoria and her sister Tennessee a considerable sum of money to leave the country, which they did.

The sisters set up home in London with Victoria's daughter, Zula Maud. Victoria began a lecture tour on the subject 'The Human

Body, the Temple of God' and on this tour she met John Biddulph Martin, the younger son of a wealthy banker. A supporter of women's rights, he was smitten with this charismatic and attractive woman and vowed to marry her despite her notoriety. They were married for thirteen years until 1896, when Biddulph died suddenly of pneumonia. Victoria, who had lived in London up to this point, inherited a healthy fortune and the Bredon's Norton estate in Worcestershire which included forests, orchards and hop fields. The main residence on the estate was a Tudor-style mansion built in 1839 and known as Norton Park, plus an Elizabethan manor house, a tithe barn, a lodge and a school, several farms and cottages.

It was at this point that, as 'lady of the manor', Victoria Woodhull Martin started to take an interest in matters agricultural. Both she and Zula Maud became subscribers to Edith Bradley's *The Woman's Agricultural Times*, which aligned well with their long-standing support for women's rights, and upon hearing of the resignation of Edith Bradley and much of the staff at Studley Castle, they made contact and, in the words of *The Cheltenham Examiner*, 'in their prompt American way, whisked the party of workers off to Bredon's Norton'[148] where they were established by the end of 1905. Edith was joined by ex-Studley sub-warden Miss May Crooke, who had been responsible for the Horticultural Department, marketing and the jam factory; Miss Mabel Carlyon, who was May Crooke's gardening assistant; Miss Bertha La Mothe, who had been in charge of the Poultry Department; and Miss Turner, a secretary. With very little delay, the team began work to set up the component parts of Edith's vision of an agricultural settlement with a training school at its heart. May Crooke set up a women's school of gardening which opened in July 1906, with Mabel Carlyon acting as assistant teacher. Victoria and Zula gave May free use of the old Walled Garden and the adjacent well-equipped glasshouses at Norton Park and May arranged with Cheltenham Ladies' College, eleven miles away, for her students to attend the College's senior botany and chemistry classes. (Pupils from Cheltenham Ladies' College were offered practical gardening instruction at Bredon's Norton in return.) Full-time students at

Bredon's Norton were housed in a hostel created from a converted farmhouse, re-named *Carmino*, the Latin word for 'ripple', suggesting an aspiration to have far-reaching effects. To keep fees to a minimum, the school sold surplus garden produce and by July 1907 the school was sending lettuces to London wholesale markets.

So far, so idyllic. An article in the suffragist newspaper *The Common Cause* certainly thought so. It described Bredon's Norton as a setting where gardening could be

> … learnt under the most pleasant conditions. Bredon's Norton is a little village a mile and a half from a station on the Midland line between Worcester and Cheltenham. It feels very remote from the rush and whirl of town life. The country is lovely, the cottage architecture suits the surroundings, there are many beautiful sixteenth-century houses and exquisite small churches, besides the great cathedrals not far off. The air is sweet, and the colouring pure. If peace is to be found anywhere it should be here, and to enjoy peace most of us need to enter into some intimate relation with Mother Earth or her offspring. The Manor-House Club, another foundation at Bredon's Norton, has a considerable library at the disposal of members, and here, in a very beautiful Elizabethan house, visitors other than students are made welcome and very happy. I will only add that Miss Crooke arranges short courses when required … A brain-worker in doubt as to where to spend her holidays might do worse than come here for a complete change of occupation and surroundings, and if a love of gardening is awakened in her, she will find it an unending source of interest and delight.[149]

Edith Bradley settled into life at Bredon's Norton and continued to edit and produce *The Woman's Agricultural Times*, the only alteration noticeable being a change of address on the magazine front cover. However, her main goal continued to be to set up the cooperative smallholding scheme. She began by renting an unoccupied farmhouse on the estate which she re-named Providence House and 'the Headquarters of the Mercia Settlement'. She was apparently led to believe by Victoria and Zula Maud that they would sell her both the farmhouse and the 285-acre farm if she could raise the money. To this end, she declared the intention of launching a private company, 'The

Mercia Agricultural Association Ltd', with the aim of raising between £10,000 and £20,000 required to buy the entire farm. To help raise awareness of the business potential of this scheme, she wrote a book on fruit bottling with May Crooke. She hoped that, 'If this little book were instrumental in arousing sufficient interest to promote this end, and were another link in the chain being forged to bring our people 'back to the land'; its purpose and my delight would be well served.'[150]

While waiting to find financial backers to respond to her calls, Edith Bradley put into action her belief that educated women could be at the heart of reviving the cultural and intellectual life of rural communities as well as their economic wellbeing. In the autumn of 1906 she gave a series of splendidly eclectic public lectures in Tewkesbury on 'Life in Imperial Rome' and 'The Place of Women on the Farm'. She had the coach house at Providence House adapted as a reading room and in February 1907 opened it as the 'Mercia Reading Room and Working Men's Club'. As well as access to books, the club offered the opportunity to play 'whist, quoits and other games' and was a venue for Women's Social Evenings.[151] Her most high-profile local endeavour, however, was to organise the first Bredon's Norton and District Agricultural Show in August 1906 which Victoria and Zula allowed to take place in the grounds of Norton Park. Victoria, a fan of new technology, arranged for a display of telephones, which she considered to be essential equipment for the modern smallholder, but it was Edith who persuaded the Earl and Countess of Coventry to perform the opening ceremony, the Midland Railway Company to offer cheap excursion tickets and Mr Bathurst to provide river transport from Tewkesbury. In her 'large white hat' she was the central and indeed only named figure in *The Gloucestershire Graphic*'s picture of the show's 'Committee and Officials.'[152] The show was such a success that it was made an annual event.

On June 17, 1907, Edith Bradley attended a drawing-room meeting in Kensington, at which Lady Wimbourne and Sir Francis Channing were appointed to a small committee to oversee the settlement plan. The following day she gave a confident interview to *The Daily News* in which she described the planned settlement: at its heart would be a training establishment comprising a small farm (with cows, sheep and pigs) and a garden with glasshouses, a dairy and marketing department where students would receive instruction. There would be fifteen smallholdings on which cottages would be built; these would be made available to both men and women, but with preference given to students who had passed through her training establishment. An essential part of the scheme was the formation of 'a Cooperative Land Holding Society, with a capital of £10,000 which is to be run on Cooperative partnership lines.'[153] The launch seemed imminent, but curiously, despite having previously declared Providence House the settlement headquarters, Edith said that a site had not yet been chosen.

This was because despite all Edith's efforts, serious financial backing was still not forthcoming, and Victoria and Zula were losing patience. They still felt the idea of an agricultural settlement had potential as a business venture, but now they changed tack. Before meeting Edith Bradley, they had embarked on a scheme to refurbish the Elizabethan Manor House at Bredon's Norton to create a Women's Club, linked with the existing Ladies' Automobile Club based at Claridge's Hotel in London. The new pastime of 'motoring', of which Victoria Woodhull Martin, like Lady Warwick, was a keen fan, allowed the wealthy to easily pass the weekend in the country and enjoy country sports, and this would offer Automobile Club members the chance to enjoy the best of country and town life. Work was well underway with this refurbishment, but now they altered their plans. They announced that the refurbished Manor House would be a Women's *Agricultural* Club and the headquarters of a women's agricultural community. In many ways it was a straightforward stealing of Edith's ideas, the only difference being the absence of a cooperative element. In August 1907 Zula gave an interview to *The Morning Post* in which she outlined the thinking behind the scheme. Like Edith Bradley, she said she favoured a 'Back to the Land' policy which was feasible thanks to new scientific methods that did not require huge acreages to make a profit. Unlike Edith, however, she said she believed there were benefits to smallholders in renting land from an entrepreneur who could organise transport and marketing, rather than trying to set up a cooperative to organise these functions themselves. Moreover, the availability of Club accommodation and meals not only reduced household chores, but more importantly eliminated the isolation that had previously deterred women from careers in agriculture and horticulture. No mention was made in the interview of Edith Bradley.

Although Victoria and Zula had capital to set up the scheme, its success still depended on attracting people to run and make a profit from the smallholdings. Yet, despite their confidence that between them May Crooke's School of Gardening and Victoria's and Zula's Women's Agricultural Club would draw in smallholders, neither flourished. Membership fees for the Club were prohibitively expensive. Looking at the Visitors' Book for the Manor House, if you discount Victoria's personal guests, overseas visitors and obvious sightseers, there appear to have been only a handful of real paid-up members. On December 6, 1908, May Crooke submitted to Victoria and Zula a memorandum in which she strongly recommended that the Club and School should be kept separate. The school would contract to supply the Club with vegetables, eggs, poultry and floral decoration 'at market prices' and while she accepted that she was still using the Walled Garden 'entirely on a courtesy basis', she hoped that they could enter into an agreement to pay a 'reasonable' rent and take more ground for a new apiary.[154] Clearly, running the School of Gardening as an independent business did not match Victoria's and Zula's vision of a 'community' and by Whitsun 1909, May Crooke had left to set up a gardening school in Ivybridge, Devon. Victoria and Zula tried to set up their own gardening school, but this did not prosper. The Women's Agricultural Club did not last much longer. Some of the cottages originally intended for the male relations and friends of Club members were let to women engaged in an eclectic range of small businesses from cake-making and dressmaking to breeding Yorkshire terriers – hardly agricultural pursuits. By October 1910 Victoria and Zula had reverted to their original plan to make the Manor House Club essentially a leisure centre for people who wanted a pleasant place to stay in the country with access to a golf course, tennis courts and fishing.

Edith Bradley meanwhile had finally realised that relying on other people, however charismatic and wealthy, to bring her dreams to fruition was not a reliable course of action. At the age of 47, after more than a decade of campaigning, she had to let go of her dream of a large-scale, cooperative agricultural community for women. Instead, she followed a much more well-trodden path and one that she could deliver for herself. In 1907 she rented her own smallholding at Greenway Court at Hollingbourne, near Maidstone. The business was set up with another woman, Cecilia Mary Baillie-Hamilton, who may have been a pupil at Bredon's Norton, and from the start it was to be 'a model smallholding, the intention being to demonstrate what can be done by women in the lighter branches of agriculture.'[155] Known to locals as 'The Ladies' Farm', Greenway Court took in pupils, but it was on a much smaller scale than Studley, and Edith, freed from the responsibilities of running a large teaching establishment, was at last able to demonstrate her proficiency as a businesswoman and commercial food producer.

In 1910 *The Times* reported that the farm had 'worked its way into prominence as a centre of experimentation and proficiency in practices suitable to holdings of restricted area, these including dairying, fruit growing, fruit preserving, market gardening, pig keeping, poultry keeping, and beekeeping.'[156] By 1913 the business had expanded as demand for training places at Greenway Court increased. A new wing was added to the accommodation which was opened with a special event for local dignitaries and agricultural experts. *The Times* reported, 'The guests were particularly interested in the pedigree Jerseys, the numerous breeds of all-white poultry to be seen in the greengage orchards or the breeding pens, the French garden tended by the French foreman, the fruit plantation and wall trees as well as the stables and bees. The farm was started five years ago with only 25 acres and accommodation for 6 students; now there are over 40 acres and accommodation for 19 students and a resident staff of teachers.'[157] Although it was not the large-scale, cooperative rural revival she had dreamed of, at Greenway Court Edith Bradley proved her point that women could make a real contribution to the rural economy.

The backyards of houses in Brettell Street, Walworth, London, in 1908.
Courtesy of London Metropolitan Archives.

6
DESIGNING GREEN CITIES

> Woman's influence is too often ignored. When the Garden City is built, as it shortly will be, woman's share in the work will be found to have been a large one. Women are among our most active missionaries.
>
> Ebenezer Howard, 1902

Despite Edith Bradley's best efforts, agricultural settlements for women did not transform the British countryside. In many ways, women horticulturists were much more likely to make an impact in towns and cities than they were in rural areas. Women were very much the minority in agriculture and only a handful managed to secure head gardener positions in large country-house gardens. Urban and suburban areas, in contrast, offered far more accessible opportunities for women gardeners, not only in hands-on gardening, but also in the fields of garden design and landscape architecture. In fact, women were at the forefront of a movement in urban planning which placed green spaces and gardens at the heart of a new vision for towns and cities, as a reaction to the squalor and overcrowding that came with rapid and unplanned urbanisation and industrialisation in the nineteenth century.

From the last quarter of the nineteenth century onwards, social reformers increasingly looked to improved urban design and planning to solve the nation's health problems. There was a recognition that fresh air, outdoor exercise and the opportunity to simply enjoy beautiful plants and trees were all vital, particularly for people who spent their lives in slums, airless workshops or noisy factories. In the later years of the nineteenth century several important charities were set up to campaign for the preservation of green spaces and the creation of new ones and women were heavily involved in all of them. In 1875 Octavia Hill's sister Miranda set up the Kyrle Society to bring 'beauty home to the people'. The society gave itself a wide remit, aiming to 'decorate, by mural paintings, pictures, gifts of flowers, &c., workmen's clubs, schools, and mission-rooms, used for social or religious gatherings, without distinction of creed; to lay out gardens and encourage the cultivation of plants; to organise a voluntary choir of singers, to give oratorios and concerts to the poor; to cooperate with the National Health Society in securing open-air spaces in poor neighbourhoods to be laid out as public gardens.'[158] This was not just a trivial or superficial 'prettification' process. These goals were heavily influenced by the ideas of John Ruskin and William Morris. In their different ways they both argued that the design of even everyday urban spaces offered opportunities to give ordinary people access to beauty. Underpinning this notion of beauty was a powerful assumption that nature was vital to the human spirit. Octavia Hill incorporated these ideas into her largest housing project, Walworth in Southwark, a twenty-two-acre area of slum housing owned by the Church of England which she redeveloped and managed. One of our six gardeners, her goddaughter the artist Olive Cockerell, worked on this project with her, although it is not clear whether Olive helped in the design of the space, which involved the creation of new Arts and Crafts-inspired, cottage-style housing, surrounded with garden squares and street trees. At that stage she was more involved in the social-work side of the rehousing scheme; her horticultural work was to come later.

Of our six women, it was to be Madeline Agar, who had taken a post as a teacher of gardening at Wycombe Abbey School, who became the most directly involved in the mission to design and create green spaces for the urban poor. It is not clear when Madeline Agar began to aspire to a career as a garden designer. There are accounts of her travelling to the United States to obtain training in the principles and practice of landscape architecture and garden design, but no record has survived of exactly where she studied or when. There is a record of a 'Miss Agar' travelling from Liverpool to New York in 1891, so perhaps Madeline did this training even before she studied at Swanley. In that case, she had such a career in mind from the very beginning and it is possible that she only took on the teaching role at Wycombe Abbey because a suitable opening was not available in garden design. Alternatively, she could have travelled to America in 1903 after finishing work at Wycombe Abbey School, but there is no record of a Madeline Agar travelling abroad at that time. There were two main schools of garden design in America, one was the Lowthorpe School of Landscape Gardening and Horticulture for Women in Groton Massachusetts which was established in 1901; the other was a short-lived landscape architecture course at Massachusetts Institute of Technology which admitted men and women from 1900 to 1909. Unfortunately, no student records survive for either institution indicating Madeline studied there. Wherever she trained, it is clear the instruction she received was highly valuable to her – she later wrote that embarking on a career in garden design required 'a severe course of geometrical drawing … a splendid drill in the use of instruments'[159] – and this technical skill set, combined with her hands-on horticultural ability gained at Swanley and honed at Wycombe Abbey School, gave her a strong foundation to become a garden designer. It seems her original plan was to set up a garden-design practice with Lorrie Dunnington, another ex-Swanley student. Their idea was that Madeline would supplement Dunnington's horticultural knowledge with 'such technical matters as surveying and levelling'.[160] Unfortunately, Lorrie Dunnington contracted bovine tuberculosis during her time at Swanley, and became too ill for this plan to take shape.

Despite this setback, Madeline Agar was not deterred. She was fortunate in that she had a trail-blazing pioneer she could learn from. This was Fanny Rollo Wilkinson, one of the founders of the Swanley Horticultural College's Women's Branch. Fanny Wilkinson was born in 1855, the daughter of an eminent physician, Dr Eason

Wilkinson. She grew up in Middlethorpe Hall in Yorkshire, an imposing late-seventeenth-century house with a large garden where, as a young girl, Fanny first developed her interest in gardening. From 1882 to 1883, after a persistent campaign, she managed to secure a place to study for eighteen months at the Crystal Palace School of Landscape Gardening and Practical Horticulture, becoming the first woman to enrol. Fanny Wilkinson was a friend of the influential Garrett family, including Agnes Garrett and her sister Millicent Fawcett, both key figures in the women's movement and supporters of the Kyrle Society, and it was perhaps the Garrett family connection that brought her to the attention of Octavia Hill and the Kyrle Society. These highly capable, committed women, at the heart of many social and political campaigns of the day, formed informal networks that often provided opportunities and openings for other women. Although the Kyrle Society's ambitions were broad, the provision of public green space was one of the most important and effective aspects of its mission. Octavia Hill said that open space offered 'that sense of quiet which whispers of better things to come ... this is true of all classes; we all want quiet; we all want beauty for the refreshment of our souls.'[161] Fanny Wilkinson was appointed to the Council of the Kyrle Society in 1883 to 'advise in matters connected with the laying-out and improvements of churchyards, gardens, squares etc'.[162] One of her first commissions for the Kyrle Society was to lay out Vauxhall Park on land previously occupied by a house and garden owned by Henry and Millicent Fawcett.

It was the Metropolitan Public Gardens Association (MPGA), however, with which Fanny Wilkinson became most involved. The MPGA was founded in 1882 by Lord Brabazon, another member of the Kyrle Society, who felt that more should be done to capitalise on the Metropolitan Open Spaces Act, which made it possible for disused burial grounds to be transferred directly to local authorities to convert and maintain as public gardens. During a career that lasted over twenty years, Fanny Wilkinson designed over seventy-five public gardens for the MPGA. They ranged in size from large parks such as Meath Gardens in Bethnal Green to small spaces such as the garden of Ironmonger's Almshouse, now the gardens of The Museum of the Home in Shoreditch. She was responsible for drawing up plans, obtaining estimates from contractors, employing labourers and ordering plants. At first, Fanny Wilkinson was not paid for the work, but by 1886 it was agreed that she should be able to charge the MPGA a percentage fee, thus making her the first female professional landscape architect in the United Kingdom. For most of the nineteenth century, the term garden designer and landscape architect were used interchangeably, but by the early 1900s the American use of the term landscape architect, to denote a designer of public parks and landscapes, was gaining ground.

From the early days of her practice, Fanny Wilkinson employed a female pupil/assistant to help her manage her many projects and in 1903 Madeline Agar was offered this role, working from Fanny Wilkinson's home at 6 Gower Street. Madeline would have learnt an enormous amount through assisting with numerous projects. Looking at the tone of the MPGA minutes it is clear that, although the motivation was lofty – to improve the health and quality of life of some of the poorest inhabitants of the capital – this was a very 'top down' style of urban planning. There is no mention of consulting with local communities about what they would like to see in the green spaces that were being created for them, and concerns are often expressed over whether the local residents will behave 'properly' in the parks provided for them. In 1887 the MPGA minutes acknowledged that, at its East End Cemetery development the 'barbed wire used to keep the children off the beds was very dangerous' but 'the Secretary noted that it was found absolutely necessary, as the children used to sit and swing on any other kind of wire fencing and steal the flowers. Miss Wilkinson agreed with this statement and, as no complaints were made from the side of the children, the matter was allowed to rest.'[163] Thankfully barbed wire does not seem to have been a frequent design choice and other parks were created that had a more welcoming approach to children. Certainly, it is unlikely that Madeline Agar, with her track record as a teacher, would have approved. The change from being a school gardener to a professional garden designer was a large one, but Madeline must have impressed in her new role. At the end of 1904, when Fanny Wilkinson resigned her position at the MPGA to become the first woman principal at Swanley Horticultural College, the MPGA had no hesitation in appointing Madeline Agar in her place.

There was a degree of irony in Madeline's new area of work because her family's fortune was to some degree founded on income from slum housing. Her grandfather William Agar was a wealthy lawyer who owned land in an area of King's Cross in North London which was named Agar Town after him. After he died, his widow sold off lots of land to be developed as low-quality housing for poor tenants. The area became known as 'Ague Town' because the poor sanitation meant it was synonymous with dirt and disease. Madeline's work for the MPGA was designed to ameliorate conditions in just this type of over-crowded and run-down area.

Many of Madeline's projects were abandoned burial grounds. During the nineteenth century increasing population numbers and high death rates meant that many of London's historic inner-city graveyards had become dangerously overcrowded, with coffins piled up on top of each other and newer graves dug dangerously close to the surface. The cholera epidemic of 1848 spurred reform and a series of Burial Acts banned burial within the most built-up parts of the city, so that many graveyards were closed and bodies relocated to large out-of-town cemeteries such as Norwood Cemetery. The Disused Burial Grounds Act of 1884 aimed to make it difficult for developers to build on these old graveyards in order that they could be developed as public parks. However, the Act did not stop unregulated development. Some unscrupulous builders, finding bones on land they were working on, would hush up the discovery and quietly cart the bones away. The MPGA and local authorities wishing to create parks from green spaces relied on the work of Isabella Holmes, a remarkable woman who volunteered as an Honorary Secretary for the MPGA. Despite having three young children, Isabella Holmes scoured historic maps for evidence of old burial grounds and then explored the back alleys and courtyards of London to find them.

Armed with only a notebook and a determined air, she managed to locate and record hundreds of disused burial grounds, sometimes scaling walls, and facing down angry builders in the process. She recorded her findings on sixty large-scale hand-coloured maps, and it was thanks to her patient work that the MPGA was able to commission Fanny Wilkinson and then Madeline Agar to work on so many parks.

Some of these new parks were quite small, modest green spaces squeezed in between tall buildings, like St Ann Blackfriars in the City of London, just north of Blackfriars Station. This was the site of a church that had burnt down in the Great Fire of London in 1666 and never been rebuilt. The churchyard had been closed for burials since 1849 and in 1907 Madeline Agar designed a small and simple garden there which still exists today. The garden is raised above ground level and largely paved, a practical decision in a small area with little access to natural light, where a lawn would struggle to thrive. Large plane trees provide a green canopy, and the perimeter is planted with robust, largely evergreen, shrubs. Some of the old gravestones are respectfully placed around the edge. It is the kind of space it is easy to take for granted as it is not visually stimulating, but it is just the kind of quiet spot of green that provides a welcome pause in a frenetic city. The MPGA described it as 'a small City Garden much used by Clerks and others'[164] and it still fulfils that function today, as busy City workers grab a sandwich or coffee on the rows of benches that Madeline placed running down the middle of the space. She also worked on larger and more high-profile spaces such as West Square Gardens in Lambeth next to the Royal Bethlem Hospital (now the Imperial War Museum), which was purchased by the MPGA and Southwark Metropolitan Borough in 1909 after a ten-year campaign to save the area from developers. Madeline Agar restored the formal eighteenth-century layout and expanded the garden square by taking surplus land from surrounding roads at a cost of £300. The design featured a rose garden with a sundial and the scheme saved several old mulberry trees from destruction.

Even though her design work was often situated in run-down

and poor parts of London, Madeline still sought to create beautiful gardens. She objected to the cost-cutting approach that some local authorities took to their public spaces, often leading to parks and gardens which, whilst practical and easy to maintain, did not create the tranquil, restful green spaces so needed in the inner city. She complained, 'In the poorer parts of large towns recreation grounds are often tar paved, which is wearisome to the eyes and feet, while it makes the only remedy against the glare – good trees – almost impossible to grow. The motive for this is partly economy in upkeep, and partly dread of stone throwing.'[165] Water featured in many of her designs, particularly the Emslie Horniman Garden in Kensal New Town, an area of North Kensington that had become a run-down slum over the course of the nineteenth century. The Emslie Horniman Pleasance Garden was a joint project with the Arts and Crafts architect Charles Voysey and featured a Spanish-style walled garden with a canal surmounted by an oak pergola. Madeline described water as 'an indispensable feature in a public park' and again wanted charities and councils to aim for a high aesthetic standard, wishing that fountains could be produced 'from a sculptor's hands' rather than 'bear the stamp of a monumental mason'.[166] The Emslie Horniman Pleasance Garden, being generously funded by the heir to the Horniman tea fortune, included the type of handcrafted detail that Madeline Agar approved of, including drinking fountains decorated with floral motifs made of Westmorland slate.

Fanny Wilkinson and Madeline Agar were not the only women to design green spaces to improve cities. In Scotland, Norah Geddes was also making her mark. Norah Geddes was the daughter of Professor Patrick Geddes, biologist, sociologist and influential town planner. Patrick Geddes had visited Octavia Hill early in his career and her ideas shaped his work on housing schemes for the Edinburgh Social Union in the 1880s. Norah Geddes was in turn heavily influenced by her father's work and ideals. She attended his university botany lectures at the age of just 14 and by 1906, at the age of 19, had decided that her vocation was a career in landscape design. In preparation she took drawing classes at the Edinburgh

College of Art and became a skilled painter and draughtswoman. Patrick Geddes felt that effective town planning needed to be based on a close observation of the way people lived and worked, together with the local geography. Norah Geddes worked as a member of his Open Spaces Committee to survey sites in Edinburgh that could provide useful outdoor recreation areas for local people. This research found seventy-five potential spaces and in 1909 Norah Geddes designed her first public garden at one of these sites in Castle Wynd. The following year she worked on another site next to the Salvation Army Women's Hostel in Grassmarket. This child-focused space was open from May to September and staffed by female volunteers. The 930-square-yard site was equipped with sandpits, swings and toys, and children were encouraged to plant their own seeds and bulbs. Norah Geddes married her father's assistant, Frank Mears, and the three worked together on the layout of the Scottish National Zoological Gardens. Although her work was rather overshadowed by the profile of her father and her husband, some of Norah Geddes' humane and sensitive gardens can still be enjoyed in Edinburgh at Chessel's Court, Johnstone Terrace and Westport. By 1908 Frances Wolseley was able to confidently claim in her book, *Gardening for Women*, that 'several municipal authorities are willing to employ women as landscape gardeners.'[167]

*

For some reformers the whole idea of a town needed rethinking. The paternalistic place-making of industrialists like Gertrude Cope's employers, George and Elizabeth Cadbury, at Bourneville, and of other 'model towns' such as Joseph Rowntree's New Earswick in York and the Lever brothers' model village Port Sunlight in Merseyside, were at the heart of a new 'Garden City' movement. This promised to deliver a more egalitarian quality of life in which everyone, rich or poor, had access to healthy and beautiful outdoor space. The term 'Garden City' was inspired by Ebenezer Howard's book *Tomorrow: A Peaceful Path to Real Reform* which was published in 1898 (revised in 1902 as *Garden Cities of Tomorrow*). Howard and his supporters demanded that access to open space for everyone should be the central tenet of urban and suburban planning. He proposed the creation of new towns and cities where, through careful planning and allocation of green space, nature would play a part in the healing of the ills caused by industrialisation. Open space and recreation would improve the health of the workforce and allow residents to enjoy the best of town and country living. The heart of every new city should be formed by a public park and factories should be built around the periphery. Allotments sited on the edge of the city near the factories could provide healthy and productive recreation after work. Beyond the town would be an agricultural buffer or 'greenbelt' that would keep the Garden City separate from other urban areas.

In its early days at least, the Garden City movement was about more than just provision of green space, it was about mobilising town planning to bring about profound societal change, including greater social equality. Ebenezer Howard's plans included provision for housing with communal laundries and kitchens so that women could be released from some of the domestic duties that prevented them from taking on careers or outside interests. The first Garden City, Letchworth in Hertfordshire, included cooperative housing facilities like communal kitchens and halls, new forms of children's education, and inclusive spaces for people with disabilities. It was renowned for attracting feminists and suffragettes, socialists, anarchists, simple-lifers, vegetarians, anti-vivisectionists; people who were often dismissed by the mainstream world as 'cranks'. Many progressive women, including Edith Bradley, supported the Garden City movement; Edith was a member of the Garden City Association, which was founded in 1899, though her focus on equipping women for rural work prevented her from taking a very active role.

In fact, despite the enthusiasm of the movement's supporters, genuine new towns were few and far between. Arguably the most widespread impact of the Garden City movement was to be seen in the suburbs, rather than the truly self-contained communities envisaged by Howard. One of the most influential of the 'Garden City'-style suburbs was Hampstead Garden Suburb, founded by Henrietta Barnett. Barnett was a Christian Socialist and, like Octavia Hill, a committed social reformer, working with her husband, Canon Samuel Barnett, to relieve poverty in the East End. She wanted to protect Hampstead Heath and the surrounding area from unscrupulous and overcrowded housing developments such as those she had seen in the East End and began by purchasing land to the Heath extension as a green 'buffer zone'. With this successfully achieved, she became more ambitious and raised money to buy land to develop a residential suburb for all incomes and classes. The aim was that people of all backgrounds would live in well-designed houses, attractively grouped, and surrounded by gardens. Although over time this dream of a mixed community was to be lost, as the suburb developed a decidedly middle- and upper-class character, there were some socially progressive features. Waterlow Court opened on Heath Close in 1909 to provide cooperative housing for single working women. Designed by M. H. Baillie Scott, Waterlow Court consisted of fifty individual three- to five-room flats, set around a cloistered courtyard. It offered access to socially acceptable, affordable accommodation for working women who were unable to live at home, could not live in a house with strangers and could not afford to rent a flat or house on their own. As most working women did not have much time for domestic chores and could not afford servants, the communal kitchens, dining room and laundry were valuable innovations. Lady gardeners were among the tenants. Lily Barbara Evetts trained at Elmcroft Nurseries run by Constance Dixon in Chichester. By 1912 she had set up a gardening business with Florence Hester Garlick who trained at Swanley. They advertised their business from their address at 28 Waterlow Court with services including: 'Care of Gardens from 7/6 per day, Gardens Designed and Laid Out, Advisory Work, Speciality Made of Pruning and Laying out of Herbaceous Borders, Rock and Walled Gardens etc. etc.'[168] In general, Edwardian developments like Hampstead Garden Suburb, influenced by the Garden City movement, took on the design principles of low-density housing and the concept of a greenbelt, rather than aiming to create experimental communities seeking a novel environmental order. And in time these middle-class suburbs with their relatively affluent residents came to offer rich pickings for female gardeners and garden designers.

Town and suburban gardens offered much more accessible employment prospects for the woman gardener than large country estate gardens. A small garden could be managed by either a single gardener working alone or with a garden boy, or as even a jobbing gardener who only visited periodically. A jobbing gardener worked for several employers, usually in smaller urban or suburban gardens that did not need a full-time live-in gardener to manage them. There were also hybrid posts such as 'lady companion gardeners' where gardening was combined with other duties. Lady companion gardeners were generally employed by elderly single women as a paid friend/assistant and gardener. As early as 1897, popular garden writer Theresa Earle wrote that single ladies living in larger suburban villas might, as she memorably put it, 'prefer a woman head gardener with a man under her to do the rougher work'.[169] This appears to be borne out by the career histories of many of the graduates of the horticultural colleges, such as Marjorie Irene Dodgshun, the daughter of a Leeds cloth manufacturer, who graduated from Studley in 1911. The college alumni register recorded her employment history as 'Gardener – Rosehill on Sea, Gardener to Mrs Williams, Cheshire, Gardener to Mrs Somers, Halesowen.'[170]

While female gardeners were obviously well placed to get the companion gardener posts, it is interesting that both proponents and opponents of women gardeners felt they had another advantage when it came to securing gardening jobs in fashion-conscious towns and suburbs. Female gardeners could emphasise the 'lady' element of the title 'lady gardener' to imply that they had reserves of education, taste and refinement not possessed by the average male working-class gardener. Frances Wolseley declared that 'a lady gardener, owing to her early surroundings, the study of pictures, gardens and beautiful objects, should possess greater capacity for appreciating fully the requirements of the lady of the house.'[171] These arguments were particularly attractive to aspirational middle-class homeowners with villa gardens in cities and suburbs. Mrs Earle claimed that, in most suburbs, 'the dullness of the small plots of ground was entirely owing to the want of education in the neighbouring nurserymen whose first idea was always to plant laurels or other coarse shrubs.' In contrast, a lady gardener 'would know how to plant for an endless variety of colour through the year.'[172]

An example of a gardener who sought to present herself in this way was Helen Colt. Born in Hampstead in 1882, she trained at the Royal Botanic Society in Regent's Park and then set up a gardening business in North London. She advertised frequently in newspapers such as *The Common Cause* and *Votes for Women*, describing herself as a 'Practical, Scientific, and Artistic Gardener, and Specialist in the Arrangement and Regular Care of Town and Suburban Gardens.' At an event titled 'The Englishwoman's Exhibition of Arts and Crafts Produced by Women' held in the Maddox St Galleries in November 1912, she exhibited 'three models of town or suburban gardens, showing how it is possible to adapt the unfruitful soil of sunless places to very delightful arrangements of rockery and grass plot.'[173]

The arguments employed in favour of female gardeners, in part to overcome prejudices against women, frequently tipped over into denigrating male professional gardeners and appeals to snobbish prejudices. Frances Wolseley complained witheringly that small gardens tended to be looked after by 'an uneducated working man, whose chief idea is to keep them tidy.' If suburban gardens were to be made more interesting and beautiful, homeowners needed to 'banish once and for all, the inferior, rule-of-thumb, slow-thinking, inartistic man-gardener whom we have tolerated for so long, and in his place require, intelligent, educated ladies.'[174] This attitude understandably increased antagonism towards women in some quarters. It must have been galling for male gardeners to repeatedly read that they were lumpen, tasteless oafs, fit only for manual labour. Even when female gardeners tried to reassure male gardeners that they were no threat, they could still manage to patronise. For instance, Miss Pollard of Swanley could perhaps have chosen her words more carefully when she declared at a horticultural conference, 'Women were not meant to take the heavier posts, but to help the men with their brains.'[175]

This emphasis on intellect and 'good taste' was part of a wider middle-class appropriation of gardening, not as a craft or a chore, but as an opportunity to express an aesthetic vision and a refined appreciation of nature. The early years of the twentieth century saw the introduction of a new style of garden design, influenced by the Arts and Crafts movement. William Robinson, the enormously influential garden writer, championed a move to more informal planting, relying on hardy perennials in naturalistic groupings rather than tender bedding plants, laid out in regular patterns. He wrote, 'The true gardener is an artist and not a weaver of carpets, and the day will come when the landscape artist will guide the garden artist and it will be thought of as barbarous to make a geometrical carpet of a garden.'[176] This approach, which placed as much emphasis on the choice and placement of plants as on their maintenance, lifted garden design beyond the mere 'laying out' of borders, and suggested that it was the garden designer who was the key person in determining the success of a garden, rather than the traditional head gardener; a shift of emphasis from brawn to brain. No less an authority than *Country Life* magazine declared that, 'Perhaps the highest form of gardening as a profession is garden design, because it needs artistic knowledge as well as keen and intense study of nature, some knowledge of land surveying and measurement, drawing and, above all an eye for colour and proportion which is not granted to everyone.' The article went on to argue that this was a definite field in which women might excel, as after all, 'Miss Jekyll's name at once occurs to everyone.'[177]

Given this burst of enthusiasm for design in the garden, it is not surprising to find that, as well as her work for the Metropolitan Public Gardens Association, Madeline Agar also designed domestic gardens for private clients. By 1908 she had moved to a suburb herself, taking advantage of the extension of the Metropolitan Railway out to Amersham in Buckinghamshire. The rail line from Amersham to Marylebone meant that Madeline was able to reach her London clients and projects easily, and the access to cheaper land and property in Buckinghamshire offered other opportunities. Just a short distance from the station, in what was to become known as 'Metro-Land', Madeline set up 'Holly Bush Nursery' on Cheshunt Lane with a Miss G. Holmes as business partner. Running a nursery gave Madeline Agar the opportunity to earn additional income by providing some of her clients with the plants required to fulfil her designs. Garden design fees from private clients and the MPGA were not high and supplementary income from plant sales was very welcome.

In terms of style, Madeline, too, was an enthusiastic follower of William Robinson and the 'wild garden' approach. She described how, 'one of the most gorgeous mixtures I have ever seen was at Wisley, in the Royal Horticultural Society Garden, where *Primula japonica*, which riots in the ditches of that enchanted wood, has spread up the bank and joined forces with *Meconopsis cambrica*.'[178] However, Madeline's design approach was eclectic, and she was not averse to formal planting in the right setting. In 1912 she wrote that it was actually better to use formal designs in smaller spaces than to try to create wild or English-landscape-inspired gardens in 'cramped spaces and villa gardens, producing laughable, pretentious muddles'. She also warned that 'one of the more terrible results of the desire to be naturalistic in gardens was the introduction of "rustic work" ... The seat or summer house constructed of peeled and varnished branches is surely the climax of bad taste.'[179]

To meet the demands of aspirational and fashionable clients, it was important to keep up to date with the latest trends and styles. In October 1912 Madeline exhibited drawings and plans of her designs at the Women's Agricultural and Horticultural International Union Show. A report in the *Lady's Pictorial* magazine described how there was 'every variety – for example, a sunk garden for a Tudor house, an arrangement for stonework, grass, brick-path, steps, knots of rosemary, and beds of old-fashioned roses.'[180]

Perhaps the hardest garden style of the period to perfect was the craze for Japanese gardens. In 1910, at the Japanese–British exhibition staged at White City in West London, Japanese gardeners were employed to lay out two large gardens, including buildings, plants and ornaments all imported for the show. The show was an instant hit with the public and press and 'Japanese gardens' became all the rage. Madeline Agar shared the widespread admiration for Japanese gardens. 'The only people who have carried the art of landscape gardening to its logical conclusion,' she wrote, 'are the Japanese … not only does a Japanese garden reproduce scenery but it also presents a definite poetical conception.' But she was, as ever, clear-sighted about the potential for translating the Japanese aesthetic on British soil. 'It can never be really developed [in the UK] because of the utter inability of the Western mind to enter or wish to enter into the symbolism expressed in Japanese landscape design. A Japanese garden in England can never mean more than a dainty arrangement of water and stones.'[181] This did not, however, stop suburban garden owners from taking inspiration from Japan, even if that was as simple as asking their gardener to include an acer or an azalea in a garden bed or buying a Japanese stone lantern from Liberty's.

Isabella (Ella) Robertson Christie, a remarkable woman who owned Cowden Castle in Perthshire, went all the way in her quest for authenticity. She travelled through India, Tibet, Russia and China, and was the first western woman to journey from Smarkand to Khiva and to meet a Dalai Lama. After a visit to the gardens of Kyoto in 1907, she was determined to build her own Japanese garden. On her return home she found a Japanese garden designer named Taki Handa studying at Studley Castle, and employed her to work on her seven-acre Japanese Garden in Scotland. The project began with the creation of a large lake, and plants were imported from Japan. Taki Handa worked for over two months in 1908 on the design before she returned to Japan where she taught botany, horticulture and English at the Doshisha Women's College in Kyoto.

In 1910 Madeline Agar published a book on garden design and landscape. Ever the teacher, her book, entitled *Garden Design, in Theory and Practice*, was educational, practical and forthright in its opinions. It was the first textbook on the subject to be written by a woman. In it Madeline Agar covered historically and geographically diverse garden styles, assessing the qualities and applications of each different style, whilst admitting that in her own country, 'There is no more a national type {of garden design} than there is an English costume, beyond a uniform delight in luxurious masses of flower which is engrafted onto any type – Italian or Japanese – whatever may be the prevailing fashion, often to the type's confusion.'[182]

This variety is reflected in her own projects – from public green spaces in London to the grounds at Place House at Fowey in Cornwall. At Place House the garden designer Thomas Mawson has traditionally been credited as the garden designer of the grounds immediately surrounding the house, which has a spectacular setting overlooking the Fowey Estuary. However, his drawings do not appear to have been fully implemented and recent research has revealed how much the appearance of the garden relied on the work of Madeline Agar. Her book reveals that she designed the rose garden and a rockery, both in a relatively formal style. Later, Madeline Agar even took the English garden to Cairo. On a trip to Egypt sometime before 1914 she met an American woman, Mrs Mary Stout, who lived in a Garden City development of Ma'adi on the outskirts of Cairo several years later. They were to write a book together which combined garden design and management tips to allow Western residents of Egypt to create lush, English-style gardens in the hot, dry conditions of Egypt.

Whilst Gertrude Jekyll was clearly the pre-eminent garden designer of her time, she was far from alone. The emphasis on town planning, the growth of garden suburbs and the blossoming of a new garden aesthetic all created new opportunities for women. Whether they were garden designers like Madeline Agar and Fanny Wilkinson, social reformers like Henrietta Barnet and Octavia Hill, or just simple suburban gardeners, women played active roles in transforming our towns and cities. They helped craft attractive and accessible green spaces that provided relief from dirty, overcrowded cities, the Victorian legacy of rapid, unregulated urbanisation.

"JOHN RADDENBURY"

Illustration from *The Violet Book* by Decima Allen and Ada Brown, published in 1913. Courtesy of the RHS Lindley Collections.

7
NO SHRINKING VIOLETS

> Girl children are brought up to believe that money falls on them by some benign plan of providence through the hands of men, fathers, brothers, husbands, whatever they may be ... An outrageous system!
>
> Marion Cran, *The Garden of Ignorance,* 1918

In 1891 Ada Brown was perhaps the most settled of our six women. She was a spinster of comfortable means, living in an Arts and Crafts style house in the pleasant suburb of Knutsford in Cheshire. But in 1899 she made a dramatic decision. She decided, at the age of 44, to sell up and move south to Sussex, where she rented a house called Holmgarth, on the edge of Henfield Common. There she opened a plant nursery. Frances Wolseley, in her book *Gardening for Women,* warned that to run a successful nursery or market garden, even two years at horticultural college was not sufficient preparation. Before setting up business she urged, 'I strongly advise apprenticeship for a year or two to a nursery gardener.'[183] Ada Brown had done neither of these things. Unlike Madeline Agar, Edith Bradley, Gertrude Cope and J. S. Turner, Ada Brown did not study or teach at a formal horticultural training school or college; she does not appear on any RHS Examination entry lists, nor did she have experience of a large garden or selling produce. Years later, she remembered that she started out equipped with nothing more than 'a small but sunny garden – a couple or so of frames, some elderly tools and much cheerful self-confidence.'[184]

On the face of it, Ada Brown had chosen one of the more accessible routes into professional gardening. Setting up an independent horticultural business did not rely on finding an employer, and for women with sufficient financial resources, this entry route could also be reassuringly gradual. Many women with access to larger gardens were able to operate in a semi-professional way, earning some income from selling surplus plants and crops. Their level of seriousness ranged from those that regarded this income as little more than 'pocket-money' to those that aspired to eventually run a serious commercial concern that provided a living.

Anna Bateson, sister of the famous geneticist William Bateson, was one such woman. She had assisted her brother with his scientific work at Cambridge, breeding plants in the Cambridge Botanic Gardens to test the theories of Mendel. Anna read Botany at the pioneering women's college of Newnham and published scientific papers. She decided to not to stay in academia but to set up a market garden business. Although she came from a progressive and liberal family which strongly supported women's rights, this decision was not welcomed. William Bateson wrote to her, 'I think it always a "regrettable incident" when those whose parents have got clear of trade, relapse into it.'[185] Undeterred, Anna began in a small way, renting an allotment of just a quarter of an acre. She explained, 'I got very much interested in it and decided to go in for a country life with a garden which I hoped to make pay its way, if not more.' She prepared herself for her new life carefully, studying gardening for two years with a market gardener in Wales before buying six acres of land at Bashley in Hampshire. She was in the fortunate position of having enough money to build a small house on the land and 'the means to live upon in a somewhat bare way', which was fortunate because 'for many years it was a most unpromising and expensive undertaking. I was entirely without business knowledge in general or any of the detailed knowledge of the horticultural trade and, also being town bred, I was led into many errors.'[186] Yet over the course of fifteen years, she managed to build a flourishing business, expanding to install five 100-foot-long greenhouses.

Anna Bateson was far from alone. The student register at Studley

Castle recorded the eventual careers of ex-students and 'working own garden for profit' crops up many times in the entries.[187] However, even with a college training, success was far from guaranteed. Amongst the positive reports of gardening careers going well, the Swanley student magazine contained a less rousing letter from Miss Ethel Lutley, who had studied at the college in 1898–99. She admitted that after leaving Swanley, she had 'drifted back to the ordinary life of so many girls'. She had tried to sell grapes from her garden at Brockhampton in Worcestershire but complained,

> we have only a small town near and although the demand for tomatoes appears to be unlimited, one cannot find a market for the better things such as grapes or peaches. The townspeople only want the cheapest of fruit, such as those Almeria grapes that come to England in barrels, and they do not care for anything better. We have not been able to sell any grapes further away, neither Black Hamburg nor Muscat of Alexandria this year, except at such a low price as not to make it worth the carriage and packaging. At least, one shilling per pound and carriage to pay did not seem to me a price worth having for grapes which were really very good ones, though of course I do not know very much of trade prices.

She ended rather plaintively, 'I feel how far beyond me the other old Swanley students have got, who have continued their garden in real earnest instead of playing at it ... Perhaps someday in the distant ages I may rise to such heights of knowledge, but in the meantime the time is far off.'[188] The fact that she had not bothered to find out about trade prices or consider switching to a more profitable crop suggests a serious horticultural career was indeed a long way off for Ethel, and so it proved. In 1911, at the age of 43, Ethel Lutley married the splendidly named Beauchamp Moubray St John of Bletso, Lord Lieutenant of Bedfordshire, and abandoned the world of horticulture altogether.

In 1901 it looked like Ada Brown was approaching her business in the same half-hearted way as Ethel Lutley. In the 1901 census she still gave her occupation as 'Living on Own Means' which suggests that her main source of income at this point was still the interest and dividends from the capital left her by her father. It seems that the nursery continued to be a small concern and was not really paying its way. But although the 1901 census return for Holmgarth does not mention the nursery business, it still gives us some interesting insights into Ada Brown's life and subsequent career. Ada is not alone in the house. In addition to a housekeeper from Guisborough and a parlour maid from Manchester, the census record includes a visitor staying with Ada Brown. Interestingly both Ada and her visitor give adaptations of their names; Ada gives her name as 'Adur C. Brown' and her guest, whose real name was Decima Allen, goes by the name of 'Dycima Allen'. It is possible that the census official miscopied the census questionnaire completed by Ada when they wrote the details up in the census enumeration book. However, it seems unlikely that both names were mis-transcribed so badly and, when you try saying the new versions of their names aloud, it seems possible that Ada and Decima were having fun with the way their names sounded when said in the local Sussex accent. This little bit of playfulness is the first sign that Ada Brown was not a conventional middle-class spinster, and it is telling that this side of her emerges when Decima Mary Katherine Allen enters her life.

Unlike Ada Brown, Decima Allen seems to have had a very unconventional upbringing, coming from a family background that was rich in incident and scandal. As her name suggests she was the tenth child of John and Elizabeth Allen. John Allen was a brewer turned farmer; his farm, 'Padnoller', at Charlinch in Somerset covered 140 acres and employed seven farmhands and two boys. The younger children were cared for by a German governess and the Allens also employed five servants. However, the family fortunes were more fragile than they appeared. John Allen died in 1870 and Elizabeth Allen, in her mid-thirties and with nine children all under the age of ten, tried to take on the management of the farm with the help of a farm bailiff. Within a year, she was declared bankrupt, and the farm was sold at auction to pay off debts. If this was not upheaval enough for the young family, at the end of 1871, Elizabeth Allen eloped with a local married man named Robert Chantor. The diaries of her husband's cousin, the Reverend John Allen Giles, record on December 5, 1871, that 'John's widow is 39 years old, and is still as wayward and headstrong as she was when she was the spoilt child of her father Mr. Crosse.' He complains that she has been 'tempted' by a 'villain of good mien and smooth tongue', and that the pair of lovers are intending to add 'folly' to their crime by 'running all over Europe'.[189] Decima herself was only one year old and it is not clear who was caring for her and her brothers and sisters while this drama unfurled. Their relative Isabella Allen Giles wrote 'What a wicked woman she (Elizabeth Allen) must be to leave her nine children and run away with that bad man! It has struck me to suggest how it would be for me to have one of the youngest and bring it up,'[190] but it appears nothing came of this adoption proposal. By April 1872 Elizabeth Allen was pregnant and living in a one-room apartment, possibly in Bristol. In January 1873 Robert Chantor abandoned her, emigrating to Canada and leaving Elizabeth behind with a baby daughter. The 'lost sheep', as she was described by her family, then moved to Brussels to start a new life as a school mistress. It is possible that Elizabeth Allen was reunited with her children at that point. Certainly, none of them appears in any British census records between 1871 and 1901, which suggests that Decima and her siblings were living abroad during their childhood and early adulthood. The family's association with scandal and intrigue did not end there. Decima's eldest brother, William, deserted his wife to join the Hussars, her other brother, Jem, was threatened with a naval court martial, and her youngest sister, Sybil, the result of the liaison with the fickle Mr Chantor, married an army officer who went on the run from the law for ten years after stealing a friend's diamond shirt stud. Sybil went on to become quite a well-known romantic novelist under the pseudonym Sybil Campbell Lethbridge, writing such thrilling titles as *A Fight for Love* and *When Love Conquered All.*

Exactly how Decima Allen and Ada Brown came to meet is a mystery. Decima was thirteen years younger than Ada, so it is unlikely they were old school friends. I have not been able to find any obvious link between their families. Whatever the circumstances, they were clearly close by 1901, when Ada was 45 and Decima was 32 years old. Decima was described as a 'visitor' in the census, but she never left Henfield and became Ada's equal partner in the nursery business. In fact, the pair renamed themselves 'The Misses Allen-Brown' and this hyphenated form of their surnames was the name they lived with and traded under for the rest of their lives.

Joint women proprietors were very common in female gardening businesses; like-minded women, whether friends, business partners, sisters or lovers, were often to be found running horticultural schools, nurseries and market gardens. Usually at least one would have training in horticulture whilst the other might provide essential administration or domestic skills. Running a business and a home was a daunting prospect for one person alone unless they were already wealthy enough to employ servants. Social convention made it impossible for an unmarried woman to work in partnership with a man, so setting up home with another single woman was a practical solution. In many cases, establishing a partnership with another woman was also the only way of amassing enough capital to meet the costs of setting up a business. Speaking at a meeting on 'Women in Horticulture' held at the Congress Hall in London in July 1910, Constance Dixon, who owned a market garden and nursery in Chichester, estimated that 'a woman setting up in this line of business ought to have a capital of not less than £1,000. She might begin with two acres and must have, of course, a small house, a promising market and a good soil.'[191] Given Decima's background as the daughter of a bankrupt, 'fallen woman,' it is unlikely she brought much money to the partnership, and the main financial contribution will have come from Ada Brown; so, in this case the initial impetus for the partnership was probably not financial.

The decision to merge their surnames suggests that Ada and Decima's partnership was much more than a business relationship or close friendship. Ada Brown's full name was Ada Eugenie Brown and it seems that Decima and other close friends called her 'Gene' (Ada's gravestone in Henfield Cemetery is marked Ada Eugenie 'Gene' Brown). We can speculate how many of the women living and working together in gardening enterprises were in a lesbian relationship, but in most cases we will never know for certain. Assessing the available evidence is complicated by the widespread phenomenon at the time of 'romantic friendships' between women, which may or may not have been sexual relationships. Romantic female friendships, often accompanied by effusive gestures of affection, were widely accepted as a phase that young women would go through, either as a preparation for heterosexual marriage, or as a natural and permissible outlet for conventional feminine attributes, such as affection and sentimentality. These small market gardens and nurseries probably made it possible for many homosexual couples to live together even within small parochial communities; however, the discretion that they had to show to avoid becoming social outcasts makes it hard today to ascertain how common this really was. What is without doubt, in the case of Ada and Decima's relationship, is the significance of the emotional support that they gained from their partnership, a partnership that enabled them to carve out meaningful and independent lives outside of a conventional heterosexual marriage.

There is one more clue as to why they chose to move to the country and set up a nursery business together. In 1908 a newspaper article on the Allen-Brown firm recounted that some years ago, the two women had 'retired to the charming little Sussex village of Henfield and commenced a business as general farmers and growers of all kinds of herbaceous plants. One of the primary reasons for the starting of the enterprise was that one of the ladies was suffering from ill health and it was thought that the light horticultural work would be a means of improvement.'[192] Although the article does not specify which of the pair suffered from ill health, it is likely that it was Ada, who may have been already suffering from tuberculosis, a disease that would ultimately kill her. Tuberculosis was one of the most common and feared diseases in the world. Known commonly as consumption, the symptoms were fatigue, night sweats, persistent coughing and a general 'wasting away.' Although much more prevalent amongst poor urban populations, where overcrowding and malnutrition aided the spread of the disease, no one was immune from this dangerous and debilitating illness, which was a major cause of death all over the world. Until the development of antibiotics in the 1940s, there was no known cure and treatments concentrated on rest, good diet, plenty of fresh air and outdoor exercise. Gardening was often specified as the ideal form of outdoor activity for tuberculosis sufferers and other invalids. Furthermore, since the 1860s, people had been aware that tuberculosis was infectious; the bacteria spread in tiny droplets coughed into the air by sufferers. Tuberculosis sufferers were encouraged to isolate in sanatoria or live in remote, sparsely populated locations. It may be that Ada Brown saw a move to a small village in Sussex, with the opportunity to take up an occupation that involved plenty of time outdoors, as a sensible choice to improve her own health and minimise the chances that she spread this dreadful disease to others. If so, she was not unusual; gardening was held up as a health cure for a wide range of illnesses. A report in *The Times* confidently declared, 'The anaemic girl, the girl (often decidedly clever) with poor eyesight, the hysterical neurotic girl, all these as a rule become changed beings after a serious course at a horticultural college. There are many girls and women whose lives would lose their dreariness, and whose minds, as much as their bodies, would become strengthened if they were in the fields at six o'clock in the morning instead of putting on the extra time at the wrong end of the day at books or pleasure parties.'[193]

Within the horticultural profession itself, there was far from universal support for this idea. There were some who worried that encouraging invalid women to take up horticulture might jeopardise the wider campaign to have women taken seriously as professional gardeners. Helen Colt, the well-respected gardener who ran a garden design and maintenance business in Hampstead Garden Suburb, was, to say the least, sceptical. In response to a talk given by a Dr Jane Walker, titled 'The Industrial Treatment of Tuberculosis', read at the Women's Congress in June 1910, Helen Colt felt moved to write a letter to the editor of *Common Cause*. She declared:

> [T]he increased practice of sending to be trained as professional gardeners, not tuberculous sufferers alone, but girls and women who are handicapped with every type of delicacy, in the belief that an outdoor occupation be their best chance in life, is becoming a menace to the interests of all concerned. The presence of such women at our Horticultural Colleges upsets the balance of work, throws an unfair responsibility on the staff, endangers the health of the patients (I cannot class them otherwise), and brings discredit on our calling. People will very naturally refuse to apply for women-gardeners when it is found that a large proportion are totally unfit to undertake the routine of manual work which forms the chief part of a gardener's life. This abuse can only be rectified by insisting upon an absolute distinction between the invalid amateur gardener and the intending professional possessed of normal health. By all means, let the former play at gardening in her own home, or practise it in a special school or sanatorium, where a man can be found for the enviable post of assistant (!), to push wheelbarrows, trench heavy ground, cut hedges, weed crops in hot weather and so on, and where the patient can stop work as soon as fatigue or any other adverse condition prevails. But need I point out that such a state of things is only possible where it is not proposed to run a garden for profit?'[194]

It seems that Ada and Decima were untroubled by any doubts that they would be strong enough, or even knowledgeable enough to succeed in their new venture as nursery owners. Looking back, years later, they admitted their naivety: 'With adoring pride, we looked around our little domain and, as it seemed to our partial eyes that every kind of plant flourished, and as we really were blessed with the gardener's gift of a lucky hand, we determined to make our mercantile career as a sort of universal producer, with all the gay insouciance of optimistic ignorance.'[195] This approach flew cheerfully in the face of all the available advice. Perhaps more by luck than design they got one thing right, however. Mr Iggulden, Horticultural Instructor at Lady Warwick Hostel, was quoted as saying that, when choosing the location of your business, 'the best neighbourhood would be near a good market' and 'within a short driving distance of the local town, or if London is to be the destination for goods, then as near as possible to a station.' He also suggested setting up business 'close to some town in which High Church views predominated because this would ensure a steady demand for flowers.'[196] Whether 'High Church' or not, Henfield luckily fitted the bill in terms of transport links, being on the railway line between London and Brighton.

The next imperative was access to a good supply of water. Ada and Decima started off sensibly enough by establishing a well in the acre of ground surrounding their house. They reported that the three wells in the garden were 'all found by the local "water-finder", with his forked twig of hazel or privet. He can trace the course of streams and tell to within a couple of feet at what depth water will be found. We know of no more interesting operation to watch; a power as yet unexplained which we believe lingers almost exclusively among dwellers in the country.'[197] However, they were far from business-like regarding the management of the nursery. For instance, they took a rather idiosyncratic approach to labelling the stock that they were selling: 'What beautiful and graceful names we gave to lovely unknown flowers! The decisions of the RHS were to us as light as thistledown.'[198]

They seemed to manage to attract customers, but that did not necessarily lead to profitability. 'Orders came from here and there and everywhere, somehow we were invariably able to fulfil them, owing partly to the fact that we did not permit the sentence "It is not worth our while" to cross our lips.'[199] It appears that it was not just Ada's and Decima's inexperience that threatened the future of their young venture. The pair were convinced that they were the subject of sabotage by some in the local professional gardening fraternity. They believed this occurred when they added bulbs to their stock: 'Certain of those who hitherto had been accustomed to purchase the various bulbs and tubers for their masters felt aggrieved when the matter was taken out of their hands, and to show how misguided said masters were, our bulbs experienced many strange happenings. Some got planted upside down, some intended for the garden were planted in the greenhouse. Choice and delicate ones were lightly stuck in the open ground. Naturally our bulbs, the pride of our hearts, suffered; so did our belief in humanity.'[200]

Whether this accusation was justified or not, their small-scale and rather amateurish nursery venture was losing money and eventually even this optimistic pair was forced to face reality. 'As time rolled on,' they later recalled, 'the thought came to be more and more forced upon our minds, what great tracts of land in England were laid out in splendid nursery gardens. Of the enormous amount of capital that had been sunk in the erection of horticultural buildings. We grasped in some degree the amount of money, education and long experience that had gone into their making.'[201] In 1905 they admitted defeat and wound up the general nursery business and had a penny sale to dispose of the stock. Ironically the sale was an 'exciting and laughable success … Smart double broughams with liveried men dashed up to our modest garden gate, and richly dressed clients descended to make a critical survey of our special "Penny Menu."'[202]

Ada's and Decima's experience chimed with the warnings given to prospective female entrepreneurs in the field of nursery and market gardening. At about the same time as Ada and Decima were struggling with their nursery at Henfield, Mr A. D. Hall, the Director of the Rothampstead Experimental Station, warned: 'The records of Swanley Horticultural College showed what openings there were for women, but with regard to the question of whether a woman with a little capital could make a living by growing flower and fruit, it was a matter which required great caution, by reason of competition.' Larger, better-established nurseries with greater resources could undercut them on price and outgun them on marketing. All was not lost though. In the same speech, Mr Hall helpfully advised that, 'The kind of business best suited to a woman was that in which intelligence was worth more than capital or manual labour, such as propagating rare and valuable plants.'[203]

Ada and Decima came to the same conclusion: to succeed, they would need to find a niche and specialise in one plant. When it came to choosing which plant to focus on, they discovered that the answer was under their noses. 'From under the high hedge, the chink of the wall, from every nook and corner, filling the air with their fragrance, grew the sweet, wild violets, purple and white and pink; and they whispered, "Oh! Foolish humans – if we, the little rustics of our race, live and thrive so happily without help, without thought, what would our smarter sisters do, cared for and tended – with all the science and the art that love can teach?"'[204] Despite this whimsical presentation of the decision to specialise, the choice of violets was a sensible one.[205] Not only did violets thrive in the Sussex sun, these pretty blue flowers, based as they were on well-known wildflowers, fitted in well with the taste for 'old-fashioned' and 'English' plants, as championed by influential taste-setters like William Morris and Gertrude Jekyll. One astute observer remarked that whilst inhabitants of small cottages 'now try to fill their little plots with geraniums and calceolarias … my lady at the Court is hunting the nursery grounds for London Pride and gentianella to make edgings for her wilderness, and for the fair tall rockets, the cabbage roses and the nodding columbines which her pensioners had discarded and 'thrown away.'[206]

There was another reason that violets were to prove a shrewd choice of plant. By the time that Ada and Decima set up their violet nursery, the women's suffrage campaign was in full swing and had developed its own iconography. In 1903, frustrated with the lack of progress made to date, Emmeline Pankhurst set up The Women's Social and Political Union. The followers of the WSPU became very skilled at image management, developing striking artwork and visual stunts to get their message across. In 1908 the WSPU chose purple, green and white as its colours. Purple stood for loyalty and dignity, white for purity and green for hope. Violets, with their purple (and in some varieties white) flowers and green leaves represented these colours very effectively and were frequently used in merchandise and imagery supporting the campaign. Violets were also reputedly associated with lesbianism thanks to references to the flower in Sappho's poems, but this symbolism was not popularised until the mid-1920s, when the flower featured as a symbol in a French play named *The Captive* on Broadway. The Allen-Browns were well known within the suffrage movement as 'great friends of the cause' and frequently advertised in suffrage-supporting newspapers such as *Common Cause* and *Votes*

Ada Brown receiving a violet plant from Mr A. Goacher in a field surrounded by glass cloches at the Allen-Brown Violet Nursery in Henfield, 1912. Courtesy of the Henfield Museum.

Decima Allen with Jerry the pony, taking goods to Henfield Station, 1912. Courtesy of the Henfield Museum.

for Women. Women wanting to demonstrate their support for female suffrage could buy flowers in WSPU colours, whilst at the same time benefiting a business run by fellow suffragettes.

Concentrating on one product also brought a new professionalism to Ada's and Decima's approach. They frankly admitted, 'From the day we took up violet culture professionally, our real hard work began.'[207] They went on to develop a real expertise in violet-growing and in 1913 they published a book outlining how to grow violets commercially. The book, simply titled *The Violet Book*, is detailed and technical, but their genuine admiration and even affection for the qualities of this little plant still shine through. They write, 'Her message is one of gentleness and love. She makes no display in courtly function, not for her the gay decoration of the ballroom, nor the glowing light of the feast. But who so welcome to the bed of the sick, to the hand of the convalescent, or on the desk of the writer, who so at one with the mourner as he places his last tribute on the grave of the beloved?' They say that 'she will not thrive on a very chalky district' but given pure air, 'she will stand scorching sun or pouring rain, bustling wind or winter frost.'[208] It is interesting that throughout the book the violet is personified as female.

The Violet Book also gives readers an honest picture of just how hard Ada and Decima worked. At first, they had no outside help and had to take on all the manual labour associated with growing large numbers of young plants themselves. Their detailed account of their first year growing violets recalled: 'In April we knelt down to plant the first spring cuttings, attired in neat apparel; the end of May found us in tattered skirt and ragged apron.'[209] Their situation was made worse by the fact that that first summer of violet production was 'exceptionally hot and dry' and they had to carry heavy watering cans about the garden 'until our heads and arms ached.'[210] The following winter was unusually cold, and the pair spent five hours a day attending to the frames, brushing off snow, opening and closing the lights to control the temperature. 'Our hands were sometimes so cold and numb that we had to stop and rub each other's to bring them back a little to life, often they were cut and bleeding.'[211] Their set-up was very basic to begin with: 'Our office was a small windowless shed, in which was done all the arranging of flowers, packing of parcels and writing business letters. The door which faced due east had to remain wide open, there being no other means of obtaining light. The cold on a winter's morning when an east wind was blowing may be imagined.'[212]

Carefully tended, different varieties of violet could provide blooms for sale for seven months of the year, although, as Ada and Decima found, this did require 'unremitting toil and care'. As they gained experience, their standards rose and 'A dead leaf was an eyesore, a footprint an unforgivable offence, a weed grieved us to the heart.'[213] From June to July, they waged a 'ceaseless war' against 'every creeping, flying, tunnelling pest, and the name is surely legion.' Their book includes a long list of threats including mildew, red spider, aphids, wireworm, centipedes, caterpillars, slugs and snails. 'It would be logical to advise the wholesale destruction of moths and butterflies,' they comment before admitting, with a hint of their initial, rather whimsical approach, 'We make ineffectual efforts to seize these jewels of the air but heave a sigh of thankfulness as they flutter safely away on their little shining wings.'[214] In fact, regarding pest control, they seem rather ahead of their time, taking a more ecological approach than most of their contemporaries who were very keen on using noxious sprays and powders. Ada and Decima pleaded, 'Let violet-growers encourage birds to nest in their gardens and nurseries. The amount of destructive grubs, insects and larvae which they destroy while feeding their young is amazing.'[215] There were limits to their tolerance and willingness to rely on natural predators, however. 'It was still in the early days of our undertaking that an immense horde of snails and slugs descended upon our garden and ravaged it. The work of extermination seemed impossible.' Any gardener who has lost precious plants to slugs and snails will identify with their response. Having tried all kinds of remedies from 'from tame toads to cabbage leaves browned in lard',[216] they went out one evening 'armed with little tin buckets containing a strong solution of salt and water, large spoons and old lanterns'. 'It was dusk, we crept along the hedge-side, under the wall, by the violet beds. The lust of battle and revenge for violets slain fell upon us. There were eager exclamations, quick scoopings, then plop, plop, another snail was in the bucket.'[217]

But it was not all hard work. There were rewards to the lifestyle they had chosen: 'It was a joy in the early dawn of an August day, ere work began, to look out from the small summer house across the sweet-smelling garden to the common beyond, lying half-hidden, half-discovered in the silver-floating mists, the air alive with melody. We dwelt for a time in fairy land. Homely bread and butter and tea in garden mugs and a dew-kissed apple from a tree by way of finish was a feast worthy of Titania's tasting.'[218]

However, for all the talk of fairyland and humorous descriptions of battles with slugs and snails, the Allen-Brown Violet Nursery did become a serious and quite considerable business. Unlike their early days of nursery ownership, Ada and Decima took the preparation and marketing of their produce very seriously. As they wrote in their book, 'There is a great deal of truth in the saying of one of our pioneer women gardeners: "Anyone can grow a flower: the thing is to sell it when grown."'[219] They even exported live violet plants abroad. 'If gathered in the cool, and properly packed, they should arrive perfectly fresh. We posted violets to Norway and heard that they arrived in good condition in spite of the long sea journey.'[220] They diversified, producing and selling a wide range of beauty products using their violets. Their violet-scented creams, soaps and perfumes, which they manufactured themselves on site, were sold all over the world. An advert in *The Graphic* from November 1910 outlined their 'Special Christmas list' which included 'soaps, scents, bath salts, toilet-powders, sachets, breeze baskets, pot pourri bowls and smelling salts, all fragrant with the old English perfumes which the Misses Allen-Brown know how to distil with unrivalled cunning.'[221] They sought aristocratic and fashionable patrons and name-dropped frequently in their extensive advertising campaigns. Over the years their customers included Queen Alexandra, Queen Mary, the Duchess of Devonshire and the actress Ellen Terry. Their customer base seems to have been predominantly female. They said that whilst men might send hothouse flowers to impress, women themselves were much more likely to purchase and give the quieter, less showy violet. Their products were designed to be amongst the 'innumerable gifts that quiet women of the British Isles send to their women-friends. It is one of our great pleasures that we are connected (though only as "middlemen") with this gracious custom.'[222] To cater for this discerning market, the Allen-Browns kept a close eye on the latest trends and fashions. They spotted an opportunity in the popularity of the new pastime of 'motoring'. In an advertorial in *The Queen* newspaper, readers were told: 'A violet motor lotion must not be forgotten, for it is the softest thing imaginable when applied to the skin, allaying the burning sensation produced by wind and sun. Most lady motorists nowadays carry it in their bags.'[223]

All this advertising and the clever product development paid off and demand rose to such an extent that the Allen-Browns decided to expand. They rented more land and erected a larger greenhouse. To cope with the expanded workload, they paid male staff to do some of the heavier work and also took on female pupils. Frances Wolseley herself recommended the training at the Violet Nurseries, explaining, 'Pupils are received on payment of 5 guineas premium for a year's tuition. The instruction given is entirely practical. Arrangements are made to obtain rooms for pupils in the village, the charges being (approximately) one guinea for a single room and board and fifteen shillings each for a room shared … The work is exceedingly healthy – above all for the open-air employment – owing to the fact that the smell of violets has medicinal qualities. The pleasure of the work proves its ample reward, apart for the pecuniary success, to all who give themselves to it unreservedly, with physical and mental vigour.'[224] The Violet Nurseries tended to attract bohemian and left-wing pupils. The Allen-Brown's pupils included Rachel Dyce Sharp, sister of Clifford Dyce Sharp, the first editor of *The New Statesman*, a magazine founded by Sidney and Beatrice Webb and other members of the left-wing Fabian Society. Other pupils were devotees of the socialist poet, philosopher and advocate of sexual freedom, Edward Carpenter. His brother, Alfred Carpenter, wrote to Edward from

Henfield on July 3, 1916, to record a visit to the Violet Nurseries and said of the female pupils there, 'Many of them are worshippers of yours and hailed my arrival (before they met me!) with joy.'[225]

A picture of the life that Ada and Decima led in these years comes from a neighbour and close friend, the American author, actress and playwright Elizabeth Robins. In 1909 Robins brought a bit of glamour to the quiet village of Henfield when she retired there at the age of 40 after a glittering career on the stage, bringing the plays of Ibsen to British audiences. Like Ada and Decima, she was a committed supporter of votes for women, and they may have met at local suffrage events. As a member of the WSPU committee, Elizabeth Robins would have been very aware of the significance of violets as a symbol of the WSPU. In fact, it was reported that, once at a dinner party with the anti-suffragette Prime Minister Asquith, she had deliberately worn a white satin dress trimmed with violets, which prompted him to remark, 'You are looking very hostile.'[226]

In 1923 Robins wrote a successful, but now largely forgotten novel, called *Time is Whispering,* which seems to have been inspired and informed by her friendship with Ada and Decima. It is the story of an unlikely platonic romance between middle-aged widow Judith Lathom and her crusty misogynistic landlord, Henry Ellerton. With a profligate adult son to support, Mrs Lathom is in financial difficulties and decides that opening a market garden is the answer. To the initial dismay of her landlord, she wears breeches and gaiters. She points out that they are less 'indecent' than conventional evening dress and infinitely more practical: 'I see you haven't any idea what it's like! At every step, stuff flapping about your legs, clinging to your knees, forever pulling you back.' The pair eventually marry so that they can enjoy each other's company without local tongues wagging. Ellerton's estranged daughter moves to the area with her female friend to set themselves up as tenant farmers and the description of this smallholding with its female pupils and workers is probably closely based on the Allen-Browns' establishment. Robins wrote, 'They worked hard and they played with a zest. Anyone who hadn't a favourite pastime was taught some game. Two evenings in the week, those who could, made music; nearly all sang, and everyone danced. There were among them as time went on, amateurs of painting, of home handicraft, of archaeology. The common bond was love of the country – but Rhodes Hall had become a School of Life.'[227]

Elizabeth Robins was certainly a supporter of the Allen-Brown Violet Nurseries. Ada and Decima dedicated *The Violet Book* to her, and it was probably Elizabeth Robins they were thinking of when they wrote, 'It is after misfortunes that the unwavering belief of a friend in one's ultimate success is of such an immense help. Pity disheartens too much, sympathy weakens the fibre, advice and criticism, that are often nonprofessional and nearly always given too late, fret and annoy – only steady, unswerving faith braces the mind, puts courage into the heart, gives new vigour to the will, so crowning the endeavour with success. These few lines are especially intended for one who, while hearing doubts, criticisms and hints of failure for many years, has remained our believing, unwavering friend.'[228]

With their successful business, catering for a largely female clientele, and their garden a training ground for bright young women wanting to make a life in the country, Ada and Decima were at the heart of a woman-centred community. Their radicalism was of a quiet type, sweetly scented with the perfume of violets. To the outside world, the most unconventional aspect of their life together was that they ran a successful business that demonstrated a new model of economic independence for women that did not rely on conventional marriage. This was a time when women were still widely expected to live lives of selflessness and empathy, and men were thought to have the monopoly on competitiveness and self-determination. The Allen-Browns and others like them proved this to be simply not true. They created their own successful business, one that made money by operating within a uniquely female economy and keeping true to their own social and political values. In 1915 Ada Brown finally succumbed to TB, dying at the age of 59. Decima Allen carried on the business, going into partnership with ex-pupil Rachel Dyce Sharp. However, the Violet Nurseries continued to trade under the name 'the Misses Allen-Brown' until Decima herself died in 1951 at the age of 81.

Caricature of J. S. Turner, titled 'An Agricultural Expert'. The drawing was made while J. S. Turner was still teaching at Glynde and gives an impression of a woman of firm opinions. Courtesy of the Archive of Frances Wolseley, Hove Library.

8
THE CALL OF EMPIRE

> Women who find a difficulty getting their living at home, would do well to think of the peaches given to the pigs, and cherry trees breaking down their weight of fruit in New Zealand or the rich, bright winters of Canada.
>
> *The Emigration of Women to Our Colonies*, A. E. N. Bewicke, 1881

Not all supporters of horticultural training for women were radical social progressives or feminists. Some advocated for women to take to the land from a very socially conservative standpoint. Opponents of female suffrage felt that these disruptive demands would disappear if only more women could find their natural destiny as wives and mothers. And if they could not find a husband at home? Well, there were plenty of single British men scattered across the Empire. Single British women should simply be persuaded and supported to emigrate and marry them. It was also argued that the emigration of 'surplus women' could reduce competition for jobs in Britain, which risked repressing wages for male breadwinners at home. But for female emigration to be a success, women would need to be equipped for their new lives as colonists. In this context, providing women with horticultural training to help them live off the land was seen as a sensible step for maintaining the social status quo at home.

It was not just a question of sending potentially troublesome women far away. There were many that saw sending British women across the Empire as essential to strengthening Britain's hold on its dominions abroad. Leading imperialists of the period were increasingly turning their attention away from military conquest – the province of men – towards building a settled, 'civilising' Empire – a mission for which women were seen as vital. Some even argued that greater female involvement was essential for the long-term viability and survival of the British Empire. An article in *The Times,* published in 1907, warned, 'It has recently been pointed out that in many parts of the Empire the British flag flies over a generation of bachelors. The men emigrate and leave their delicately nurtured women at home. This is not colonisation; this is not Empire.' For its supporters, true colonisation required a settled and growing white population, and that meant wives and mothers.

But preparation was needed before women could leave home to bring 'the best traditions of English womanhood to our colonies'. *The Times* article went on to argue:

> It needs more than mere sentimental desire to make colonisation a success. It needs more than 'love in a cottage' ideals to run a household where there are few of the aids of civilisation. Success can only follow thorough scientific and business-like training. The colonist's home needs a woman, whether help or helpmate, who, besides the main essential of good health, possesses practical training in all branches of simple housekeeping, adaptability, and common sense. Even some women who consider themselves domesticated would be surprised to find how much they lack when Peter Robinson [a chain of department shops] and the Stores were separated from them by an ocean and perhaps a desert ... One thing above all others, the woman who intends to colonise must not be afraid to soil her hands.[229]

Agriculture and horticulture were seen as essential tools in bringing the 'wildernesses' in Britain's colonies under control, and in this context, it was perfectly acceptable for women to do outdoor work, as their physical labour was seen as serving a higher imperial and patriotic cause.

There was undoubtedly a racist and eugenicist element to this argument for a specifically female role in British colonies. Jessie M. Saxby in her book *West-Nor-West,* published in 1890, even framed it in gardening terms: 'We should look upon the British Isles as the cradle and nursery of the world – a nursery garden where the best kind of seedlings and saplings are trained into vigorous young life for the purpose of transplanting into wide gardens, lawns and woodlands!... We ought to send to our colonies – to the whole uninhabited or sparsely-peopled, or savage-haunted places of the earth – "well-assorted specimens" from our home nursery garden.'[230]

Of course, not everyone who promoted horticultural training or emigration for women was doing so from this standpoint, but unquestioning support for the British Empire was a popular view that influenced most parts of public life, and horticulture was no exception. As uncomfortable as it may be to acknowledge today, a commitment to colonialism did underpin some of the efforts to equip women with horticultural and agricultural skills in this period. The campaign to send women to the outposts of Empire was to become one of the most popular and prominent movements of its day. Most active female supporters of imperial expansion were not feminists in the sense that they did not challenge existing gender roles or inequalities. And yet, even if they did not believe in female suffrage or emancipation, they did share with feminist campaigners a pride in female achievement and a belief that women could make a valuable contribution. Our picture of the Edwardian women's movement and gardening's role within it is only a partial one if it ignores the motivation to create an active female role in the British Empire.

From the 1880s onwards, numerous charities were set up, many run by women, to promote and support female emigration and these eventually coalesced under the umbrella of The British Women's Emigration Association (BWEA). One of the highest-profile and most popular national movements of the time, it had agents in practically every provincial town in the country and established hostels in Liverpool and London where women could stay before departure. It employed a network of cooperative 'correspondents' across the Empire who informed the Association of the local demand for female emigrants and arranged for safe reception, lodging and respectable employments. The BWEA recognised that the women would initially need to be employed. Although the ultimate goal of sending women of breeding age abroad might have been to consolidate colonies, it was seen as unseemly to explicitly send young women husband-hunting, and in any case, female emigrants would probably need to earn their keep while they waited for a marriage prospect to materialise. Horticultural training, as well as offering practical skills for life as a housewife on a colonial homestead, offered a promising means of earning a respectable living before or, if the worst came to the worst, instead of marriage. As with the case for female head gardeners at home, the natural recipients of these opportunities were explicitly defined as being women from the middle and upper classes. Working-class women were encouraged to emigrate, but via distinctly separate routes, with the assumption that they would obviously be destined for positions in domestic service.

Propaganda for female emigration was heightened during the Boer War, when there was a general upswelling in patriotic and imperial feeling. Horticultural schools and colleges quickly adapted their courses to meet the demand for training that would prepare women keen to start a new life in the colonies. In 1901 Lady Warwick was introduced to Cecil Rhodes by the famous newspaper editor W. T. Stead and became a sudden and dramatic convert to Imperialism. She immediately decided that Cecil Rhodes was a man of genius and wrote him gushing letters of support. Her hero-worship of Rhodes inspired her to set up a colonial training programme at the Lady Warwick Hostel in Reading in 1901 while Edith Bradley was still warden. She managed to persuade Alicia Amherst, a well-known advocate of female emigration and wife of Conservative MP Evelyn Cecil, to become a patron of the Lady Warwick Hostel and be on her college's General Committee. A staunch supporter of British imperialism and an active member of the South African Expansion Committee of the BWEA, Alicia Amherst was a keen gardener and botanist and went on plant-collecting trips to Mozambique, South Africa, Rhodesia (Zimbabwe), Ceylon (Sri Lanka), New Zealand, Australia and Canada. However, Lady Warwick's socialist views and racy private life meant that her efforts were never well integrated with the better-established organisations promoting female emigration.

Another reason for her lack of impact in this area may be that the real engine of activity in her horticultural work was Edith Bradley, and her eyes were firmly fixed on making room for women in the British countryside with her cooperative smallholding schemes.

Swanley Horticultural College was also swept up in the enthusiasm for colonial training and opened a Colonial Branch in 1903. Students stayed in a designated residence block where they could live 'as far as possible under the conditions of colonial life'. The idea was to educate a class of women who could fill skilled occupations in teaching, gardening and agriculture in colonial settlements. The curriculum included botany, agricultural chemistry and soils, in the same way as the core Swanley horticultural courses did. Emphasis was also placed on practical domestic work and there was 'expert instruction in those first essentials for the country colonist, sanitation, first aid and nursing'.[231] Students at the Swanley Colonial Branch could study for a twelve-week Certificate course or a Higher Certificate course which took a year to complete.

Of our six women, it was to be the stocky, no-nonsense Lincolnshire countrywoman, J. S. Turner, who was to be most involved in the movement to prepare women for colonial life. Like her employer at the Glynde College for Lady Gardeners, Frances Wolseley, she was a wholehearted supporter of the British Empire. J. S. Turner had grown up in a conservative household; with her father she had attended many political meetings supporting Conservative and Unionist election campaigns. She was also an active supporter of Tariff Reform, a campaign to put high import taxes on goods coming from outside the Empire and spoke at events for The Women's Tariff Reform League. In 1909 she called for the government 'to treat our colonies better than the foreigner and knit up the bonds of Empire while there is still time.'[232]

In 1907 she decided to leave Glynde and set up her own training school 'where ladies could be made familiar with the old-fashioned farmhouse life' specifically to prepare them for emigration.[233] A report in *The Girl's Realm* explained that this decision was prompted by a conversation with Alicia Amherst who had told J. S. Turner that, 'one of the great wants of our colonies was well-trained, ladylike girls who would make good wives.'[234]

However, it is hard to imagine that J. S. Turner was only interested in preparing women to become colonial wives to breed new settlers. Her own rural upbringing, her experience of estate management at Dochfour and her experience at Glynde had clearly convinced her that there was absolutely no reason why women could not manage their own farms, smallholdings and market gardens even in the toughest environments. Looking back on her own childhood, she recalled, 'when she was a girl in Lincolnshire, women worked on the land and were much better and healthier for it.'[235] Whilst she was at Glynde, she was outspoken in defending the capacity of women to undertake hard physical labour – and encouraging pupils to do likewise. At Glynde, which Frances Wolseley described as 'a rough, bleak spot for the first few years, without trees or hedges to break the wind', J. S. Turner observed, 'We have taken in hand five and a half acres of ordinary agricultural land and converted the greater part into a garden, entirely by the work of the pupils.'[236] Frances Wolseley later recalled 'the sound of the pick as it fell at regular intervals, hewing down the hard rock to form this sheltered, hidden garden'.[237] Whilst East Sussex was not exactly the Australian outback or the Canadian plains, J. S. Turner clearly felt, that with the right training, women had the ability to manage independently without the need of a husband. The impressive list of patrons that she recruited for her new school also suggests a broader range of views about women's potential role in the British Empire. True, Alicia Amherst was socially conservative and actively opposed to women's suffrage. On the other hand, one of J. S. Turner's most active patrons was Lady Frances Balfour, a prominent campaigner for women's suffrage. The list of names supporting the Arlesey House Colonial Training School shows that support for female emigration to the colonies spanned the spectrum of opinion on women's rights. If Alicia Amherst felt that the best role for women emigrants was a traditional domestic role, albeit in a more physically challenging and basic setting, feminists like Frances Balfour believed that the colonies, far away from the social restrictions of home, were places where

Photograph of J. S. Turner at the top of a ladder, putting up a pergola at Glynde School for Lady Gardeners *c.* 1906/7. Courtesy of the Archive of Frances Wolseley, Hove Library.

women's roles could be reinterpreted as something bolder and more equal to their male counterparts. Other patrons included J. S. Turner's old employer at Dochfour, Lady Burton, and – her biggest coup – Princess Louise, Duchess of Argyll, as President of the patron group. Queen Victoria's sixth child was a keen supporter of higher education for women. Her husband was Governor of Canada from 1878 to 1884 and Princess Louise maintained a lasting interest in Canada, which may explain her involvement in a colonial training scheme.

J. S. Turner found a large former vicarage with four acres of land to rent in Arlesey, a small village on the Bedfordshire/Hertfordshire border between Hitchin and Biggleswade. The Arlesey House Colonial Training School opened early in 1907. The large house was well suited to conversion into a school with 'two spacious wings, which contained among other rooms a delightful drawing-room, handsome dining-room, and an excellent sitting-room for the students, which were connected by a veranda which opened onto the lawns, gardens, and orchard'. The land surrounding the house was also promising, as the soil was 'particularly good, a fine, well-enriched loam with gravel below, but not too near the surface'.

The school was small to begin with and at first took only eight students. J. S. Turner was owner and principal of the school, and she appointed ex-Bredon's Norton pupil, Dorothea Kitson, as her assistant. Each student had their own bedroom and the course cost £80 a year, the same fee as at Swanley. In return students could expect instruction in 'plain cooking', care of pigs, poultry and 'gardening in all its branches'. After six months' general training, for an additional fee, students could also take special courses 'in riding, driving and stable management, laundry work, dairy work and simple carpentry.' They were also taught first aid. The students were expected to wear 'business-like garb' with 'very short skirts, shirts with sleeves rolled up to above the elbow and the thickest of gardening boots'.[238] This was hands-on, physical and practical work. J. S. Turner was later to warn women wanting to emigrate that, 'In England there are very few posts where you can wear gloves and a shady hat and give orders, but in the colonies, there are absolutely none.'[239]

The work of the school was described enthusiastically in 1910 in *Every Woman's Encyclopaedia*: 'The students take it in turns, week by week, to act as gardeners, housemaids or cooks and the whole work of the farmstead, both inside and out, with its pig sties, poultry farm, beehives, orchard, greenhouses, cucumber frames and kitchen and flower garden covering some four acres of ground, is carried on entirely by the girls themselves.' The course was perfect, the article explained, for 'the high-spirited and enterprising young English girl of the upper and middle classes who is not bound by home ties, is being drawn more and more strongly towards the idea of emigrating to the Colonies, and seeking a living in the Empire beyond the Seas – in Canada, South Africa or New South Wales – rather than staying at home to fight in the already over-crowded market for a post as secretary, journalist, governess, companion or lady's clerk.' In a separate section headed 'The Type of Girl Wanted' it went on to explain, 'Miss Turner firmly believes that for the well-equipped young gentlewoman, equipped with a thoroughly practical preliminary training for colonial life and able to work for herself, a place is ready and waiting in our possessions beyond the seas.' J. S. Turner herself was described as 'an ardent advocate of emigration for girls of the upper classes' and 'a distinguished lecturer on horticulture and smallholdings'.[240]

The impression that this was a school designed exclusively for 'ladies' is confirmed by an account in *The Queen* magazine written in 1908 shortly after the school opened. It declared that 'the new school offers girls a particularly pleasant way of learning how to do properly the many tasks which women instinctively like but find so little opportunity of performing in their own fully servanted households' – a neat way of saying that these cossetted students had to be prepared to do all the household work themselves. The school made it clear that, to prepare for the rigours of life in the colonies, students needed to be able 'to meet with perfect equanimity the impossibility of getting any hired help at all.' There was, however, a maid employed at Arlesey, 'to do the roughest work'.[241] There were limits, after all.

Although many supporters of the British Empire might want women to emigrate to take on traditional roles of wives and mothers, a lot of these 'high-spirited and enterprising' young girls were attracted to a new life abroad precisely because it offered the opportunity to live a different kind of life altogether. In previous decades, intrepid female travellers had found a greater degree of personal freedom the further from 'civilisation' they ventured. The traveller and archaeologist Gertrude Bell wrote in a letter in 1892, 'I shall be sorry to leave this wonderful freedom and be back within walls and gardens'[242] and during her travels in India, Marianne North declared, when she returned to the British settlement in Coonoor in 1878, that she wanted to move on 'to the dear old sun and heat again. I fancy it will suit me better than the dressy gardens and trim-shaved roads of this Anglo-Indian paradise.'[243] This image of the Empire as a setting for adventure was heavily promoted in the popular culture of the day. In the late nineteenth century, British authors of adventure fiction for girls created resourceful and courageous heroines who rose to the challenges of the rugged environment of the colonies. These enormously popular books followed in the footsteps of equivalent books for boys by writers such as Rider Haggard. Female authors such as Bessie Marchant, despite having never once left England herself, set her novels aimed at young girls in romantic, faraway settings like the Canadian Rockies. At the same time as being shameless propaganda for the British Empire, these books portrayed strong and capable heroines, used to hard work out of doors and independence and bravery were shown as desirable female qualities. For more adventurous women, who by the early 1900s had grown up on a diet of these books, colonial schools like Arlesey or the course at Swanley offered them training that seemed to promise access to this kind of adventurous outdoor life. In 1912, in a column in *Pearson's Weekly* called 'What Clever Men and Women are Saying', a columnist named Mrs Pember Reeves gave a ringing endorsement of the colonial training at Swanley saying: 'The type of girl at Swanley Horticultural College is very like the Colonial type – practical girls, who know what to do if a baby has a fit.' Aside from the ability to calmly handle convulsing infants, a further clue as to the qualities 'colonial types' required can be found in another article on the same page. It advises anyone wanting 'an exciting occupation' to consider travelling to Africa to live-trap wild beasts for exhibition, with the warning: 'Gorillas are the most difficult to take alive, though Giraffes can give a good deal of trouble.'[244]

The horticultural and agricultural training offered needed to go beyond rugged self-sufficiency to teach skills that would allow women to seek posts as gardeners or establish their own commercial farms, smallholdings or market gardens. To meet this need, the Arlesey House Colonial Training School had a vinery and special greenhouses for chrysanthemums and cucumber-growing. Students also had access to a large farm next door where they could learn about dairy work and livestock management and were taken on visits to famous gardens in the surrounding areas. The horticultural component of the course involved passing practical examinations. These were held in the garden of Hatfield House by permission of the Marquess of Salisbury and the examiners were Mr Prine, Head Gardener at Hatfield House, Mr Hazelton, head gardener at North Mimms Park, and Miss C. M. Dixon of Elmcroft Nurseries in Kent. After taking the full two-year course, the graduate was declared fit to farm and work her own land. Pupils were also able to sit RHS national horticultural examinations, though not many did (only six Arlesey students feature in the RHS examination list of 1907–14). Nevertheless, the training provided at Arlesey was generally well regarded. One reporter remarked, 'It would be a happy thing for the employers who await them across the water' if more potential emigrants were trained at Arlesey. The report commented on the school's excellent horticultural and agricultural library and the fact that J. S. Turner gave the students two evening lectures a week in addition to their hands-on training during the day.[245]

Advocates for female emigration promoted the idea that it was easier for skilled women gardeners to find paid work in the colonies than in Britain. In *Gardening for Women*, Frances Wolseley wrote, 'From our Colonies, too, comes a cry for skilled and well-instructed "heads". There they have plenty of hands to do mechanical work, numbers of "coolies" to do menial jobs, but they want more intelligent directors and guides to industry.'[246] It was taken as read that it was the role of white settlers to lead and direct. The racism cut right across the political spectrum. Even many liberals and progressives, like Frances Balfour and Lady Warwick, did not see arguments for equality extending to the indigenous peoples of the lands that Britain conquered and colonised. Indeed, in this context, the proponents of a more active role for women abroad were simply arguing that British women deserved the same rights to exploit and gain from the Empire as British men.

The colonies most frequently quoted as offering the best job opportunities for 'genteel' British women were South Africa and Canada. In the wake of the Anglo-Boer wars, many issues of the British Women's Emigration Association journal, *The Imperial Colonist*, were devoted to propaganda encouraging women to emigrate to South Africa. It proclaimed that women should 'transform the blood-stained veldt' into 'a loyal and prosperous community living in peace and harmony beneath the British flag'[247] and featured case studies of ex-Swanley students who had settled in South Africa to encourage others to follow suit. In fact, J. S. Turner was highly sceptical that South Africa offered many real prospects for British women to be employed as gardeners. In 1910 she was quoted as saying, 'In countries such as South Africa, where native labour is chiefly employed, a (woman) gardener as a paid worker could not suitably be employed.'[248] She was not alone in believing it unthinkable that a white woman should do hands-on labour in the garden or field alongside Black workers. The only acceptable role for a woman was as a head gardener or overseer of labour on a market garden, farm or plantation. But then there was the difficulty, as at home, of persuading employers that a woman would be skilled enough to manage a workforce. In South Africa this was compounded by anxiety about leaving a white woman 'unprotected' amongst Black African labourers. In *Gardening for Women*, Frances Wolseley, too, raised this issue, but ever the Imperialist, she believed it was only a matter of time:

> In small gardens, with only one boy, this danger is reduced, but in large ones it is almost a necessity that two ladies should protect each other. The proportion of men to women is about seven to one, and, therefore, some may consider that South Africa will not be, as regards lady gardeners, a woman's country for another fifty years. That it will be so then, we who are anxious to see the better cultivation of our great colony, upon lines indicated for us by Cecil Rhodes, venture to hope. When Englishwomen have firmly established a good reputation as landscape gardeners, directing experts and teachers in the mother country, they will doubtless be welcomed with enthusiasm in our colonies.[249]

Frances Wolseley's strident confidence, voiced thousands of miles away and based on very little first-hand experience, was misplaced. In a letter to the Swanley Horticultural Magazine in 1906, Mary Hewetson, a Swanley graduate who became a head gardener in Pietermaritzburg in 1906 and in 1907 took up a forty-acre plot of her own in Natal, shows attitudes that were not at all likely to establish a good reputation for women managers or make them 'welcomed with enthusiasm'. 'I have a dozen or thirteen "boys" of all kinds,' she wrote, 'some utterly raw, ignorant, unintelligible and stupid – others with fixed ideas of what they should or should not do – a difficult team to drive and often at night I wondered how I should get through the next day.'[250] Although she was for a time the poster girl of South African emigration, she clearly held her workers in contempt and made no effort to earn their respect or question her own prejudices. In May 1907 Mary Hewetson died suddenly and there was speculation that she had been murdered. Following this there was rather less promotion of South African opportunities.

Increasingly J. S. Turner focused on training her students for a new life in Canada. The prairies of Canada were widely seen as the brightest agricultural prospect in the Empire. Organisations such as the Colonial Intelligence League (CIL) sought to send women to Western Canada to farm. Founded in 1910 by novelist Caroline Grosvenor, the CIL aimed to operate as an agency to investigate and communicate local employment opportunities for trained women. Caroline Grosvenor was convinced that Canada was ideal for 'the girls who have been brought up in the country, who amidst the moorlands of Scotland or Ireland, the dales of the North of England, the broad pastures of the Midlands, or the wind-swept downs of the South have got into their blood the love of outdoor life, of outdoor things and animals.'[251] She might have been describing Turner herself, a countrywoman to her bones, and it is easy to see how she became swept up in the enthusiasm for Canadian emigration.

The foundation of the Arlesey Colonial Training School also coincided with a high-profile campaign led by several female imperialists to encourage British women to emigrate to Canada and set themselves up as homesteaders. The Dominion Land Survey of 1871 had established the sovereignty of the federal Canadian government over the land. Although, under the Indian Act of 1876, no 'Indian' or First Nation people could be homesteaders, white male settlers could claim a free grant of 160 acres of land from the federal government of Canada. They simply paid ten dollars and then had to cultivate and live on the land for a minimum of three years before claiming legal ownership. A white woman could homestead only if she was sole head of a household with children – generally interpreted to mean a widow. Although adverts appeared for several years in *The Imperial Colonist* proclaiming '160 Acres in Western Canada Free. Healthy Climate. Good Crops, Free Schools, Light Taxes, Abundant Water', there was no mention of the fact that most women were not eligible for this land. [252]

From around 1908 to the outbreak of the First World War, however, campaigners sought to obtain homestead rights for single British and British-Canadian women. The campaigners, while they might have been in favour women's rights, were still riding roughshod over the rights of the indigenous peoples. They also promoted the idea of women homesteading as an explicit alternative to granting homesteads to 'ignorant, uncouth, lawless foreigners'.[253] This played to anxieties about British culture in Canada being 'swamped' by invaders, since Americans and Europeans had begun to arrive in significant numbers in the later nineteenth century.

J. S. Turner was a keen supporter of emigration of British women to Canada, working closely with one of the main figures in the campaign to award homesteads to women: Georgina Binnie-Clarke. Born in Sherborne, Dorset, she had made her living as a journalist. In August 1905, after a visit to her homesteading brother, she had purchased a 320-acre farm at Fort Qu'Appelle in Saskatchewan, despite having no experience of farming herself. She had to learn how to milk cows, make bread, clean out stables and do all the other work on the farm that she could not afford to have done for her. She threw herself into the role and became an ardent promoter of farming as a vocation for British women. She was a passionate advocate of the British Empire and believed that women could 'contribute to the spadework of British expansion'.[254] To promote her ideas, she published many newspaper articles and wrote two books about her experience. She also visited England for lecture tours and in March 1910 J. S. Turner invited her to read a paper at an 'at home' event at Arlesey House, chaired by Lady Frances Balfour. Binnie-Clarke assured Turner's students that the produce they were cultivating at Arlesey was exactly what they could grow in Canada. She illustrated her talk using lantern slides with images of the fruit and flowers of British Columbia as well as her own farm in Saskatchewan. As a wheat farmer she exhorted her listeners to think big and grow grain on large acreages, as this gave the most profitable return.

Also in attendance at the event was the prolific garden writer, Marion Cran. Long before social influencers or reality TV stars were ever dreamt of, Marion Cran made a living writing about her own family life, dispensing lifestyle advice, gardening tips and messages about female empowerment. She, too, was a devoted imperialist and ardent believer in the superiority of the British 'race'. Two years before the meeting at Arlesey, having been asked by the Canadian government to investigate the condition for British women immigrants in Canada, she had spent six-and-a-half months on a fact-finding visit to Canada. Whilst Marion Cran was fully supportive of British women coming out to marry settlers, she was not convinced that farming wheat on the prairies of Western Canada was a realistic possibility for most women.

Marion Cran felt it was important that women could 'farm or work in some way to secure their absolute independence. They want, every nice woman wants, to be free to undertake marriage as a matter of choice, not of necessity.'[255] But like Edith Bradley in England, she felt that horticulture and 'the lighter branches of agriculture' were more suitable occupations. Her view was that women should avoid the 'big gamble' of wheat farming and should instead grow fruit and vegetables on smallholdings within easy reach of the markets in cities such as Saskatoon, Regina, Edmonton and Calgary.

The following month, J. S. Turner and Georgina Binnie-Clark appeared together again on the platform at a meeting at the Royal

Colonial Institute in London. Binnie-Clark gave a talk entitled 'Land and the Woman in Canada'. Although there was lots of support at this meeting there was also some opposition – one speaker saying that it was telling that the agricultural colleges in Canada did not teach women ploughing, sowing and reaping because they were clearly physically incapable of doing these tasks. J. S. Turner held her ground, saying the Canadian colleges only taught women to cook and sew 'because men did not like to do that sort of work themselves' and that 'any woman who had stamina and common sense had very much better go back to the land than sit about or run after mothers' meetings or act as a sort of junior curate, as so many of our daughters did now.' J. S. Turner pointed out that Scottish women did half the labour on farms in Scotland. She claimed to have trained many women who had gone to Canada, two to South Africa and two to Australia and those who went to Canada had done the best.[256]

The reality was more complex. Whilst British imperialists might confidently assert that there were plenty of openings for well-trained, well-prepared female horticulturists and farmers in Canada, Canadians themselves were often less convinced. Local newspapers featured copious correspondence from local men and women openly doubting that ranch or prairie work was possible for most single women. For some the desire to maintain traditional gender roles was reinforced by a keenness to demonstrate Canada's status as a 'civilised', 'developed' society, capable of greater self-determination within the British Empire. Most paid employment opportunities for women in Canada were in the field of domestic labour. This was an uncomfortable truth that many of the emigration societies struggled with, as they tried to encourage middle-class women to emigrate. Imperial advocates did their best to sell the idea of domestic service, re-branding servants as 'mother's helps' or 'home helps' and stressing that it was not demeaning for genteel women to do paid domestic work and they would be treated as respected members of the household. Others put a positive spin on the idea by stressing that domestic service was the ideal preparation for the more hands-on life of a colonial settler's wife: 'Such a girl, if she takes a post as a mother's help, will prove a real help, and when she marries, will be a true helpmate to her husband.'[257] But the use of the word 'when' rather than 'if' regarding marriage here is telling and it appears that the real priority was the perceived needs of the Empire, rather than self-fulfilment and independence for women. The biggest indication that these campaigns were more interested in what emigrant women could do for the British Empire rather than what emigrating could do for them, was the fact that the advocates for Canadian emigration never mentioned that single women could have a free grant of land if they moved to the American West. British women were directed only to British colonies. Indeed, *The Imperial Colonist* journal warned British women who were considering going to the US that there would be no one to meet and care for them, leaving them at risk of being lured by Mormons into a life of polygamy![258]

The Colonial Intelligence League, despite its name, appears to have done little effective research on paid employment opportunities for women in the British dominions and the intelligence they did gather was hardly encouraging. A report from Calgary in 1912 noted that there was no work for jobbing gardeners because of the 'long idle season. We are so high up that our gardens are always spoilt very early by a crushing frost. Last year it was in August, and after that there is nothing to do but gather up and burn the debris, cover all with manure and wait until April.'[259] For J. S. Turner this was further evidence that the lady emigrant needed to be adaptable and face up to the fact that 'practically the lady gardener who was only a gardener was not wanted in any of the colonies but that she might find employment if she combined cooking and housework with gardening.' However, she claimed that resort to domestic work may be just a temporary status, while new settlers acclimatised and raised money to set themselves up as independent market gardeners or farmers. She reported that whilst many women who went to Canada had started out as domestic helps, they were now 'following Miss Binnie-Clark's example' and farming independently.[260]

The truth was that most of the pupils from the Arlesey Colonial School never left Britain's shores. In 1908 *The Queen* newspaper explained that 'Miss Turner started her undertaking at the instigation of ladies who wished educated girls to be trained for colonial life. But so far, the effect of training girls to do well in the colonies seems to be to make the pupils so valuable in this country that the idea of emigrating is abandoned in favour of other inducements.'[261] This was putting the most positive gloss on things. After six more years running the Colonial School, J. S. Turner admitted, 'It is rather curious how often we are asked for women gardeners by elderly ladies, with nice places in the country. Such ladies are often really afraid of the men they have employed who keep the house short of flowers, fruit and vegetables, to whom it seems like a wicked act if the owners venture to cut a few of their own roses, and who continually demand expensive seeds and tools. They apply to us thinking how much pleasanter it would be to have an agreeable, well-trained lady with them, who would sometimes come in for a chat in the evenings, and in several instances, this is proving a happy arrangement for both parties.'[262] Working as a gardener for a timid old lady who wanted someone agreeable to talk to was hardly the adventurous frontier living promoted by the arch Imperialists. Nor was Arlesey an isolated case. At Swanley the Colonial Branch had 65 students between its opening in January 1903 and the issue of its 1907 annual report, but only 20 had actually 'sailed for various colonies'.[263]

It may have been just as well that relatively small numbers of women actually emigrated after completing their training course. Like the other colonial training courses, J. S. Turner's school spoke in a broad-brush way about 'the Colonies' even though the British Empire covered an enormous range of climates and landscapes. There was also more than a hint of naivety in thinking that the gentle English countryside of Kent, Bedfordshire or Hertfordshire could replicate such varied and extreme conditions. There appears a touch of role-play and make-believe in the privations that some of the schools inflicted on their students to supposedly prepare them for this new life. At the Lady Warwick Hostel, the students were taught to manufacture substitutes for ingredients, such as making yeast from potatoes. As one description of the course breezily put it, 'The training in fact, will consist very largely in doing without things.'[264] One critic of the course provided at Arlesey complained of the 'vagueness' of the training, as it was not clear for which colony or region the women were being trained: 'You might keep house for fifty years in most parts of New Zealand and never want to do most of the things taught at this school.'[265] A journalist from *The Bystander* noted that one subject J. S. Turner 'makes a great point of is carving of joints'. Neatly carving a nice joint of meat seems a slightly niche concern for a school determined to prepare its students for a life far from home. That some prospective female colonists had little idea what awaited them is indicated by the preparatory hints given by J. S. Turner's old employer Frances Wolseley in her book *Gardening for Women*. She felt it necessary to advise women planning to emigrate to South Africa that their furs might be best left at home.

Even if the horticultural and agricultural skills and information they were given had been relevant, the most striking feature of the accounts of these schemes for female emigration is the complete lack of interest in or even curiosity about the lands to which they sought to send women, or about the people already living there. As Sarah Carter has pointed out in *Imperial Plots*, her excellent book on British women in Canada, women of the Doukhobor, Hidatsa and Mandan peoples had cultivated the land on the Canadian Plains for centuries and were the mainstay of the traditional agrarian economy. Yet they were completely invisible in the imperialist propaganda of this period, and their rights were never acknowledged in the vision of the Empire as a blank canvas for white British men and women to shape to their needs and desires.

Drawing by Olive Cockerell entitled 'Aches and Pains' from *A French Garden in England*. Courtesy of the RHS Lindley Collections.

9
THIS ENCHANTED PLACE

> What we think, or what we know, or what we believe, is in the end of little consequence. The only thing of consequence is what we do.
>
> John Ruskin, 1866, 'The Future of England', from *The Crown of Wild Olive*

Delicate, reserved and artistic, Olive Cockerell was an unlikely recruit for the army of professional women horticulturists. Nevertheless, she became a professional gardener, and her decision was driven by high ideals and involved a profound personal transformation. Today, many of us are drawn to gardening in response to the climate emergency and biodiversity collapse. We want to do something small but significant, to nurture and nourish a small patch of ground, to grow sustainably and maximise the biodiversity in our gardens. If we are blessed with the space, we might put in a pond, leave the lawn unmown, aspire to a mini meadow and generally try to create a space for nature on our doorstep. These feel like modern concerns – a world away from the neat, regimented lawns of our grandparents and great-grandparents. However, Olive Cockerell's story shows us that the roots of this ecological approach to gardening run further back in time than the scientific understanding of global warming. More than a century ago, there was already an awareness of the damage being done to the planet and to people by rampant industrialisation and some sought a path to a better life, closer to nature, through growing.

In 1898 Olive returned to London from nearly five years in New

Mexico as the main carer for her nephew Martin. She did not return to the family home but instead took lodgings in Denmark Road, near the new Camberwell School of Art, and aimed to restart her career as an artist. Before she left for America, she had enjoyed some success as a book illustrator. She had illustrated a book of fairytales entitled *The Queen of the Goblins*, written by Wilhelmina Pickering. Olive's illustrations of mischievous sprites, imps and goblins received positive reviews. Wilhelmina's sister, Evelyn, was herself a successful artist and was married to William de Morgan, the pottery and stained-glass designer who worked closely with William Morris. Like the de Morgans, the Cockerell family were part of the network of artistic and socially progressive people that gravitated around William Morris. Olive's brother Sydney Cockerell was close to Morris and his family, attending his lectures from a young age and eventually working as Secretary to William Morris's Kelmscott Press. When William Morris died in 1896, Sydney acted as one of the executors of his will and supported his widow Jane in winding up the Kelmscott Press. When she returned from New Mexico, Olive re-entered this artistic set, working on portraits of family and friends. She also began work on another set of fairytale illustrations, this time for William de Morgan's sister, Mary. Mary de Morgan was a remarkable woman; in addition to being an author, she worked as journalist, embroiderer, typist, East End volunteer and prison reformer and was a member of the Women's Suffrage League. Her book *The Windfairies* was a set of four different tales which, although aimed at children, displayed allegories for feminism and early 'green' sentiments. Princesses in these stories were active rather than passive figures and could be strong as well as beautiful. The human characters encountered enchanted plants and personified elements like the wind and rain – these elemental forces were presented as actors in the stories, rather than mere resources to be exploited. In a story entitled 'The Pool and the Tree' plant collectors and gardeners were shown in a negative light because they are obsessed with acquiring 'rarities' rather than caring for nature. Olive provided the book with beautiful black-and-white drawings, which were clearly very heavily influenced by the Arts and Crafts

Self-portrait by Olive Cockerell, *c.* 1900.
Courtesy of the William Morris Gallery.

movement and the work of artists like Walter Crane. With highly decorative borders, her illustrations were vividly detailed and lavishly decorated, with background patterns reminiscent of the fabric and wallpaper designs of William Morris. Her 'windfairies' were dressed in long robes which swirled and swooped about their feet, entwined with the locks of their hair. This was not the twee or simplistic illustration seen in many children's books of the time. The drawings also suggested a rich imagination, a world away from the nursery and sickrooms that had been the actual setting for most of Olive's life to date. The book was beautifully produced in a cloth binding with gilt edging and sold at the relatively expensive price of 5 shillings. Both the stories and Olive's illustrations were praised in the press. A review in *The London Illustrated News* described it as 'a charming, old-fashioned story book, some of the illustrations being particularly graceful and full of delicate imagination.'[266]

However, despite this achievement, Olive's family were concerned about her wellbeing. Whilst in America, she had been briefly engaged to a man that her family unanimously considered a disastrous choice. Olive's godmother, Octavia Hill, described herself as 'profoundly grieved' by the incident and even if Olive eventually came to share her family's perception that she had had a lucky escape, she herself must still have been saddened by the affair.[267] An undated self-portrait that Olive made at around this time survives in the collections of the William Morris Gallery in Walthamstow. She has drawn herself wearing a simple smock-like garment, tied at the neck with a bow, and she stares intently at the viewer with a slightly furrowed brow. The soft, tentative pencil strokes give a sense of a delicately featured young woman with large, intense eyes.

As no diary and hardly any letters survive to give us an opportunity to hear from Olive directly, our impression of her at this time must rely instead on this self-portrait and the mentions of her in the letters of her more famous relatives whose correspondence was deemed worth archiving. She appears frequently in correspondence between Octavia Hill and Sydney Cockerell. From these letters it is apparent that soon after arriving home from caring for her brother, Theo, and nephew, Martin, in New Mexico, Olive suffered two further blows in quick succession. Her mother died in 1900, and the following year she received the news from America that little Martin, for whom she had been a surrogate mother, had fallen ill and died. She was living as a lodger with Charles Abbey, an architectural sculptor, and his wife in Richmond, but although Olive's occupation in the 1901 census is listed as a 'Black and White Artist', she did not have another project to work on after *The Windfairies*. Her family appear to have been very worried about her.

In October 1901 her brother Sydney used his connection with the Morris family to introduce Olive to William Morris's widow, Jane. Letters between Sydney and Jane Morris make it clear that Jane Morris invited Olive to visit as a favour to Sydney in return for all his help winding up the Kelmscott Press after William Morris died. Jane Morris wrote, 'I am so glad Olive came. I foresee we shall be great friends; she must come very often. Her sweet natural ways were very consoling to me. She has promised to come for a long stay in spring which will be a great pleasure for us all. I need scarcely add how glad I am to find a way of serving you – after all your exceeding goodness to me.'[268] Sydney replied, 'She is utterly guileless and unselfish, but she thinks so little of herself that undiscerning people take her at her own valuation and this makes her silent and difficult. She came back radiant from Kelmscott ... and she was full of your kindness and the curious fact that you had not seemed to find her the bore that she considers herself to be.'[269]

Olive was to visit and stay with Jane Morris several times over the next two years. Even if the friendship began as an act of charity, in practice it was of as much benefit to Jane Morris as it was to Olive. Jane's elder daughter Jenny, who was eight years older than Olive, had suffered from acute epilepsy since the age of 15. There was no cure and Jenny Morris's seizures were unpredictable and distressing. There was a great deal of stigma attached to epilepsy, as the condition was still seen by wider society as a form of insanity. Many people with epilepsy were housed in asylums, hidden away and isolated. William and Jane Morris refused to do this, but caring for Jenny placed a considerable burden on Jane Morris, particularly after her husband died. Jenny could never be left unattended, and her mother felt unable to entertain anyone other than very close friends when she was with Jenny. Olive, with her experience of nursing others and her quiet, calm demeanour, became just such a trusted friend. In 1902 Jane Morris wrote, 'Olive Cockerell is coming to stay a month with me, which will be cheering – as she is nice and companionable, an excellent walker, too.'[270] Although it must have been exciting to be close to such a famous figure, the muse of William Morris and Dante Gabriel Rossetti, the visits to Jane Morris were of necessity quiet and uneventful. In between visits to Jane and Jenny Morris, Olive also helped her sister Una, who had given up acting to marry and gave birth to a baby in 1901. In summary, Olive's life as an artist had stalled, and she was living the peripatetic life of a genteel spinster; visiting friends and relatives whilst being helpful and mildly diverting, always accommodating herself to the plans and needs of others.

Although Olive was quiet and uncomplaining, this life was not enough for her. She had inherited her father's and godmother's sense of social conscience and their desire to make a practical difference to the lives of the poorest in society. Though she did not write long sermonising letters like her brother Theo, or attend political meetings like Sydney, Olive, too, was gripped by the socialist ideals of William Morris and John Ruskin. The art and social critic John Ruskin was a particularly influential figure for Olive. Through his books and lectures he had laid bare the hypocrisy of the conventional views of society, demonstrating how far people had drifted from Christian teachings in their refusal to face up to the ugliness, suffering and exploitation that underpinned a consumerist lifestyle. As he pointed out, by seeing workers only as a means of producing wealth, 'The rich not only refuse food to the poor; they refuse wisdom; they refuse virtue; they refuse salvation.'[271] Although John Ruskin had argued that the sexes performed distinctive functions and should stay in their respective spheres, his harsh criticisms of modern industrialised society, and his emphasis on the high moral qualities and powers of womanhood, provided a rallying call for many women to take up an active role in changing society for the better.

Olive was an avid reader of Ruskin's writings, but she also had a personal association with him. Ruskin had provided the funding for her godmother Octavia Hill's first housing project and Octavia Hill was a devoted 'Ruskinite', until a misunderstanding led to Ruskin writing a harsh and public criticism of his one-time disciple. In fact, in 1888, when she was only 18, Olive and her brother Sydney had visited John Ruskin at his home at Coniston in the Lake District on a mission to attempt a reconciliation between them. The visit was viewed by the pair almost like a pilgrimage to see a god-like figure. On finding out they were visiting, Octavia Hill advised, 'You will gather memories which life will never take away.'[272] Certainly, the meeting was emotional. Ruskin gave them a tour of his home and showed them his art collection which included several sketches by Turner. When Sydney broached the need for a reconciliation with Octavia Hill, Ruskin at first was obdurate but as Sydney later recalled, 'Olive seconded me bravely and we continued the attack until finally he could surrender to our alternate demands and entreaties … Then he kissed us both, joined our hands, gave us an affectionate blessing and bade us farewell, we being touched to the heart and in tears.'[273] Growing up in an atmosphere like this, it is hardly surprising that Olive wanted to put John Ruskin's ideas into practice in a more real and practical way.

At some point in 1903, Olive approached Octavia Hill and asked to become one of her rent collectors. Octavia Hill had reservations, knowing how demanding the work was, but relented. As she later wrote to Sydney Cockerell, 'You know perhaps that I had never dreamed of her coming to work in the houses but had imagined her at art work, but she came to us, very low and herself proposed it and seemed to long for the human work.'[274] As a firm believer in the morally redeeming power of work, Octavia Hill could see that socially useful work could give Olive dignity and independence. As she told Sydney Cockerell, 'There is her spirit to think of as well as her body. She must be happy as well.'[275] Octavia Hill gave Olive work on her largest and most ambitious housing project. A hundred-year-old lease had expired on 22 acres of land on the Walworth estate in Camberwell in London owned by the Church Commissioners. Octavia Hill used her considerable powers of persuasion to prevent the Church Commissioners from selling the land for profit and to instead give the estate over to her to develop and manage as a social housing scheme. The scheme involved widening and re-arranging the streets, establishing a cooperative shop, setting aside an acre for recreation, an area for a new parish school and accommodation for 790 families in cottages and cottage flats in three-storey tenement houses. Olive was recruited to work as a rent collector on this scheme. However, this was not a simple case of collecting money. Being a rent collector for Octavia Hill involved building close face-to-face relationships with tenants and developing detailed knowledge of every aspect of their lives. This allowed rent collectors to provide tailored support, but they were also expected to monitor and, to a degree, police the lives of the tenants. Octavia Hill strongly disapproved of simple charity; she felt that social progress could only be made if working people developed habits of personal responsibility and were encouraged to better themselves. This was intense and emotionally draining work and Olive threw herself into it wholeheartedly. During the course of 1904, Octavia Hill, who herself frequently worked to the point of collapse, became more and more concerned. On December 7 she wrote to Olive pleading with her to come and visit so 'that we might get those fragments of time which come between work together'. She reassured Olive that she would not have to stop work on the visit: 'You would be quite free to go off to your work when and how you wished and should have a quiet room to write in if you must write in the evenings.'[276]

Perhaps one of the reasons Olive did not spare herself was that she was now in contact with a group of similarly driven women, all battling daily with the consequences of urban poverty and deprivation in a world before the welfare state. One of them was Helen Nussey, who worked as an almoner at Westminster Hospital. It is possible that Olive and Helen met through a case, with Helen Nussey following up on a referral letter for a resident of Walworth that Olive was working with. Although six years younger than Olive, Helen was much more experienced in the field of social work. The daughter of a wealthy solicitor, she had benefited from a modern education at Cheltenham Ladies' College and from there had immediately volunteered to work at Mayfield House in Bethnal Green, one of the poorest areas in East London. Mayfield was a 'settlement house' sponsored by Cheltenham Ladies', where the students of the College could volunteer to live in poor communities and give their time, enthusiasm and abilities to improve the lives of local residents. Settlements like Mayfield House (which later moved and became known as St Hilda's East) acted as educational, social and often religious centres for the areas they served. The residents ran activities and clubs and offered educational classes for adults and children. Helen Nussey concentrated on teaching disabled children while she was there.

In 1900 Helen was appointed to a paid role as Almoner at Westminster Hospital. An almoner was effectively the hospital's social worker. In the Edwardian era most hospitals catered exclusively for patients who could not pay for medical care. They would be treated in hospital but immediately they improved, sent home, often back to the appalling conditions that may well have caused their illness in the first place. To improve outcomes, hospitals began to employ almoners to organise after-care for patients. At the same time, almoners like Helen were also expected to identify patients whose families were able to make a financial contribution. They had to make hard-headed assessments of what a family could truly afford to make sure that scarce charitable resources went only to those in desperate need. In June 1905 Helen wrote an article entitled 'Medical Treatment for the Working Classes' for *The Monthly Review* in which she noted: 'Poverty is a relative term. The line has to be drawn somewhere by most people, and many draw it at paying their doctor's bills who would never think of drawing it at paying for music halls, drinking or betting.' In the same article she also observed, 'At present the work of a Hospital Almoner, whose duty it is to eliminate the unsuitable from those who enjoy the privileges of hospital treatment, is frequently rendered abortive by the attitude of the "visiting lady".' In her opinion, volunteer female social workers gave letters referring people for free treatment far too freely, which she felt acted as a disincentive for the more morally satisfactory solution of saving to pay for medical care.[277]

It is easy to imagine that upon first meeting Olive, the briskly practical Helen Nussey might have assumed that she was one of those naive and soft-hearted 'visiting ladies'. An inexperienced illustrator of fairytales with only amateur nursing experience and a head packed full of idealistic socialist ideas would, after all, be easy to dismiss. Nevertheless, by the end of 1906 a bond had formed between the pair to the extent that, to the surprise of all who knew them, they began to plan a completely new life together, far away from London.

The plan the two women hatched together was a radical one. They would leave inner-city London to grow fruit and vegetables on a small plot in the country, living a simple and self-sustaining life on the land. When she learnt of the plan in November 1906, Octavia Hill wrote to Olive warning her of the risks involved: 'I have known several people try to make various forms of country work pay and every one of them has failed to make it a financial success.' She was also worried about the physical strain on Olive, warning, 'Pray beware of potato digging and over fatigue!' She conceded that social work in the city had not suited Olive, admitting, 'I can well realise that the work as you do it may be too great a strain of fatigue, also that Miss Nussey's leaving Westminster would leave you lonely and feeling still more strain.'[278] Yet in presenting this decision as a simple wish to abandon work that was fatiguing and to be with Helen, Octavia Hill failed to understand just how much this decision was driven by Olive's deeply held beliefs and her desire to live according to her values in a very practical way. This was much more than just a change of scene: the desire to start afresh growing food fitted in with the Ruskinian ideal of physical labour as a form of artistic expression and represented a rejection of the industrialised world which, Ruskin taught, exploited both people and the environment. Olive's other hero, William Morris, also advocated turning away from wasteful consumption to build a world that did not rely on the exploitation of the many to fuel the luxurious lifestyles of the few. He and his followers favoured 'useful toil' and engagement with the earth which fed and clothed people over industrialisation which alienated workers from the fruits of their labour. In his classic novel *News from Nowhere* he declared, 'Wealth is what Nature gives us and what a reasonable man can make out of the gifts of Nature for his reasonable use.'[279] *News from Nowhere* painted an enticing picture of Britain in the future, reimagined as an agrarian utopia. It seems Olive wanted to do more than represent these ideas in her art; she wanted to live them.

Olive and Helen were far from the first to attempt to create a simple life in the country. Several agrarian socialist, cooperative and anarchist communities formed in the last quarter of the nineteenth century, inspired by thinkers such as Ruskin, Tolstoy and Thoreau, seeking to simplify life and remove waste and needless luxury. The members of these communities tended to wear homespun, loose-fitting garments, and eat a simple vegetarian diet. Some followed Tolstoy in striving for a purified fellowship between men and women, which, they believed, banished altogether the complications of sexual desire. Others experimented in 'free love', communal living and freedom from private property to the amusement and/or horror of many critics. The high-minded ethics of these groups often mingled with affected aesthetics and a lifestyle very different to that of the traditional peasant they aimed to emulate. As G. K. Chesterton observed, 'There was more simplicity in the man who eats caviar on impulse than in the man who eats grape-nuts on principle.'[280] There was often nothing simple about their commitment to the simple life. Although Olive and Helen shared some of the characteristics and ideals of these 'Simple Lifers', as they were known, it is interesting that they did not seek to join any existing group. They preferred to go it alone, to create their own private utopia.

Olive and Helen were also more realistic than many of these commune members; they knew that even the simplest existence needed some income and that they would need to find a way of earning some money. They decided that their best hope was to grow fruit and vegetables in a way that made a modest profit. Their optimism was fired by news of a new approach to market gardening that had recently been brought over from France. French Gardening was a specialised commercial system for growing early seasonal vegetables under glass. Early vegetables, principally lettuce, radishes, carrots and cauliflower, were 'forced' (cropped early) in glass-covered wooden frames known as 'lights', about one-foot high, and in hundreds of bell-shaped glass cloches. Both frames and cloches sat on a thin layer of soil laid above long beds of decaying manure which provided the heat. The beds were also protected from frost at night by special grass mats. It was not actually that much of an innovation – many of the horticultural technologies for growing under glass dated from the seventeenth and eighteenth centuries – however these techniques were much more widely used on the continent than in traditional British market gardens. The person who can be credited with the early introduction of French Gardening to this country was seedsman Charles McKay. In 1904 he led a deputation of market gardeners from Evesham in Worcestershire to visit market gardens around Paris. He decided to set up a garden on French lines in Evesham and began advocating the approach in the press, partly to promote the sale of glass cloches which he also sold. The claim was that relatively small plots of land could produce impressive yields at a time of year when prices were at their highest. However, these market gardens required constant attention and the system required expert judgement in managing crops so that they matured and marketed at the most advantageous time, since peak prices were only available for brief periods.

With no personal experience or family background in commercial growing, the pair were aware they had a steep learning curve ahead of them. In early 1907 they rented rooms in a house in Lime Street in Evesham so that they could spend a year working and training in the French Gardens owned by Charles McKay. The work was hard; they later recalled that this was where they 'learnt what a Frenchman means by "hard work".'[281] Their families were worried about this radical step, which involved leaving behind family and friends and sinking their savings into a very uncertain venture. In time French Gardening was to become very well known, but Olive and Helen were 'early adopters' and Charles McKay was an unknown quantity. As Octavia Hill wrote to Sydney Cockerell, 'I know nothing of this man or scheme but have a profound suspicion of those who charge a fee for teaching beginners a lucrative business which involves in addition some capital expenditure … My experience (very small) of ladies trying gardening was not encouraging.'[282] It may seem strange to find that Octavia Hill, a founder of the National Trust, was not supportive of this new life in the country, but she was in many ways a very socially conservative person. Philanthropic work in inner-city slums sat more easily within her definition of appropriate feminine behaviour than manual labour in the countryside. Jane Morris was much more encouraging. Before meeting and marrying William Morris, she had grown up in poverty with a drunken and violent parent, so she was aware of the emotional and psychological burden that Olive faced working in deprived neighbourhoods. She wrote: 'I am glad Olive has given up that dreadfully hopeless work. My love to her please. I shall send her my portrait like yours when she is settled at Evesham.'[283]

After a year of training at Evesham, Olive and Helen felt ready to take on their own plot of land and began looking in the southeast of England, where they felt that the climate would be more conducive to that type of gardening. It also had the advantage of plenty of good rail links to get their product to market in London. They started their search with a bicycle tour of properties for sale in Hampshire. However, finding the perfect plot and the perfect house was not easy, particularly as neither seemed prepared to compromise on their aesthetic standards. Although they wanted a simple life and described themselves as determined to be 'sternly utilitarian', as true followers of William Morris, they found that their aesthetic sense could not tolerate 'bungalows which in their endeavours to be artistic, with their gimped balconies, their varnished walls and extraordinary paint, filled our minds with terror'. They viewed 'a little monstrosity, built of shiny tiles of a peculiarly offensive vermillion, which the proud owner proudly informed us would never lose its colour.' Despite their reservations this property was for a while the front-runner, but they pulled out when they found it did not have a good water supply and, even worse, 'the occupier intended to start building another exactly like it next door.' This clinched the matter as they felt 'it would be criminal to aid him in such a nefarious project.'[284]

Eventually help came via a connection from Olive's brother Sydney, who for a time had worked as a secretary for the poet and author, Wilfrid Scawen Blunt, another associate and follower of William Morris. Blunt, a wealthy radical with often controversial, atheist and anti-imperialist views, owned a large estate called Crabbet Park in Sussex with his wife, Lady Anne Blunt, daughter of Ada Lovelace. Blunt was also a close friend and ex-lover of Jane Morris so it may also have been through her that he heard of Olive's and Helen's search for a suitable plot of ground. He offered to rent them 'Gosbrook', a small bungalow on his estate which came with a couple of acres of unpromising land. Although the land had previously been seen as unfit for commercial growing, Olive and Helen were undeterred, as the French system involved growing on copious amounts of manure, so the initial quality of the soil was not critical. A water supply was essential, and Blunt offered them labour from his estate to dig them a pond. As they later recalled, as soon as they saw the site, they had no doubt: 'We could see miles of wooded country and the blue line of the South Downs swelling up to Chanctonbury Ring in the distance before us … We knew that here we should make our home.'[285] Within a week of seeing the property in late November, the pair had signed a lease, and a week after that they moved in.

Even with a year training in Evesham under their belts, Olive and Helen were absolute beginners and from the very outset their inexperience was evident. At dawn on December 1, 1907, they set out to mark out the ground for their plot. They later recalled, 'One of us had a tape measure, the other a hammer with which to drive in landmarks.' Wilfrid Scawen Blunt sent his bailiff with men to do the heavy digging for them. 'We timidly held out the tape measure and the landlord's bailiff smiled. Our only previous experience in measuring land was marking out a tennis lawn.'[286] They managed to measure out four rods of land (66 feet wide). This was wide enough to fit fifteen lights (glass-topped wooden frames) on either side of a central road with a grass path around the edge. This area of the garden measured just one acre, of which half was to be 'under glass' in the form of two hundred lights and bell glasses. They sowed another acre with clover for fodder and rye which would eventually provide material for the mats that would keep crops warm at night.

Although the pair clearly threw themselves wholeheartedly into the venture, Olive did not put her artistic and literary interests entirely behind her. Over the next twelve months, the pair recorded the experience of their first year together in the form of a small book, illustrated with charming line drawings by Olive, entitled *A French Garden in England*, and published in 1909. It is thanks to this book that we get a sense of what life was like in the little bungalow in Sussex. Although the drawings are credited to Olive, the words are jointly authored, and they wrote the book as an indivisible 'we'. In the opening paragraph they described themselves as 'two women, not very robust but accustomed to hard work, who started a French market garden a year ago with a small capital, two acres of raw field and a year's training in French Gardening, but up to then no horticultural experience whatever'. They described the book as 'a record of our experiences, of the mistakes we made and the difficulties we had, no less than the small successes achieved'.[287]

The mistakes and difficulties were many and varied. Under the French gardening system, the beginning of the year was really October, so by starting their business in January, they were starting with a disadvantage. 'By rights our lettuces and cauliflowers should have been little plants, ready to go in the hotbeds but we had not yet sown a seed.'[288] As a result, their first year was not really productive and they lived off savings, burning through money as they purchased sheds, frames, bell jars and a water pump. They ordered one thousand cloches from France, but many arrived broken and had to be painstakingly mended with white lead, linseed oil and dryers (a chemical to set the glue). They also purchased 'lights' or wooden frames with glazing to sit on top of plants. They spent nearly £400 on the garden during the first eight months alone (corrected for inflation, this would be the equivalent of at least £46,000 today). They had to learn many lessons the hard way. They bought the wrong kind of manure for the hotbeds and the wrong kind of straw for mat-making.[289] They ordered rye straw as recommended by French gardeners but found it had already been threshed so the stems were too broken to be of use for mats. They had to settle for making mats from wheat straw, even though they knew these would not last so well. The book gives details of how to make the mats and it certainly looks a laborious and strenuous process. They observe that 'mat-making is worthwhile if the maker is an expert … a novice will waste string and straw to such an extent and be so slow, that it may be cheaper to buy.'[290] William Morris style craft-based living was harder than it looked.

They did everything they could to be true to the 'Simple Life' philosophy, paring the furnishing of 'Gosbrook' down to the bare essentials and eating a restricted diet so they could maximise the hours they could work in the garden. Although not total vegetarians, they decided to eat as little meat as possible, declaring: 'We could not have joints of raw beef desecrating such a sanctum … We meant to spend our lives out of doors, and to hamper ourselves as little as possible with cooking and dishwashing, and we lived therefore chiefly on nuts and cheese, which we shared with the robins and tits who became our daily companions.'[291] This was where their bohemian backgrounds came in handy, as removing meat was 'no hardship to us as the food we ate was what we would naturally have chosen and was what we were accustomed to.'[292] They got up at 6 am and had breakfast of homemade wholemeal bread and butter with 'crushed nuts and sometimes eggs.' They cleaned the bungalow and then were in the garden by 8 o'clock and worked continuously until 12 o'clock when they had a simple lunch of bread and cheese and hot milk. After lunch they would rest and read a book and then it was back in the garden until it was dark. Supper was 'usually a kind of stew of crushed nuts, sometimes flavoured with vegetables and often served with eggs and a dish of rice, macaroni or potato; and then perhaps figs or other fruit, and we had hot milk before going to bed.'[293] Like every gardening female of the time that put pen to paper, they had to give full details of their gardening outfit. Their clothes were also as simple and pared down as possible. They wore 'merely plain blouses and short skirts, as near the colour of the earth as possible, and in bad weather we used skirts with about fifteen inches of waterproof cloth at the bottom.' Appropriate footwear was harder to come by. They confessed that, 'we soon had a collection of every kind of footwear. Wooden clogs lined with felt were warm in the winter but very tiring if worn all day.' They also tried traditional, vernacular costume, with 'Sussex clogs' which could be slipped over their shoes for 'clashing through the mud'.[294]

Despite working hard to prepare the manured beds properly, they could not get their beds hot enough for their cucumbers to germinate. 'We were almost in despair as we had now lost nearly

Olive and Helen looking in dismay at glass cloches broken in transit from France. Illustration from *A French Garden in England*. Courtesy of the RHS Lindley Collections.

eight weeks and were no nearer getting our cucumbers than when we started. It was not until March 31 that we were even able to prick out our seedlings, by which time we should have been planting them out.' Even then their troubles were not over: 'A horrible little fungus which, in ignorance of a more scientific nomenclature, earned the name "smutty", sprang up everywhere in the lights.'[295] Mold was not the only challenge to their crops. They had carefully erected a wire fence, some six feet tall, around their one-acre plot to keep out 'undesirables' but, in their eagerness to start, had failed to notice that 'a rabbit had with some forethought made a nest right underneath and the babies were on the inside, near some of our precious cauliflowers, dainty morsels for her young offspring.'[296] In addition to rabbits, they found that the field was riddled with mouse runs and 'all measures we have taken have not exterminated our foe, though we have materially weakened his strength in numbers.' The clever mice learnt to avoid traps laden with bacon and cheese so 'finally, we introduced a kitten into the garden who began to make a havoc among the mice, but the fear of her being trapped in the midst of a gaming country such as ours, led us to feed her lest she should wander, and since then her life has been one of luxurious pauperism.' However, like Ada Brown and Decima Allen, they reserved their greatest resentment for slugs and snails, which is hardly surprising, as they estimated that they lost over 15,000 cos lettuces to these 'great pests'. They tried soot, superphosphate and salt. They laid down empty orange-peel traps 'into which the slugs would not go' and tried the 'advertised slug destroyers' but found that these killed the seedlings. Olive made a humorous little drawing to illustrate their efforts, showing one of the pair forlornly pursuing a gigantic slug with a bucketful of salt. As with the mice, they tried bringing in a predator to help, this time in the form of a pair of ducks who they planned to eat eventually. However, soon they were just as attached to the ducks as to the cat, explaining that they 'established such personal relations that it was impossible to contemplate their death when they began to fatten'.[297]

The challenges of growing and protecting produce paled into insignificance when compared to the challenges of selling it for a reasonable return. The key to making a profit with a French Garden was timing, the aim being to adjust the speed that crops ripened so that they came to market at the time when prices were at their highest. Helen and Olive recalled how they 'anxiously watched the prices at Covent Garden lest they should come down in a rush before our crop was ready. We sent our first specimens to a London friend and were cheered to hear that West End shops were asking fabulous prices for lettuces like ours ... but a week later when our main stock was ready, the outdoor produce was already coming in carts from Worthing' and they found that the price had collapsed. They tried selling in Brighton, but that was no better. 'We realised that we must get private orders if we wanted to make anything of our lettuces this year. The difficulty was how to get up a connexion (sic) in a hurry – we could not bother our friends, and we knew of no one to whom to send and up to the end of May we only had four private customers on our books.' Then Helen had the brainwave that they should use the contacts and knowledge she had gained as a hospital almoner. 'We wrote to various London hospitals suggesting that we might supply them at a low price. In this way we got up a connection for all future produce which was not quite up to our usual standard – everything perfectly good but rather late in the season, or a little damaged in appearance, or perhaps rather small to attract a public, which prefers its vegetables large.' Sometimes, ironically, the orders were simply too large for them to cope. 'A telegram from one shop nearly cleared us out. It came in the afternoon of a pouring wet day with a request for the goods to be sent out immediately. We squelched about in the mud until dark searching for carrots large enough to send, and were out again by dawn continuing our quest – for it was a terrifying time.' They had to admit that their carrot crop 'spelt utter failure' as they 'had not even nearly paid for the manure on which they had been grown'.[298]

Fortunately by September things began to pick up. As word got around, they received 'so many unsolicited demands from private customers that we began to feel quite like partners in an old established firm. Private custom was what we now turned our attention to … we steadily increased the number of hampers we sent out weekly.' They established a customer list that was probably composed of bohemian people like them, who were prepared to pay a premium for hampers of vegetables produced on a small artisan scale. They reported that their customers 'liked their vegetables fresh – direct from a garden and many of them wrote encouraging letters saying how different they were from those which had been through the market and the shops'. Putting hampers together was hard work, however. 'Each consignment takes time and thought to arrange and, understaffed as we were, we had many a scramble to get the baskets off to catch the train. Nevertheless, we enjoyed this part of the work.' This work, even in a small way, clearly gave Olive an outlet for her artistic sensibility, and their book declares, 'Bunching carrots and turnips needs an artistic touch.' Again, Olive provides a telling little illustration complete with commentary. The caption reads: 'This illustration shows the artist [surely Olive] at work on her carrot pyramid. The other partner, standing outside the picture, is watching her carefully add carrot to carrot, literally champing with impatience to carry off the bunches.'[299] This affectionate, self-mocking little picture gives an insight into their partnership. They were a team, working hard, but prepared to laugh at themselves and have fun. Early in their first year, they ordered eighty bushels of soot to get rid of grubs which they decided to spread themselves so that they could 'experience all the disagreeables as well as the pleasures of our trade.' Wearing waterproof aprons and handkerchiefs to cover their hair, they remembered how they 'spent an entire day making an acre of land and ourselves black. We returned in the evening, tired, but so triumphant that we still had spirit enough to enjoy each other's feeling of discomfort and sable hue, every inch of us being completely black except eyeballs and teeth!'[300]

As heartening as their progress was in overcoming challenges and gaining customers, this was clearly not primarily a commercial enterprise. Their book makes clear that their motivation was to build a new life for themselves and live in a way that suited them, rather than to make money. They rejoiced in the open-air life and the opportunity to live and work close to nature. 'All through the changing months there was the steady delight of the healthy life in the open with the sun and the breezes from the sea over Chanctonbury; the pleasure of six days' labour with the larks pouring out their songs over our heads and the plovers pee-witting around us … We never thought of the time, we just worked till dark; and when the moon shone we worked under the stars.'[301] It feels as though they set out to build their own separate little world in what they called 'this enchanted place', which was 'quite hidden in the woods, entirely to our liking, for the life we were going to lead was to be free, as near the life of the woods as we could make it.' As with Ada Brown and Decima Allen, we can speculate as to whether Olive and Helen were lovers as well as partners in this venture. Their book leaves little doubt that they loved their life together. Alongside the honest descriptions of hardship, there is a fairytale, happy-ever-after feel to their description of life in their cottage in the woods. They describe the cottage as being 'in a clearing where primrose roots and violets, anemones and daffodils rioted in profusion. Squirrel Nutkin was there, and Peter Rabbit and the birds of every feather; and we knew that the fairies danced o' nights because we saw their many-coloured toadstools and dainty traces everywhere.'[302] In this atmosphere, the simple act of growing from seed was a magical one: 'Our first seed sowing was almost as awe-inspiring a proceeding to us as throwing little messages into the Ganges is to a Hindoo … How vivid it still is, the never-to-be-forgotten thrills when the first seeds germinated.'[303] Even the biochemistry of manure receives a fantastical treatment in their book. The freeing of nitrates from stable manure to nourish plants is described as 'almost like a fairytale. Millions of bacteria, acting as scavengers, are ever busy with their beneficient cleansing work. All they require is lime with which to accomplish it; they are powerless without it! ... It is when it is deficient that the soil becomes foul because the bacteria is thrown out of work.'[304] This explanation is illustrated by Olive with a comical picture of weeping 'bacteria' men, sad that they are unemployed owing to the lack of lime.

Their book was published in the summer of 1909 and was an immediate success. One reason was that, whilst Olive and Helen were quietly working away in their isolated garden, the whole topic of French Gardening had become something of a national craze. This was largely thanks to *The Daily Mail*. Its focus on agricultural issues was part of the wider anxiety about the state of the nation. Agricultural depression, urban living conditions and rural depopulation meant, *The Daily Mail* told its readers, that the stock of healthy manhood, the backbone of the British imperial power, could be compromised; Britain was at risk of becoming a second-class nation. The answer to all these problems, it believed, was smallholdings. And as a campaigning tabloid, the *Mail* took up the cause. In January 1908 the newspaper even ran a competition to find a tenant for a 'Daily Mail Farm' – a fourteen-acre smallholding in Lincolnshire which was won by a railway clerk from Grimsby. By spring 1908 *The Daily Mail* had discovered French Gardening and began to promote this technique as the most profitable way to run a smallholding, claiming that an annual profit of £500 could be made from just an acre of land. Over the late spring and summer there were more articles. The newspaper even produced a book entitled, *The French Garden: A Diary and Manual of Intensive Cultivation*, written by Olive's and Helen's mentor, C. D. McKay, which was advertised heavily in the paper. *The Daily Mail* set up a small working example of a French garden at the Ideal Home Exhibition in Olympia in 1908. Other magazines and newspapers followed suit. The gardens at Evesham had to introduce an entrance charge to control the flow of visitors wanting to see the gardens at work.

The techniques of French gardening were particularly attractive to women setting up smallholdings, as they promised high returns on small plots of land with limited capital outlay. One particularly successful example was the Thatcham Fruit and Flower Farm, near Newbury in Berkshire, run by Miss Lily High Jones, where French Gardening was taught to female pupils, the most famous of whom was Beatrix Havergil who went on to found the Waterperry Gardening School. Other horticultural schools caught on quickly and began to offer courses in French Gardening. May Crooke, Edith Bradley's old colleague at Studley, and principal of the Bredon's Norton Gardening School for Ladies, began using French gardening methods after visiting Evesham in 1906. Edith Bradley herself employed a Frenchman to teach the techniques at her own garden in Kent. As ever, Lady Warwick's efforts were never far from the headlines. After Studley began teaching French Gardening to its pupils, *The Gardening World* ran a story headlined 'Lady Gardeners in Brittany' which claimed:

> The Countess, we are told, is responsible for an official scare all along the coast of Brittany. The lady gardeners turned out by her classes have been trying to buy small plots in that country near the mouths of rivers, where their produce might be marketed cheaply. They have even offered fancy prices for holdings not on the market. Nothing is known in France of Lady Warwick's educational zeal, or of the reasons why her pupils have found it difficult to buy land to their minds in England; and so there is an official circular to the notaries of sea coast departments instructing them to draft no more deeds of sale to foreigners, and to give an account of all such deeds drafted during the last 10 years. For all that can be seen, Lady Warwick's young ladies may be preparing an English invasion.[305]

Even the Allen-Browns jumped on the bandwagon. Although they concentrated on growing violets, they also began to advertise their Henfield nursery as a 'School for French Culture', able to take two or three pupils under 'a resident French expert'.[306]

In this atmosphere, Olive's and Helen's first-hand account of what it was like for two women to run a French Garden on English soil was bound to be popular. *The Clarion* described it as 'a brightly written, really helpful little book'[307] and a copy was even sent to the King who had expressed an interest in French Gardening. These endorsements, combined with the couple's evident health and happiness, reconciled even their sceptical friends and relations to their new life. Octavia Hill and her companion Harriot Yorke paid a visit to the cottage. They enjoyed the lovely view of the South Downs and saw for themselves how well settled the pair were. In March 1909 Octavia wrote to Sydney Cockerell, 'Olive and Miss Nussey do seem happy and the book one thinks will be a great success. Everyone seems charmed by it.'[308]

In 1909 Olive and Helen looked forward to building on the foundations they had laid the previous year. They took on enthusiastic pupils and began making plans to expand the range of crops. They planned to get their melons and cucumbers started earlier in the year and aimed to try adding mushrooms, early potatoes and early beet. Now they had established a discerning private clientele for their hampers they wanted to try 'various French vegetables and herbs which we think may be liked by English people'.[309] They had proved the doubters wrong and had every reason to be confident about the future, having found a lifestyle that gave them everything they wanted. They had ended their book with a breathless, gloriously multisensory list of all the things that they had experienced in their first year and could look forward to enjoying into the future: 'Health, bright skies, congenial companionship, the visits of our friends, the sympathy and help of all around, the knowledge that we were making steady progress in what we had set out to do; the many creature comrades who live with us in the wood, the freshness of the dawn, the awakening of birds, the smell of the mossy earth, the pushing of the growing things in spring, the moon behind the trees – the colours of it all! And then the long winter evenings with a log fire and a pleasant book and the consciousness of a good day's work done.'[310]

Sadly, this idyllic existence was not to last. Just over a year after the publication of their book, in July 1910, Helen Nussey wrote an urgent letter to their landlord Wilfrid Scawen Blunt. Writing from a flat in Kensington, she wrote:

> Dear Mr Blunt,
>
> Miss Cockerell has cancer – and they find this morning that they can do nothing by operation. They think she will not live more than about 3 months but say they do not think she will suffer as much as in some cases. When she is out of hospital, which will probably be in about 3 weeks, I should like to bring her back to Gosbrook. She loves it more than any other spot. Of course, we should have to have a nurse living with us. Mr Cockerell is not quite sure whether we should not be too far from a doctor. I shall be up here as much as I can during the next three weeks – I have taken rooms here with Mrs Lowe, her sister. [311]

Olive had never been physically strong, but this was devastating and shocking news. Octavia Hill and Sydney Cockerell rushed to help. Olive was cared for in St Thomas's Hospital in Lambeth and her uncle, Sir Richard Douglas Powell, who had been employed as physician to Queen Victoria's household, oversaw her care. However, it was to no avail; it was rapidly apparent that she did not have long to live. She was in terrible pain. Helen Nussey described her as being in 'awful agony, worse she says than she could ever conceived as possible',[312] but as Octavia Hill said, Olive was 'brave and unselfish' throughout.[313] On July 23 Helen Nussey sent her landlord an update on her plans: 'I went down to Gosbrook the night before last for a flying visit and have given the pupils there three months' notice so we shall close the garden in October. Gosbrook is very crushing alone and I cannot live there, beside which I want to be with Olive.'[314] Octavia Hill offered Helen space in her home in Westminster, but she preferred to stay in a rented flat with Olive's sister Una. The hopes of taking Olive back to 'Gosbrook' had to be abandoned as she was just too ill. Sydney Cockerell wanted to arrange for her to spend her last days in Cambridge near his family. Octavia Hill wrote, 'If she can really be brought to a little house near you, with Miss Nussey and Una to watch over her, and able just to see the children, with quiet and a few trees and flowers and a little grass, it will be a blessed thing.'[315] But this, too, proved impossible as Olive's condition deteriorated far too quickly. She died on July 24 of cancer of the abdomen and a pulmonary embolism, just a day after these letters were written. She was 41 years old.

Their dream of a free 'life of the woods' was over. Helen Nussey was distraught and could not face moving back to their cottage alone. She only returned to 'Gosbrook' briefly to try to find other people to rent the house and garden. She hoped to let it as a going concern to recoup some of their considerable investment but, despite writing to all the female horticultural colleges, she could not find anyone willing to take on the tenancy. It was not to be until February the following year that a new tenant came forward, but in the meantime, Helen had to sell off stock and equipment separately, breaking up everything she and Olive had built together. In September 1910 Sydney Cockerell took Olive's ashes up to the Lake District to be scattered over the waters of Lake Coniston; the same lake by which Olive and Sydney had first gone to meet John Ruskin in their youth. Helen was not invited to attend. She was staying with Octavia Hill and Miss Yorke who seem to have taken her under their wing. On

September 22 Octavia Hill wrote to Sydney Cockerell to thank him for his letter describing the commitment of Olive's ashes, saying, 'It must have been very impressive and beautiful … You would think much of Ruskin and be glad to have memories of him haunting you … Your letter arrived the evening we returned from Devonshire and Miss Nussey, whom we took with us there, was staying here that night. She was of course much interested.'[316]

Helen Nussey returned to life in London and for a time worked for Octavia Hill in her old field of social work with poor Londoners. The garden she and Olive made together had disappeared and the time in Sussex must have seemed a distant memory, but at least she had the beautiful little book they made together as a record of their year in the country. In large genteel families one daughter, especially if she was physically frail, could find herself trapped in the role of spinster sister, whose destiny in life was to endure all the dull domestic routines whilst caring for elderly parents, siblings, nieces and nephews. As Florence Nightingale vividly described it: 'Living from breakfast to dinner, from dinner till tea, with a little worsted work and … looking forward to nothing but bed.'[317] This confined, monotonous life of helpful virtue was the one Olive Cockerell seemed destined to lead – until she met Helen Nussey. Their escape was a brief one, but for a time they worked together to live a life that had meaning and joy and, as they wrote at the end of their book, 'Surely there is little else that heart of human can desire?'[318]

10

MRS BULL WANTS A SPADE

John Bull and Mrs Bull have got
A cultivated garden plot,
Where both work hard, in rain or sun,
Though he has tools, while she has none.

'Mr and Mrs Bull's Garden',
Common Cause, May 12, 1910

Although Olive and Helen will not have noticed, sealed off as they were in the hushed world of terminal illness in a hospital room, the summer of 1910 coincided with a time of tension and anticipation for women up and down the country. The steps women were taking to forge independent careers were happening in parallel with steps to change the law so that they could also become full citizens with the right to vote. The year had begun with a General Election, in the run-up to which supporters of votes for women campaigned vociferously to ensure prospective MPs took notice of their demands. The new Liberal government under Asquith seemed to indicate that legislation to give at least some women the vote was a possibility. However, by early July these hopes were hanging by a thread. Prime Minister Asquith had decided not to include votes for women in a planned Electoral Reform Act; instead hopes now rested with an all-party committee under Lord Lytton. The committee proposed a new Parliamentary Franchise Bill named the Conciliation Bill, which, as a compromise, would give just one million property-owning single women the vote. Married women were excluded; wives could not vote from the same property as joint householders with their husbands. Some of the women who are the focus of this book would have been beneficiaries – as unmarried property owners, Ada Brown, Decima Allen, Edith Bradley, Madeline Agar and J. S. Turner would all have gained the vote under this measure; Gertrude Cope, living in a cottage that came with the job, would not. The prospect of the Conciliation Bill, which looked likely to gain all-party support, brought a brief period of calm and optimism. Militant campaigners for the vote declared a suspension of their disruptive activities to allow the Bill to be debated in a peaceful atmosphere.

The connection between the rise of women gardeners and the campaign for female suffrage goes beyond the fact that both were motivated by attempts to improve the status of women. Women gardeners were often directly involved in the campaign for the vote, gardens and parks were important scenes of protest, and flowers were used as evocative imagery in propaganda material. When it comes to our six women, the evidence is patchy, but it seems that they held, like the rest of society at the time, a range of opinions on the question of female suffrage and how it should be achieved. There is no definite record of Olive Cockerell's or Helen Nussey's opinion on the question of votes for women. As a follower of William Morris and coming from a progressive family, it is likely that Olive was supportive in principle. However, we cannot take this for granted. Her godmother Octavia Hill, despite being a formidable social campaigner, and a great advocate for women's role in public life, was an opponent of female suffrage. On July 15, 1910, *The Times* published a letter from Octavia Hill in which she declared 'how profoundly sorry I shall be if women's suffrage in any form is introduced into England'. She felt that men and women should operate in different spheres and that 'party struggle and political life' would distract from 'that large field of public work in which so many are now doing noble and helpful service … out of sight, silent work which really achieves something.' She did, however, admit that this was not an opinion shared by 'some of my earnest young fellow workers'.[319] Both Olive and Helen were both from that younger generation, so it is likely that they would have disagreed with this rather Victorian characterisation of the role of women, but there is no record of their participation in any suffrage-supporting activity to prove this. Nor is there any record of Gertrude Cope's stance on the question of women's suffrage. Her employer at Northfield, Elizabeth Cadbury, was very active in supporting women's right to vote but she would not be the first or only employee to differ from her employer's views. As we have seen, J. S. Turner worked with both Alicia Cecil, who was actively anti-suffrage (she was a member of the National League for Opposing Woman Suffrage) and Lady Frances Balfour, who was a prominent and longstanding campaigner for votes for women. In the absence of evidence either way, the fact that these women led independent lives as active, hands-on professional gardeners makes it more likely than not that they supported the idea of enfranchising women. Certainly J. S. Turner was politically active all her life, speaking on public platforms on behalf of Tariff Reform and the Empire, so it seems unlikely that she would not want the power of the vote as well.

Despite the frustrating absence of evidence to pin down the opinions of particular individuals, where it is possible to tell, it seems that most women involved in professional gardening were suffragists rather than suffragettes. Suffragists were the moderate voices in the campaign for women's votes and were represented by the National Union of Women's Suffrage Societies (NUWSS). They argued that gentle, lawful demonstrations and petitions had already made progress and could make more. Many of those involved in the early days of promoting horticultural training opportunities for women were part of the network of influential and pioneering women who argued for the vote in this way. Women like Elizabeth Garett Anderson, Fanny Wilkinson, Lady Frances Balfour and Emma Cons had managed to advance the case for the vote in crucial, indirect ways, particularly by establishing themselves as both voters and elected councillors in local government. Years of patient and persistent campaigning had won the limited concession to enfranchise female ratepayers and grant them the right to stand for election on local government boards. The creation of elected county councils in the 1880s had opened further opportunities.

Suffragists argued that demonstrating seriousness and competence in professional, public and charitable positions was the best route for women to persuade legislators to give them the vote in national elections. Women who took professional horticultural exams, managed large gardens or independent horticultural businesses reinforced this picture of women as responsible citizens, deserving of a say in the way the country was run. As Scottish medic and suffragist Dr Elsie Inglis said, 'The ordinary male disbelief in our capacity cannot be argued away. It can only be worked away.'[320] Some, however, felt that this gradualist approach was simply too slow and did not acknowledge the simple truth that women should have the right to vote, and patience was not the answer when rights were denied. In 1903 Emmeline Pankhurst set up the Women's Social and Political Union (WSPU) with the motto 'Deeds not Words', determined that women should make their demands impossible to ignore. The term suffragette was first coined by *The Daily Mail* in 1906 to belittle women campaigning for the vote, but the term was embraced by followers of the WSPU as they began to adopt spectacular and often violent tactics to focus political and public attention on their cause. It was far more common to be a suffragist than a suffragette.

To begin with, the split between the two groups was not an uncrossable chasm; some women gave support to both NUWSS and WSPU activities. Anna Bateson, the ex-Botanist who turned to market gardening in Bashley in the New Forest, was a case in point. Along with her mother and two sisters, she was a founding member of the Cambridge Women's Suffrage Association in the 1880s. After she moved to Hampshire to set up her market garden, she became Secretary of the New Forest Suffrage Society which was affiliated to the moderate NUWSS; yet in 1908 she donated money to the WSPU. Anna Bateson was a pillar of the local community, a Poor Law Guardian, a school governor and a member of the Lymington District Council and there is no evidence of her ever taking part in any violent or destructive acts of protest. As the WSPU began to become more militant most women, including gardening women, felt uncomfortable with its increasingly extreme and violent acts of protest. Membership of the WSPU was always much smaller than the NUWSS; however, for obvious reasons, it was the suffragettes that gained the headlines at the time and who have dominated the history books since.

Madeline Agar was a member of the Mid Bucks Women's Suffrage Society which was affiliated to the moderate NUWSS. She provided exhibits for NUWSS horticultural shows to raise funds. She was probably converted to the suffrage cause while working for Frances Dove as a gardening teacher at Wycombe Abbey. Frances Dove was the first woman councillor in Buckinghamshire and a prime mover in the foundation of the Wycombe branch of the NUWSS. Edith Bradley was a vocal and active campaigner for women's rights, though I have not been able to trace any association with a formal suffrage group. It is clear, however, that she did not share Lady Warwick's views, either in terms of socialism or her approach to the question of the vote. In her autobiography, Lady Warwick was keen to stress that although she was 'keenly interested in helping to forward women's work on new lines', she did so 'without taking any part in political movements such as "Women's Rights"'.[321] Endowed with wealth, beauty and social status, Lady Warwick probably felt she had far more powerful levers for political influence than a single vote could offer. In contrast, when women finally got the vote in 1918, Edith Bradley was quick to encourage her fellow women to use this new right. She gave lectures to attentive groups of women explaining the process, such as one she gave at Bearsted Village Hall in December 1918, entitled 'How Women Ought to Vote and Why'.[322] At a meeting in Ulcombe she called on 'all women electors to look upon voting as a duty and power for good and urged all to take an intelligent interest in the affairs of their country.'[323]

Decima Allen and Ada Brown were the only ones of our group who can firmly be identified as suffragettes and supporters of the WSPU. They were part of a committed band of gardening suffragettes living in and around Henfield. Ex-Swanley students May Martin Le Lacheur and Gladys Ellen Sherris set up a nursery garden called Flowers Farm on Upper Station Road in Henfield in 1909, a short distance from the Allen-Brown Violet Nursery. May Le Lacheur's whole family were committed to the cause of votes for women. Her mother Judith was the Treasurer of Tunbridge Wells Women's Suffrage Society and her sister, Kate Le Lacheur, a farmer in Berkshire, was described as 'a Socialist and a Suffragette' who 'has her farm hands, both men and women, sitting at the same table as herself'. She also delivered her milk by 'chauffeur and a motor float'[324] and in 1910 the milk float was used to distribute suffragette leaflets. The Allen-Brown's close friend Elizabeth Robins, to whom they had dedicated their book on violet-growing, was another Henfield suffragette. She wrote a hugely successful play entitled 'Votes for Women!' which advocated militancy as the only means of achieving female suffrage. The play was performed by suffragette groups up and down the country and in 1907 made into a novel titled *The Convert*. In one scene, a character called Ernestine Blunt gives a speech in Hyde Park which makes use of gardening metaphors to highlight the hypocrisy of a society that depicts women as fragile flowers, whilst simultaneously exploiting them. '"We are too delicate – women are such fragile flowers." The little face was ablaze with scorn. "I saw some of those fragile flowers last week – and I'll tell you where. Not a very good place for gardening. It was a back street in Liverpool. The flowers (oh, the contempt with which she loaded that innocent word!) – the flowers looked pretty dusty – but they weren't quite dead … what had they been doing there in that – garden, I was going to say! – that big grimy building? They had been making cigars! Spending the best years of their lives, spending all their youth in that grim dirty street making cigars for men … But a vote would soil our hands."'[325]

Flowers, which played to conventional views of femininity, were natural symbols for a women's movement that placed such a lot of emphasis on appearance. However impractical, suffragettes appeared at marches, demonstrations and public meetings wearing large hats and long fitted dresses decorated with floral trimmings. Mrs Pankhurst was eager to avoid shocking male prejudice and she refused to concede that women had to become like men to be worthy of the vote. Their dress and use of floral decorations (often violets sourced from the Allen-Brown's nursery) projected the importance of femininity and feminine values even as women were performing unfeminine acts. The popularity of violets among suffragettes may have been a factor in the success of the Allen-Brown business. Violets were often included in bouquets given to suffragettes on release from prison or to speakers at suffragette rallies. The flowers were also a popular motif in artwork on posters, leaflets and banners, and the platforms at large WSPU meetings would be decked with floral decorations in purple, white and green. Female growers of other flowers also got in on the act. Miss Smith of Sussex also advertised sweetpea seeds in the colours of the WSPU; varieties included 'Dorothy Eckford' (white), 'Lady Grisel Hamilton' (mauve) and 'Mrs Walter Wright' (violet/mauve).[326] While the suffragettes were particularly adept at using flowers for visual spectacle, they did not have the monopoly; the suffragists could also put on a good show and mobilised floral art to do so. At the NUWSS meeting at Sutton Coldfield Town Hall in December 1910 'the platform and tables were artistically decorated with plants and flowers – red, white and green, the colours of the Union, only being used.'[327]

Hiring and decorating halls for meetings, printing posters and handbills and paying expenses for speakers all cost money and selling plants and flowers was a popular way of raising funds for both suffragettes and suffragists. The pages of the campaigning newspapers *The Suffragette, Common Cause* and *Votes for Women* were full of advertisements and announcements of plant sales to raise funds. These efforts ranged in scale. The WSPU held annual 'Self Denial Weeks' when supporters were asked to donate flowers from their gardens and volunteer as flower-sellers to sell them in the street in large towns and cities all over the country. Although newspapers carried alarming accounts of anti-suffrage men shouting abuse at WSPU flower-sellers, the WSPU Treasurer reported that this was rare, and described how 'Flower-sellers have sold out almost before they had time to get settled at their various pitches … Men and women stopping to buy a bunch of violets have time and again put down 1s or 2s 6d and refused change.'[328] WSPU flower-sellers were also sent to large events such as the RHS flower shows held at the RHS headquarters in Vincent Square in London.

Some women became regular sellers of plants to raise funds, such as Miss Lowe of St Edmunds Cottage, Grayshott, in Hertfordshire, who frequently advertised 'Plants, Perennial Seedlings etc for Sale. Proceeds to Suffrage', and the Misses Evans of the Vale House, Stamford in Lincolnshire, who regularly advertised the sale of rock garden plants 'for Suffrage' in *Common Cause*. Other sales were more sporadic and clearly represented surplus from a small private garden, such as this report of a member of the Bournemouth branch of the NUWSS: 'One member offered plants from her garden to be sold for the good of the cause. She quickly raised 10 shillings which she handed over towards the expenses.'[329] Lucky shoppers at the Guildford NUWSS shop could buy plants from the garden of Gertrude Jekyll. She was an active suffragist and in 1909 was elected Vice President of the Godalming branch of the NUWSS. In November 1912 the Surrey, Sussex and Hants branches of the NUWSS hired a shop in Guildford to hold a 'Grand Sale of Plants from Famous Gardens of Surrey' to raise funds for the cause, to which Gertrude Jekyll naturally donated plants.

In some advertisements, it is not clear whether the sales are to raise campaign funds or the seller is just making reference to their political allegiance to encourage purchases from like-minded buyers, such as this advert in *Votes for Women* in 1909: 'Suffragette offers Daffodil Bulbs from a country garden, trumpets and narcissi, mixed 50 for 1s 6d, Mrs Rowe Holford, near Bridgewater.'[330] Ada Brown and Decima Allen advertised their Allen-Brown violets in *Votes for Women* for many years, confident that not only were they supporting a newspaper that promoted their views, they were also reaching a female clientele likely to be interested in their products. They also funded the work of the WSPU more directly; they were listed as frequent donors to the WSPU '£20,000 Fund' to support the creation of banners and other material for WSPU campaigns.[331] In 1909 they even donated a diamond ring worth £8 10 shillings to the WSPU Treasurer's Fund (about £1,500 in today's prices).[332]

Women gardeners were also visible in the mass marches and rallies organised by both the NUWSS and the WSPU. In 1908, two years before the Conciliation Bill, another bill to extend the franchise to women had been debated in the Houses of Parliament and actually passed its second reading. Although it would ultimately be blocked, at the time this was the greatest progress that a suffrage bill had made since 1897. While the bill was still under discussion, the leaders of the NUWSS thought that the time was right to show the country how well organised and united women were in demanding full citizenship. In May 1908 Miss Stillington, an organiser for the London Society for Women's Suffrage, wrote to Frances Wolseley to ask her to allow her students at Glynde to attend. She wrote, 'I think there can be few professional women to whom the possession of the Parliamentary Franchise would mean so much as it would to women gardeners, who have still to meet and overcome the prejudice which most unfairly attaches to women taking up a new profession, which has been regarded as one for men only.' She also mentioned, perhaps hoping this would swing the decision, that, 'Miss Wilkinson has asked a very large number of her past and present students to join her on this occasion.'[333] It is hardly surprising that Fanny Wilkinson, the Principal of Swanley Horticultural College, was happy to support this march. As well as being a pioneering female landscape architect and educator, she was a member of the Central Committee of Women's Suffrage, led by her relative, friend and neighbour, Millicent Fawcett. On June 13, 1908, thousands of marchers assembled in eight blocks on the Embankment, just along from the Houses of Parliament. The blocks were assigned to different organisations and professions. Gardeners were in Block 4, marching six abreast alongside farmers, physical training instructors, artists, writers, actors, musicians and homemakers. Each group had their own banner, designed by members of The Artists' Suffrage League, which included Jane Morris's daughter, May Morris. The gardeners' banner featured a design of a rake and a spade in earthy brown and green (unfortunately, no image of this banner survives).[334]

The following Sunday, June 21, the WSPU organised an equally impressive 'Women's Sunday' march to Hyde Park and women gardeners were again called to attend. *Votes for Women* carried an appeal from the organiser Miss Lennox: 'A feature of the Hyde Park Demonstration will be the group of women gardeners and florists. Already the different horticultural colleges have been approached and there is every indication that a large number of women gardeners will respond. Friends are asked to send their names at once.'[335] Some Swanley students wanted to join the WSPU march. The college authorities were more nervous about this association; they agreed that students 'might walk as women gardeners but it was undesirable that they should use the college name.'[336] May Le Lacheur and Gladys Sherris from the Flower Farm in Henfield were both there, driven to the event by May's father in his motor car, which was brilliantly decorated for the occasion, with rosettes in green, white and purple. A small 'Votes for Women' placard was fixed on the front of the car and a large notice advertising the demonstration hung out at the back.[337]

By 1910 years of patient suffragist work and increasingly noisy and disruptive suffragette activity had made votes for women one of the foremost political issues of the day. Hopes were high that the new Liberal government would at last deliver electoral reform that gave women the vote. For most feminists, enfranchisement was essential, but it was only part of a wider drive for change. Underlying the suffrage campaign was an insistence upon radically redrawing the relationship between women and men and between women and society. The ultimate goal was to give women the power to change society itself.

Even as the campaign for the vote reached new heights, work to advance women's educational and professional place in society continued alongside. On the horticultural front, Edith Bradley was, like the suffrage campaigners, in a cautiously optimistic mood. Although battle-weary from years of unrewarded work in the cause of horticultural and agricultural training for women, she found herself drawn once more into the fray. The source of her renewed hope was a meeting organised as part of the Women's Congress, an international gathering of women held as part of the Anglo-Japan Exhibition that had done so much to popularise Japanese gardens at White City in West London. The meeting, held on July 5, 1910, and entitled 'Women in Agriculture', was arranged by Frances Wolseley of the Glynde College for Lady Gardeners and Fanny Wilkinson, the Principal of Swanley. It brought together all the main institutions and figures involved in horticultural and agricultural training for women. Edith Bradley was invited to speak as an expert on 'Fruit Growing and Fruit Preservation'. Other speakers included her friend and ex-colleague Bertha La Mothe, who spoke on beekeeping, and Miss V. Courtauld, who gave a talk about 'Lady Farmers'. J. S. Turner spoke with her usual bluntness on working in the colonies. The event, in the heady atmosphere of gleaming White City, surrounded by exotic Japanese gardens and other exhibits, re-ignited Edith Bradley's enthusiasm for a more organised and ambitious movement for women in horticulture and agriculture. After the various presentations ended, she stood up and proposed a resolution that:

> The time has arrived for the Movement to be organised under four distinct headings:
>
> Education – more coordination between all the colleges, schools of gardening and teaching institutions. Schemes of training and the different curricula could be planned on more uniform lines, which would have the effect of giving dignity to the profession and raising it to a foremost position, aiming at securing an agricultural degree as the highest prize.
>
> The organisation of trained students with regular meetings to build 'esprit de corps'.
>
> The organisation of the sale of produce and purchase of plants, produce etc.
>
> The organisation of smallholders or small owners. This class will develop rapidly and will need all the help which can be obtained to make the movement successful.[338]

The resolution represented a neat summary of all the plans that Edith Bradley had long fostered but had never managed to see to fruition. Her vision was bold and all-encompassing: a well-thought-out uniform curriculum culminating in a respected degree-level qualification and the creation of a cooperatively organised ecosystem of smallholders. She must have felt delighted when her resolution was passed at such a gathering, filled as it was with representatives from all the interested parties. Following the meeting, brimming with excitement, she wrote to Frances Wolseley, whom remarkably she had not met before, even though both had moved in similar circles for years:

> It seems we have a nucleus of a very important combined action within our reach, and I am very pleased indeed to know that you agree with me … We do not want to make it in any way an organisation identified with one college or any particular body of Agriculturists but that it should be as widely representative as possible.[339]

Just as with the campaign for the vote, success felt tantalisingly close; just one more coordinated push and women could look forward to a brighter future as gardeners and farmers.

In October 1910, acting as 'Honorary Secretaries', Frances Wolseley and Edith Bradley sent out impressive invitation cards to an event on October 25 at the Lyceum Club, titled 'The Organisation of Agriculture as a Profession for Women'. Edith Bradley, Fanny Wilkinson, J. S. Turner and Frances Wolseley all attended on behalf of their respective organisations. However, bringing together the different competing horticultural and agricultural colleges and schools was never going to be easy. In the aftermath Edith Bradley wrote to Frances Wolseley: 'I wonder what your feelings are after the curious turn of events? … The atmosphere in the room was distinctly suggestive of a packed meeting was it not? Miss Turner's attitude towards Miss Wilkinson was a curious inversion, it made me wonder why?' The meeting was not a success. Reading between the lines, it seems that, despite in the past having been harshly critical of the training at Swanley as being too academic and impractical, J. S. Turner had decided to back Fanny Wilkinson in order to overturn Edith Bradley's idea of a new unified curriculum and a focus on practical support for smallholders. Edith Bradley was frustrated by 'the exaltation of Horticulture as expressed by Swanley College' and complained of Fanny Wilkinson's focus on large-scale farmers like Katherine Mina Courtauld: 'Fancy quoting Miss Courtauld or Miss Edwards as representative agriculturists! How can we hope to get on to broad and far-reaching lines? I am sure that we shall not, and it makes one grudge valuable time taken from other things.'[340] Outnumbered in the meeting, Edith Bradley's desire for a new organisation, representative of all the schools, which focused on the lighter branches of agriculture and smallholdings, was rejected. There was still a move towards coordinated action, but it seems Fanny Wilkinson decided that this should best be done via the Women's Agricultural and Horticultural International Union, the group which had been established at the Women's Congress in 1899. After the Lyceum meeting, it changed its name to Women's Farm and Garden Union and established an educational sub-committee which set out to administer its own examinations. Edith's vision of a unified and consistent qualification, focused on the lighter branches of agriculture, was thwarted.

Bitterly disappointed, Edith Bradley once more returned to Greenway Court in Kent to continue her work on her own farm. For a woman who espoused the idea of cooperation, she was stubbornly reluctant to work with others who did not exactly share her views. She remained convinced her whole life that the Women's Farm and Garden Union was too closely associated with Swanley Horticultural College and therefore was not close enough to the practical concerns of female smallholders, being too academic and focused on gardening rather than agriculture.

Things were even more frustrating on the political front. The Conciliation Bill had passed its first reading on July 12, but Prime Minister Asquith refused to give the Bill parliamentary time to progress into law. He was locked in a battle with the House of Lords to pass welfare measures and decided to call a second general election for December 1910 to try to increase his majority. This shelved any immediate prospect of any extension of the franchise to women. Supporters of votes for women of all political persuasions, militants and moderates, felt betrayed. The WSPU marched on Parliament on November 18, 1910, and Asquith refused to see a WSPU deputation. The suffragettes stayed in Parliament Square and tried to enter the House of Commons. These efforts were met with violent aggression by the police, who beat and hit the suffragettes, and threw them into the hostile crowds for further ill-treatment. Known as 'Black Friday', this event hardened the militancy of many WSPU supporters. Previously, WSPU direct action, though disruptive, had been only sporadically violent, and their attacks almost exclusively aimed at government figures and officials. After the betrayal of 1910, however, suffragette violence was directed increasingly at commercial concerns and the general public. This was explicitly planned by Emmeline and Christabel Pankhurst as a self-described 'reign of terror'. Emmeline Pankhurst's stated aim was 'to make England and every department of English life insecure and unsafe'.[341] Their goal was to create a state of national crisis that the government could not ignore or dismiss.

One of the first opportunities for women on all parts of the political spectrum to express their frustration was the 1911 census. Like most people who regarded themselves as law-abiding suffragists, Edith Bradley, Madeline Agar, J. S. Turner and Gertrude Cope all completed the 1911 census in the conventional way. However, Decima and Ada Allen-Brown do not appear in the 1911 census, and there is no record of their having left the country, so it is likely that, in common with many suffragettes, they evaded the census in protest at the exclusion of women from the electorate. Helen Nussey is also missing from the census record and does not appear to have left the country either. Other evaders included Gertrude Cope's old employer, Rhoda Anstey. Along with all the staff and students at the Anstey Physical Training College, she refused to provide details for the census. Instead, she wrote across the form: 'No Vote No Census! I protest against the injustice done to women ratepayers by the continued refusal of the government to give them the vote, and hereby refuse to fill in the census forms for my household.' On the form the registrar noted in red ink that: 'From the information obtained from several sources it is estimated that on the night of April 2nd 40 females slept on the premises and this number has been enumerated.' Some did not avoid the census altogether, but made their views known on the form itself. Both May Le Lacheur and Gladys Sherris completed the 1911 census, putting their occupation as suffragist and nursery gardener. May's mother, Judith Le Lacheur, stated that her occupation was 'Treasurer Tunbridge Wells Women's Suffrage Society' and her female members of staff, the cook Sarah Turner and nurse Caroline Merchant, both put 'suffragist' next to their names. The wealthy landowner and farmer Katherine Mina Courtauld wrote on her census form, 'As a householder and ratepayer I deeply resent being denied the privilege of a citizen in the exercise of the Parliamentary franchise.'

This was too mild for the WSPU. The WSPU 'reign of terror' included window-smashing campaigns for which its leaders were imprisoned and fined. The Allen-Browns showed their support by contributing money towards a fund to pay the enormous fines levied on Emmeline Pethwick-Lawrence, Treasurer of the WSPU, and her husband Frederick, after they were imprisoned for conspiracy to organise a window-smashing campaign in 1912. Once arrested, many militant suffragettes went on hunger strike. The infamous 'Cat and Mouse Act' was rushed through parliament in 1913 to ensure that none of the women in prison on hunger strike could become martyrs. Eagle House in Batheaston, outside Bath, became known as 'The Suffragette Retreat' because its owners, WSPU supporter Emily Blathwayt and her husband, invited suffragette hunger-strikers to stay there to recover. From April 1909 to July 1911, trees were planted in the grounds in honour of individual suffragettes; at least 47 were planted in a two-acre garden which became known as 'Annie's Arboretum' after suffragette Annie Kenney who stayed with the Blathwayts frequently. One tree, a *Cupressus Allumii*, was planted by Lady Constance Lytton who had written a contribution for Mrs Theresa Earle's bestselling gardening book, *Pot Pouri from a Surrey Garden* and who was related by marriage to Edwin Lutyens, Gertrude

Jekyll's architect partner. Constance Lytton became a convert to the suffragette cause in 1908 and was arrested and went on hunger strike in 1910. Using an alias, Jane Wharton, to avoid being given special treatment due to her aristocratic background, she was force-fed. Constance Lytton never fully recovered from the experience of force-feeding and died in 1923. The Blathwayts, alarmed by the increasing violence of the attacks, eventually became disillusioned with the tactics of Emmeline and Christabel Pankhurst and resigned their WSPU membership. The family continued to care for Annie's Arboretum but unfortunately, after their daughter Mary died in 1962, the garden was sold to developers and only one tree now survives.

Whilst the Blathwayt's garden had a symbolic and commemorative purpose, most suffragettes and suffragists used their gardens in more practical ways during these campaigning years. As well as raising plants and flowers for sale, private gardens provided ideal spaces for meetings and garden parties where speeches could be given without official interference and commitments and networks could be established and reinforced. The suffrage newspapers are crammed with references to garden parties, both WSPU- and NUWSS-affiliated. For instance, a 'splendid event' was held in the garden of 1 Fitzjohn Avenue in Hampstead where the Actresses' Franchise League gave a performance, followed by 'dances by Annie Spong's children', which presumably moved at least some of those attending to donate more money.[342] Mrs Kate Harvey of Brackenhall, a suffragette who refused to pay Imperial Taxes or the National Insurance for her gardener (rather ironically named Mr Asquith) as an act of protest for the Women's Tax Resistance League, held an unusual garden party in July 1913. It was reported that, in order to prevent tax collectors entering her property, her house was 'barricaded and has been in a state of siege since the beginning of May'. Nevertheless, on July 10 she gave a garden party to raise money for The Women's Tax Resistance League, 'the guests entering through a hidden gateway or else by scaling a fence, an act which the law does not permit a tax collector'.[343] Equally, garden parties held by anti-suffrage campaigners and official figures could also be a target for suffragette activists. At Fulham Palace in the same month, a garden party was infiltrated by 'a woman who persistently spoke to the Bishop of London on the subject of forcible feeding and another woman who attempted to hold a meeting were both ejected.' They were 'roughly handled, one of them, it is said, coming away with her face streaming with blood.'[344]

Despite the risks of injury, imprisonment and force-feeding, the suffragette attacks continued through 1912 and 1913. The attacks were wide-ranging, but it is interesting how often gardens, parks and green spaces were targeted. The Edwardian era was in many ways the golden age of public parks. They were highly valued expressions of civic pride, with their bandstands, boating lakes, tea pavilions and elaborate bedding schemes. As such, they made tempting targets for suffragettes wanting to puncture the complacency of local and national politicians and disrupt the workings of 'civil' society. Empty at night, protected only by easily scalable iron railings, public parks were sitting targets. In the early hours of the morning of February 8, 1913, two women snuck into the Royal Botanic Gardens at Kew and attacked the orchid house. A total of 37 panes were broken, letting in the cold night air, damaging and killing valuable exotic orchids and 'others were torn and twisted from their pots and the blooms were trampled underfoot.' Almost as if determined to cause the maximum distress to the gardeners, the attackers destroyed the name labels which greatly complicated the task of rearranging and protecting the plants that survived. Police found a card with the motto 'Votes for Women' on the scene and a piece of paper stating that 'orchids can be destroyed, but not woman's honour.'[345] The choice of the orchid house as their target – home to fragile, exotic blooms from across the Empire – feels a deliberate political statement. Orchid-collecting was a rich man's hobby, the preserve of exactly the type of powerful elite men who stood in the way of female enfranchisement. Two weeks later, the Tea Pavilion at Kew was the subject of an arson attack. This time the perpetrators were caught at the scene. They included Olive Wharry (aka Joyce Lock/ Lilian Lenton). Once in prison she went on hunger strike and was released having nearly died during a particularly violent force-feeding episode. After recovering, she went on the run adopting a number of disguises and aliases and gaining nationwide notoriety. The author Rebecca West wrote about the incident for the socialist newspaper *The Clarion*, in an article called 'The Mildness of Militancy: A Storm in a Tea House'. She wondered why 'an active young woman should destroy beautiful flowers when the Albert Memorial still stands in Kensington Gardens and there is gunpowder in the land'. But she understood why the tea house was a target:

> For I spent a little time of sleepy peace there one sunny day last summer. At the next table sat a dear old person with silver hair and gold-rimmed spectacles and a pale young curate. During the three-quarters of an hour I was there they talked with delicate gravity and an air of profound culture about a correspondence in *The Spectator* about the decay of the subjunctive mood in modern English. The burning of the tea house was an honest attempt to overcome the difficulty felt by reformers of getting in touch with people who are snowed under by decaying subjunctives.[346]

Kew was the highest-profile garden to be the subject of suffragette attack, but it was far from the only one. The previous month, two devices were planted at the Kibble Palace glasshouse in Glasgow Botanic Gardens. One bomb was defused by a night watchman, but the other then exploded behind him, nearly killing him and shattering the glass in a conservatory. The tea pavilion in Regent's Park in London was completely destroyed by a fire set by suffragettes using cans of petrol. In April 1913 the tea pavilion in Armstrong Park in Newcastle was burnt down and three large hyacinth beds destroyed. In November an unexploded home-made bomb was discovered in the palm house in Sefton Park in Liverpool and there was a large explosion of a gunpowder-filled pipe bomb in the cactus house at Alexandra Park in Manchester.

Golf courses, representing a world of male privilege, were another popular open-air target. In the small hours of February 15, 1913, a coordinated attack was launched on golf courses in Cromer, Pontypool, Acton, Chingford and Bradford Moor. Greens were attacked with knives, spades and acid, and notes were left reading 'No Votes, No Golf'. Even the smallest, most innocent-seeming green spaces did not escape attack. In August shrubs and trees in the school garden at Doulton Road School in Rowley near Dudley were pulled up and papers left scattered across the garden which read, 'Militancy Must Go On'.[347]

The determination to continue militancy was tempered by an awareness that violence was hardening resistance to the suffrage message. In an attempt to counter the picture of suffragettes as irrational and violent extremists, the image-conscious WSPU turned to the garden, the natural location for calm femininity. In June, 1913, the WSPU staged the Suffragette Flower Fair and Festival in The Empress Rooms in Kensington. The festival organiser, Miss Joan Wickham, made it explicitly clear that the role of the show was to show that women who wanted the vote were 'a band of the most intelligent and charming women in the country … not only will public misunderstandings be dispelled but members of the WSPU will have a much-valued opportunity of friendly intercourse.'[348] To ensure that the right impression was given every element of this visually striking event was planned down to the last detail. Exhibitors were told 'the uniform of the stall-holders will consist of flowered muslin dresses and picture hats.'[349] Picture hats were wide-brimmed hats, elaborately trimmed with ribbons, flowers and feathers; this was an outfit designed to emphasise their status as 'ladies'. There were to be no short gardening skirts or knickerbockers here. There were flower stalls, a miniature rock garden, a golf green, bookstall, a hat stall, farm- and garden-produce stall and a boat swing. The centrepiece was a seventeenth-century-style garden, the design of which was very deliberately chosen to transport visitors to a calmer time. *The Suffragette* newspaper described it as a 'riot of June flowers restrained to a certain orderliness and formality. There will be yew hedges and smooth lawns.' As if this were not enough to reassure visitors that suffragettes were models of femininity, the account continued, that since no garden would be complete 'without butterflies and the Little People that every child believes to lurk in the flowerbeds … children will be flitting about dressed as brownies, elves and butterflies.'[350] The event was deemed a big success, but it is likely that the event only attracted existing supporters rather than changing minds, given the more shocking headlines that suffragettes were making.

A contrasting picture of the role of flowers in the suffragette campaign can be seen in the events of March 9, 1914. Emmeline Pankhurst attended a large WSPU meeting at St Andrews Hall in Glasgow whilst under threat of arrest according to the terms of the Cat and Mouse Act. As usual for large meetings, the hall was elaborately decorated with flowers, and Mrs Pankhurst was presented with a large bouquet. Just as she began her speech, a group of policemen from Scotland Yard stormed the hall to arrest her. They were met by a 'fusillade of flowerpots' and when they caught hold of the platform railing to storm the platform, they discovered that 'beneath the decorations of bunting and flowers, barbed wire had been concealed'. After vicious hand-to-hand fighting, Emmeline Pankhurst was arrested and bundled from the stage. 'The whole floor in front of the platform was seen to be littered with broken flowerpots, earth, splinters of tables and chairs, tickets and pamphlets and trampled flowers.'[351]

By 1913 a bitter stalemate had developed. As the militant suffragettes became more extreme in their activities, the government dug its feet in harder and introduced more draconian measures, prompting in turn a more extreme response from the suffragettes. Anti-suffrage cartoons in magazines and postcards depicted suffrage campaigners as violent harpies who were poor examples of womanhood. In 1913 the windows of the office of the Canadian Pacific Railway were smashed by suffragettes as part of a campaign to punish businesses for not speaking out in support of votes for women. Even though the Canadian Pacific Railway was a frequent advertiser in suffrage journals such as *Common Cause* and *The Suffragette*, encouraging women settlers to lease land in Canada from the railway, they boarded up their windows and covered the boards with promotional posters and a large banner with the words 'We are looking for Settlers, Not for Suffragettes.'[352]

The suffragists tried their best to distance themselves from the violent methods of some of the suffragettes. In July 1914 students

Cartoon from *Punch* in 1913 showing reaction at a garden party to rumours that suffragettes may have infiltrated the event. Courtesy of the RHS Lindley Collections.

from Studley had a stall at a local Suffrage Fete, organised by the Conservative and Unionist Franchise Association, and organisers were at pains to stress that the event was 'non-militant' and money raised would 'not be devoted to burning churches, breaking windows or anything of that type'.[353] However, as positions hardened, even the moderate suffragists found themselves subject to a strong backlash. In June 1913 the NUWSS organised 'The Great Pilgrimage'. This was a march to London from points all around England and Wales along six set routes. The idea was to take the message out to the countryside and provide a focus for the moderate women working quietly in small groups in smaller towns and villages up and down the country. But even this decorous and peaceful procession met with hostility. In Cirencester, male students from the Royal Agricultural College 'rushed' the lorry that the pilgrims were using as a platform to give speeches from. Rushing was a popular form of Edwardian protest which involved people linking arms in a long line and lurching backwards and forwards in an increasing number of steps at a time to create an irresistible momentum. One of the suffragists, Annie Ramsay, said she thought she was going to die as the breath was squeezed out of her with each surge of the crowd. To add insult to injury, some of the male students dressed up in drag. The crowd tried to overturn the lorry and physically assault the speakers and they only just managed to escape to a house to hide, bruised and terrified.[354] Even a quiet place like Cirencester could be a violent and threatening place for women who dared to speak up.

There was a strongly negative response to the extreme tactics of the WPSU in the world of horticulture, too. The attacks on parks and gardens provoked outrage in the horticultural press, aghast at the 'wanton destruction' of valuable plants and buildings and risk of serious injury to park users and staff. Nor did the attacks help the cause of introducing women to the gardening profession. Even women who quietly and studiously devoted themselves to building a horticultural career still met with a frosty reception. Although by this time female gardeners were no longer such a novelty, and the anxious or vitriolic correspondence bewailing the entry of women into horticultural colleges had abated somewhat, female gardeners were far from well established in the profession. By 1913 women had been excelling in the RHS examination result list for a decade, yet they were still rarely considered for good horticultural jobs and were not welcomed into the profession. The popular weekly gardening magazine *The Gardener* ran a regular column profiling eminent figures in horticulture. In 1913 not a single woman was featured. In fact, in the whole year, apart from the occasional reference to an aristocratic lady opening a flower show, there were only two references to women in *The Gardener* – and they were both reports of suffragette attacks on parks. In horticulture and agriculture, although there were individual success stories, the same old arguments and glass ceilings remained firmly in place. Women could not be ignored, but equality was still tantalisingly out of reach.

11

THIRTY THOUSAND WOMEN CAN SAVE US!

All the boys have been in Flanders for the last three years or more,
All the girls are doing jobs they never did before.

Women's Land Army song, *The Landswoman*, March 1918

The outbreak of war changed everything. When Britain declared war against Germany and her allies in August 1914, both the NSUW and the WSPU immediately suspended their campaigns for the vote and called on women to rally around the war effort. In the world of horticulture, because the consensus was that the war would be short, the main concerns were about the immediate economic impacts on commercial horticulture. Three weeks after war was declared, the RHS felt moved to advise its membership (then known as Fellows) that, in time of war, 'whilst rightly denying oneself such unnecessary luxuries as for example the more expensive wines, cigars etc., it is in our opinion an act of the highest patriotism to live our normal lives as far as possible in all other respects, cultivating the same area of land, employing the same staff, transacting in fact all our usual business and household arrangements. To act in any way otherwise must of necessity throw numbers of men and women out of useful and remunerative work.' Fellows should not fall victim to 'the mistaken idea that gardening is a luxury and should for that reason be reduced.'[355] This letter speaks volumes about the RHS's picture of the world and its own membership at the time, but it is notable that the message includes a rare admission that the horticultural workforce included women as well as men. If the RHS felt the key thing was to carry on as normal (barring fine wine and cigars of course), women with horticultural skills were quick to realise that war would bring profound change. Frances Wolseley noted that, 'In the early autumn, after war was declared, my young women realised that, at last, their chance had come. And that, if they could work with precision and method, those doubts so often cast upon their capability would once and for all be dispersed.'[356] Tens of thousands of young men were enlisting, and it was clear that this would leave gaps to be filled in gardens and horticultural businesses up and down the land. Surely even the most sceptical employers would turn to women, who were ready and waiting and well trained by Swanley, Studley, Glynde and all the other gardening schools over the past twenty or so years?

In February 1915 *The Journal of Horticulture*, a weekly gardening paper aimed at professional gardeners, published an article by its columnist W. Pea which agreed with this analysis. He wrote, 'I am going to prophesy a great advance on the part of female gardeners' even though he knew 'the effect which that has on the average gardener of the other sex.' He saw that not only were male gardeners heading off to war, but those left behind would be 'so badly needed on the farm that gardens will have to be run by women or not at all.' Mr Pea was in favour, as 'there is splendid grit in girl gardeners' and the physical side of gardening work was often exaggerated. Just in case he felt his views were not provocative enough for the 'average gardener', he declared that female gardeners would have no trouble working in public parks as 'I very rarely go through a public park without being struck by the almost unmanly nature of the tasks which strong grown men are performing. And the pace at which they work is funereal.'[357] If *The Journal of Horticulture* had hoped to provoke a response from its readers, it was not disappointed. Angry letters filled the pages of the newspaper for the next couple of months. The tone of the letters and the arguments put forward show that, in many ways, little progress had been made in winning over male gardeners in the previous two decades. The letters made the very same points with the same vehemence as when women first outperformed men in the horticultural examinations. The following extracts give a feel of the views:

> 'The day that women displace men in gardens will see the genesis of the decay of British gardening. N.Green' [358]
>
> 'Mr W. Pea … I should like to give you control of a place where female help only was allowed – six months would settle you.'[359]
>
> 'That women gardeners can do as much as a gardener of life experience is too absurd to discuss. George Felton'[360]
>
> 'When one sees the advertisements in the horticultural papers week after week, more especially for head positions, I think it is deplorable that experienced men should suggest bringing women into the profession … When women take the place of men in our gardens, we shall see the deterioration of our noble profession. George Robinson'[361]

Yet, regardless of the concerns expressed by some in the gardening profession, employers had to adapt to the new reality of a war of mass mobilisation. In the summer of 1915 the Royal Botanic Gardens at Kew, which had suspended their experiment of offering spaces for women as 'improvers' in 1903, began to recruit women to replace the young men who went to war. They were able to call on several excellent Swanley graduates. Lucy Joshua went to work at Kew in August 1915 and recalled 'feeling at once at home in the company of old Swanley friends, Macintyre, Stubbington, Champion, Taylor, Merryweather and Allen, all well-trained women, keen and fond of their work.' Lucy Joshua had graduated from Swanley in 1912 and had gone to Switzerland to become a head gardener and lecturer in a small gardening school but returned to Britain after war was declared. At first the Swanley-trained candidates were restricted to menial tasks. Lucy Joshua and her friends were put into the team working in the Herbaceous Ground. She recalled, 'It was dull work, trimming edges and helping to push round a heavy and very lop-sided mower (the poor thing had been accustomed to having a douche of cold water instead of an oil can and a few feathers) but we felt it was war work and kept cheerful.' As the labour shortages bit harder, however, the women were assigned across all garden departments. Lucy Joshua was promoted to sub-forewoman in the Temperate House Pits and described how, 'The Decorative Department was for a time entirely run by women, so much so that it received the name of Coutts' Harem' (after the head of the department, John Coutts). Even though the women were well qualified, and this was not the first time women had worked in the gardens at Kew, the women were not paid the same rate as the men and to begin with faced hostility. According to Lucy Joshua, 'At first, the women workers met with some suspicion from the men, but when we had shown them that we were prepared to do our full share of work, including fumigating, the ice was broken, and there was real comradeship. I laugh now when I think of the excitement in the Melon Yard when one day it was known that a woman was fumigating the pits. Mr Taylor came rushing in to make sure I was all right and not overcome by smoke (those were old days of tobacco paper and shreds). I was certainly the first woman to tackle this job in Kew and I believe I am the only one who has helped to fumigate the Temperate House.'[362] During the course of war, Kew was to employ a total of ninety women to replace men who had been called up.

As the war dragged on and conscription was introduced in January 1916 for all men aged 18 to 41, more male gardeners were called up and for the first time the advertising columns in the gardening press began to feature large numbers of job adverts aimed specifically at women gardeners. In a single issue of *Gardeners' Chronicle* in January 1917 the following advertisements appeared:

> Wanted two women for glass department, must have some experience, one to act as Forewoman, good Bothy, Manor Gardens, Little Berkham, Hertford
>
> Wanted two lady gardeners with some experience, chiefly inside. Particulars and wages expected to W. Chaplin, Frognall Gardens, Sunninghill Ascot.
>
> Wanted Good Practical Woman Gardener for the Glass Department, under Forewoman; also one for the Rock Garden

> and Herbaceous Borders, & c., good wages. Bothy and usual perquisites. Arthur Freshwater, Head Gardener, Pains Hill, Cobham, Surrey.[363]

Even so, some employers still managed to make it clear that they saw employing a female gardener as very much a 'second-best' option: 'Gardener – A vacancy occurs for a capable MAN who understands Greenhouse work – a lady gardener would be entertained. T. H. Rose, 6 Rawlinson Road, Oxford.'[364] Some stubbornly refused to entertain employing lady gardeners at all, even at the risk of coming into conflict with the authorities. When conscription was introduced, the expectation was that all able-bodied men would report for military service unless their existing occupation was deemed essential for the war effort. Some determined employers tried to argue that their male gardeners should be declared exempt, but they were generally given short shrift by the authorities and told to try employing women instead. A Dunmow florist complained, 'She [a lady gardener] would want too much money. He paid his man gardener who cultivates flowers and tomatoes 27 shillings a week.' His appeal was overruled.[365] Likewise, at Nantwich in May 1916 the local workhouse asked for an exemption for the man who oversaw work by inmates in the workhouse garden. The Chairman asked, 'Have you tried a lady gardener?'[366]

Often the positions that were becoming available were in precisely the larger, more prestigious gardens – public and private – that had remained stubbornly inaccessible to female gardeners until now. For the first time, large municipal parks opened their doors to women workers. The 'First lady Official Gardener in Bradford' made front-page news in the *Bradford Weekly Telegraph* in 1917: 'The lady gardener has made her appearance in Bradford's parks, the first appointment being at Manningham where Miss Beale has been given charge of the botanical section. This young lady has special qualifications for the position.'[367] Horticultural women who had been a voice in the wilderness for years did little to hide their glee at this change of affairs. Frances Wolseley reported that owners of large private gardens who 'had maintained that men-gardeners alone could do the work and that women were all right as companion gardeners or to do jobbing gardening in seaside towns, but altogether impossible to consider for the supervision of large places, have quickly altered their opinion.'[368] By 1916 the *Gardeners' Chronicle* reported that the United Horticultural Benefit and Provident Society, a medical insurance company, was for the first time considering accepting women members since there were now sufficient numbers of them to make it financially worthwhile.

Not all the new wartime opportunities were for paid work. Many women took it upon themselves to use their own gardens and gardening skills for the war effort. One area of concern was the disruption to the supply of imported medicines and medicinal ingredients caused by the war. The government appealed to civilians to grow medicinal herbs to help fill the gap. Maud Grieve had been running a herb garden called The Whins, at Chalfont St Peter in Buckinghamshire since 1908. She was a member of The Daughters of Ceres, the Studley alumni group set up by Edith Bradley, and she helped set up the National Herb Growing Association which organised the collection and drying of medicinal herbs. Other local initiatives sprang up, mostly organised by women, many of whom saw themselves as part of a long tradition of 'wise women' herbalists. For instance, in Suffolk, women formed a County Association for herb-growing 'with the object of making it a permanent country industry, to discover what herbs grow wild or admit to cultivation in the district, also to obtain spaces on which they can be cultivated'. A kiln for drying was established in Ipswich and reports noted that, 'The lady in charge has qualified herself as to the manner of drying.' Two receiving centres were also set up and 'parties of ladies go on expeditions to seek those plants needed that are in season.'[369]

There were also voluntary gardening roles in the new institutions that sprang up to support men wounded in the war. When war broke out, wealthy property owners offered some of their large houses to be converted into hospitals, staffed by women volunteer nurses. In November 1914 Lord Leverhulme offered Cedar Lawn, an old-fashioned house with extensive grounds in Hampstead, to

Members of the Women's Army Auxiliary Corps tending the graves of fallen British soldiers in a cemetery at Abbeville. Courtesy of the Imperial War Museum.

the War Office for use as an auxiliary hospital. Hilda Leese, who had taken the RHS National Examination in Horticulture in 1898 and since then lived at home in Finchley with her mother, working as a jobbing 'lady gardener', took on the role of volunteer head gardener at the Cedar Lawn Auxiliary Military Hospital from 1915. Wartime had given her the opportunity to take charge of a large garden for the first time. According to the British Red Cross Volunteers' Register for 1914–18 Hilda 'superintended work with excellent results'.[370] The peace and tranquillity of gardens in hospital grounds were recognised as important assets in healing soldiers, damaged in mind and body by war. The patients at Cedar Lawn were encouraged to play cricket and other sports and generally spend time outdoors in the gardens. Hilda was far from alone in managing this type of therapeutic garden. In November 1915 the 'Lady Gardener at Summerdown Convalescent Camp Eastbourne' made an appeal for 'cartloads of plants – wallflowers, forget-me-nots, alyssum and all kinds of seedlings, plants and shrubs' to brighten 'the hut gardens of

3,000 wounded Tommies.'[371] A sadder volunteering role was carried out by twenty young women gardeners in 1917. Following a brief period of training at Kew, they were sent to France to tend military cemeteries. A further contingent was sent to cemeteries in Belgium by the Women's Army Auxiliary Corps.

Gardening at scale in wartime brought special challenges. Imports of plants and seeds from the Continent were of course interrupted and there was a great deal of concern in the gardening press for the fate of the French and Belgian horticultural industries. The Army had requisitioned horses and the very shortage of labour that opened up opportunities for women also made gardens harder to manage and run well. Inevitably, many large ornamental gardens suffered. Even the more naturalistic 'wild gardens', made up of hardy perennials that were fashionable in the years immediately before the war, were hardly low maintenance. If a large garden also had formal borders designed to take tender bedding, large lawns, many glasshouses and a well-stocked kitchen garden, the workload was considerable. Many women who took charge of gardens, or departments in large gardens, found they had depleted staff to work with, consisting of inexperienced women, old men or young boys. Even Gertrude Cope, who had always had female assistants at Northfield, was affected. As Quaker pacifists, Gertrude Cope's employers' response to the war was to concentrate on reducing suffering. George and Elizabeth Cadbury continued to hold large parties in the garden for deprived children. Every summer throughout the war the garden played host to parties of hundreds of children such as the 'Birmingham Slum Children's Treat' on June 23, 1916, at which a thousand children enjoyed tea and games. However, quite early on in the war, Gertrude Cope found that she would have to manage with fewer staff to maintain the garden. In June 1915 her assistant, Marjorie Merryweather, left to answer the call from Kew for replacement gardeners. Marjorie, a descendent of Henry Merryweather, the nurseryman who propagated and popularised the Bramley apple, had worked with Gertrude Cope at Northfield since graduating from Swanley in 1913. She did well at Kew, eventually becoming a deputy in the alpine yard. It is not clear whether Gertrude managed to replace her.

In 1916 the RHS issued a special pamphlet titled 'Economy in the Garden' to advise gardeners how to adapt to the realities of running a garden in wartime. In it they warned garden owners that, 'Supplies even of unskilled labour are difficult to obtain and the number of women able and willing to undertake garden work is insufficient to meet demand.'[372] This is borne out by the fact that when the Board of Trade set up a special register for women to nominate themselves for war work, of the 33,000 women who had registered by April 1915, only 500 put gardening as their preferred occupation. Frances Wolseley felt that the large garden owners only had themselves to blame. 'If only those many hundred owners of large gardens who have recently been writing pitiful letters to Horticultural Colleges, asking to be supplied with women gardeners to take the place of men who are enlisting, had in past years evinced some interest in the profession of a woman gardener, their wants could now have been readily supplied.'[373]

The shortage of well-qualified female gardeners was exacerbated by the fact that many horticulturally trained women did not choose to take up gardening posts when war came. Ada May Cassidy, the head of the group of three female gardeners who looked after the gardens at Bignor Park in Sussex, supported the war effort but in a clerical rather than horticultural capacity, becoming a volunteer clerk at the Star and Garter Home for Disabled Soldiers and Sailors in Richmond. Likewise, Irene M. Dodgshun, who had made a living as a jobbing gardener at various places after leaving Studley in 1911, volunteered for the YMCA in the war, running canteens for soldiers, munitions workers and their families. In 1919 she was awarded the Women's Service distinguished conduct medal for long service in YMCA work. Frances Wolseley felt many women decided to volunteer in this way because they felt that this type of work had 'the glamour of real warfare, a feeling of being closer to the fighting lines' than working in a garden, even if doing so freed a man to fight.[374]

As the nation began to worry about wartime food shortages,

women with horticultural and agricultural skills may have seen working in food production as a higher priority than gardening. Whilst only 500 women on the Board of Trade Register offered to work as gardeners, 1,700 nominated dairy work and 2,000 specified agricultural work. Even at the very beginning of the war, when people were expecting it to 'be all over by Christmas', there were already concerns about food supply. Just a few weeks after war was declared, Edith Chamberlain wrote in *Common Cause*, 'All ordinary trading is disorganised and many sources of supply will be altered … It is thought by commercial men that even if the war ends quite soon, it would be two years before the sugar supply regained normal conditions.' Her advice to women smallholders was to breed more chickens. 'Not only shall we need chicks, but if France and Belgium are at peace by spring, they will want eggs or young birds to make good their losses.' She also recommended planting trees on wasteland to replace those used in the war and plant willows for basket-making, as 'soon there will be a larger demand since we have imported so many of our lighter makes of basket from Germany.'[375] It was rapidly apparent, however, that the rural war effort needed to go beyond chicken-breeding and basket-making. Despite the best efforts of proponents of rural reform such as Edith Bradley and Lady Warwick, in 1914 Britain was heavily dependent on food imports and British agriculture was in a weakened state following decades of low investment and depression. From 1915 onwards, concerns about the German submarine campaign and threats to British shipping and supply lines meant farms needed to radically increase production if food shortages were to be avoided. Studies have shown that 240–270,000 men left agriculture during the war.[376] In these circumstances, it seemed obvious to many women that they should apply their skills and efforts to help feed the nation.

Initially, the Liberal government took a very hands-off approach, leaving it to local organisers and voluntary agencies to try to meet labour shortages. This lack of action in mobilising women caused a great deal of frustration. In January 1915, in an article headed 'A Chance for the Outdoor Woman' the *Common Cause* noted:

> The Report issued by the Board of Trade on the state of unemployment in December points out that there is likely to be a difficulty in getting the necessary agricultural work done in the spring, even in districts where there is sufficient labour for winter needs. Already shortage of labour is marked in the Wold district of Yorkshire, and in the Home Counties in the case of milkers and market gardeners. Yet no appeal is made by the Government to the women of England. When will our own Government begin to realise that the women of the nation can be an asset, not a burden? When will they cease to regard them as mere 'dependants', and make full use of them? Frenchwomen may at present be more efficient for they are more accustomed to work side by side with their menfolk in commerce and agriculture, and to take responsibility – but if Englishwomen were trained and encouraged, instead of being made to feel themselves a drag upon the State, they could do as good work as the women of any Continental nation. This should be the chance of the outdoor, athletic girl, of whose splendid physique little or no use is being made.[377]

Edith Bradley naturally joined the call for a more coordinated approach. On April 6, 1915, she wrote to the editor of *The Kent Messenger and Gravesend Telegraph* to outline her plan for mobilising women's labour on the land:

> The Board of Trade admits that in seeking the assistance of women, it has reached the rock bottom of its resources. Therefore it surely CANNOT BE that the women of England will fail to rise to this opportunity for patriotic endeavour when women are solving the agricultural problem in Russia, Belgium, France and Germany. I am convinced that it is only lack of organisation which stands in our way.

She then enumerated the elements of her scheme:

> a) Trained women agriculturists.
>
> b) A centre or centres for training in each county.
>
> c) Registers of employers and employees.
>
> d) The cooperation and assistance of the Board of Agriculture, of Educational Committees, of the County Councils, of the Dairy Farmers Association and the Farmers Union.

e) County and District Committees composed of influential men and women who will make it their business to collect and give information relating to all matters likely to hasten forward this work on successful lines.

f) A keen and energetic Organising Secretary, with the whole-hearted interest in the movement, able to organise and address meetings and conduct the work on thorough business lines.

There can be few prizes for guessing that Edith Bradley had herself in mind when she was describing the ideal Organising Secretary. She ended her letter 'My personal assistance I shall be glad to offer if it is required.'[378]

Edith Bradley's plea for co-ordination, while an amplification of what she had been saying for years, was not unwarranted. For the first two years of the war, co-ordination was in short supply. At the beginning of the war, Edith had high hopes that the Guild of the Daughters of Ceres, the alumni organisation for old students of Lady Warwick Hostel and Studley that she created in 1901, might have a key co-ordinating role. In 1910, as part of her proposals for better co-ordination in the profession, she had tried to expand its membership to encompass all female horticulturists and agriculturists, regardless of where they had trained. However, her hopes that The Daughters of Ceres would become a vibrant, self-supporting membership group never came to pass. In a letter to Dr Hamilton in 1915 she wrote, 'How deeply I regret that the comprehensive scheme I organised seventeen years ago for Women engaged in Agriculture is not in full working now. What a chance, a golden chance for Women it would have been.'[379]

Yet it was not only Edith who encountered barriers to the establishment of a coordinated system to place trained women on farms. William Palmer, 2nd Earl of Selborne and President of the Board of Agriculture and Fisheries, was tasked with overseeing the country's food supplies. In Autumn 1915 War Agricultural Committees were formed in each county in an attempt to increase food production. Working with the Board of Trade, Lord Selborne also set up Women's County Agricultural Committees to try to recruit and register volunteer women workers. Like Edith, he had envisaged a national campaign to recruit, train and place these women but this never materialised under the laissez-faire Asquith government and, although the Women's County Agricultural Committees worked hard, without a central approach to training and placements, they were not well placed to overcome reluctance on the part of many farmers and War Agricultural Committees to employ women. A plethora of voluntary organisations attempted to step in to fill this void. The Women's Defence Relief Corps, founded in September 1914, at its peak managed to place five hundred women (mostly from London) on farms. The Women's Legion was formed in December 1914 and set up an Agricultural Section which received an annual grant from the Board of Agriculture, but this was later withdrawn, as the Legion was not that effective at recruiting and training women. The same fate befell the Land Council set up by the National Political League. This organisation was run by suffragette Mary Adelaide Broadhurst and for a time ran eleven training centres to prepare women for work on farms, but it also was assessed to be ineffective by the Board of Agriculture. The Women's Farm and Garden Union (WFGU), the organisation originally known as the Women's Agricultural and Horticultural International Union, was more successful in gaining official backing. In February 1916 the WFGU sent a deputation to meet with Lord Selborne and managed to persuade him to give them a grant of £150 to organise training for women farm workers. This was done under the auspices of a new offshoot of the WFGU called the Women's National Land Service Corps under the direction of Mrs Louisa Wilkins. They launched an experimental twelve-week practical course for women to introduce them to farm work and by September of that year nearly eight hundred women had been trained.

The National Land Service Corps, led as it was by longstanding proponents of horticultural training for women, had its eyes firmly set on recruiting and training educated middle-class women. This approach was partly an automatic continuation of their pre-war efforts to train 'lady' gardeners and farmers. It was also because there was an assumption that mobilising and training 'educated women' to act as leaders and trendsetters in farming would be the most effective way of increasing food production. There remained a real and enduring tendency to dismiss the rural working-class women already engaged in agriculture, or to assume that they would only be useful if led and supervised by a woman with formal training and qualifications. Despite this confidence in the value of 'educated women', the response of British farmers was very reminiscent of that of Canadian farmers to lady settlers before the war. In October 1915 Edith Chamberlain, in an interview in *Common Cause*, admitted that there was a mismatch between the type of female volunteers that they were recruiting and the demands made by farmers: 'A large number of demands have come into the Farm and Garden Union for women of the servant class, who would help in the house as well as outside, or for widows with sons of 15 or so. The volunteers on the other hand were for the most part of quite a different class and had different views of what they wanted to do. Hence many of the demands could not be met on either side.'[380]

Nevertheless, the WFGU persisted with its approach and when it launched the Women's National Land Service Corps in February 1916, it announced that it wanted 'only such workers as are capable of making a good impression' and that the women it trained would be 'organisers of village women'.[381] The longstanding assumption was that working-class girls in rural areas had turned their back on traditional agricultural occupations and required the example of their social betters to make them see that manual work was not beneath them. In a letter to *The Times*, Louisa Wilkins, a leading light in the WFGU, wrote, 'One educated woman, by her mere example and encouragement and powers of organisation, has been the means of making available 20 village women at the same time as herself doing farm work ... We want 2,000 women, not merely to work for 2,000 farmers but to be the means of making available the labour of 40,000 village women.'[382]

As the WFGU had been around for many years, and many key figures in women's horticulture and agriculture were already members, the Women's National Land Corps got strong backing from women in the profession. Madeline Agar became Honorary Treasurer and was involved in raising money to pay accommodation expenses for women attending training courses organised on farms in Essex and Northamptonshire. Fanny Wilkinson was also heavily involved, along with a number of other Swanley alumni. Even though the Corps was associated with Swanley, Lillias Hamilton, despite having reservations, decided to give it Studley College backing and urged Edith Bradley to do likewise. 'I do not approve of all Swanley does,' she wrote, 'I dare say you do not approve of all I do, but if we stuck together like a bundle of sticks, we could make more progress.'[383]

But Edith Bradley, despite her complaints about others' lack of willingness to join forces in a coordinated way, did not budge. Instead, she remained outside this new venture and concentrated on working at a local level as a volunteer for West Kent Women's County Agricultural Committee. On their behalf she sent out leaflets and letters to the female residents of the 23 villages in the Hollingbourne rural district, near her home at Greenway Court. The tone of the letter that she wrote, headed 'War Work, Women and Agriculture' on December 27, 1915, gives a sense of the almost desperate desire felt by Edith and many other women to be active and useful in this time of national need.

> Dear Mrs —
>
> May I ask you to read the enclosed official Leaflets? They relate to the all-important question of our FOOD SUPPLY. All women living in the Country are asked to help. We have been called the SECOND LINE OF DEFENCE. By ORGANISATION we can justify this title. Lord Selborne outlines the plan of the Organisation, as you will see. It is left to the Women of every Country and in every Rural District to draw up their plan of campaign. I have been requested to represent the District of Hollingbourne with its 23 villages. I have to find a Registrar for each village, and to mobilise the entire District, during the first month of the New Year. As personal acquaintance is most essential, it seems advisable to hold Meetings to discuss plans

> in four at least of the Villages and I suggest Ulcombe or Sutton, Lenham, Detling and Hollingbourne.
>
> Mrs Deakin, The Manor House, Hollingbourne, has kindly promised the use of her Drawing Room early in January. The Date will be announced in *The Kent Messenger*. Residents from any of the Villages will be most welcome, and are indeed urged to attend, especially those from Hollingbourne, Harrietsham, Broomfield, Leeds and Langley.
>
> Suggestions, and the offer of Rooms at Ulcombe, or Sutton, Lenham and Detling will be gratefully received by me. The Morning (about 11 o'clock) would be, I think, the most convenient hour. Personal interest and willing help must be the key-note of the movement because the Call has come to EVERY Woman, rich or poor, gentle or peasant, strong or weak, to do something, and to do it NOW.[384]

Just reading about all these leaflets, letters and drawing-room meetings is exhausting. In February 1916 Edith Bradley became even busier when she was appointed by the Board of Trade as Agricultural Organising Officer for Kent, Surrey and Sussex to help deliver Lord Selborne's scheme for placing women on the land. She embarked on a whirlwind round of lectures and meetings trying to drum up interest among both women and farmers across the three counties. At a meeting in Sutton Valence, she 'earnestly appealed to the patriotism of all present to make this work a great national success. The help and assistance of all classes working together for the common good was needed, and for everyone in the great field of agriculture there was a place. Only by organisation could the women of England earn the proud title of our second line of defence.'[385]

Despite her energy and drive, her efforts were not always appreciated or welcomed by local farmers. At a meeting held at Session House in Maidstone in May 1916, her ideas for recruiting and training women from Maidstone to work on farms was rebuffed by local farmers. One farmer, Bernard Champion, claimed, 'Farmers were getting more or less good work out of the women and they asked the Committee to leave them alone ... Mr Champion went on to deprecate systemised training, saying the only training the ladies needed would be obtained in their own gardens by carrying water and digging because farmers wanted women with muscles and back; then they would train them as the work shifted from fortnight to fortnight.' He was concerned that trained women would 'probably ask for more pay than the ordinary workers. At the same time, he could hardly conceive well-bred women roughing it on a farm, unless four or half a dozen managed to secure a cottage.' Another farmer, Percy Cox, suggested that Edith Bradley and her volunteers had been 'canvassing the wrong class of people, and thought if ladies would go out in parties where their help was urgently needed, possibly the Village Hall could be obtained for their accommodation.'[386] It seemed the farmers of West Kent were only interested in cheap labour they could call on at short notice as needed and not, as Edith Bradley hoped, in integrating trained women into their farm's workforce. Many farmers believed that the educated middle-class women Edith was suggesting as labour were more trouble than they were worth. Farmers were also clearly worried that the more women they took on, the more likely it was that the government would feel free to draft more male farm labourers into the military. Undeterred, four months later Edith Bradley went above the heads of the West Kent farmers and attended a meeting of the Kent branch of the National Farmers Union. There she made the case, 'In Sussex there was a desire that there should be an arrangement for training but in West Kent a different view prevailed.' She proposed that the three counties of Sussex, Surrey and Kent should work together and after a show of hands in the meeting 'the majority of members declared themselves in favour of training.'[387]

The question was where could women go for training? The existing colleges and schools did their best to meet the demand but, without government subsidy, they were dependent on students paying for their own training. Many women did pay and the demand for places at gardening schools and colleges increased. Elmwood School of Gardening near Cosham in Hampshire had been established as a small private gardening school by Ruth Cornelius Wheeler, an early student at the Lady Warwick Hostel. For more than a decade the school had accommodated around ten to fifteen students a year, supplementing its income by providing hampers of fruit and vegetables to local private customers. By 1916 demand for training places was so high that the school expanded and moved to Aldersey Hall in Cheshire, offering a broader range of courses geared around food production. J. S. Turner's school at Arlesey experienced a similar uptick in demand. In 1915 she moved her school from Arlesey House to a much larger property near Iver in Buckinghamshire. Huntsmoor Park was a large house set in 96 acres of parkland. J. S. Turner and Dorothea Kitson rented 46 acres of the estate, with hopes of raising enough money to eventually buy the whole estate. The land rented included glasshouses and space to raise cows, pigs and bees. In December 1915 they told *The Daily Telegraph* that they were 'hoping that some large-hearted person would help them to more scholarships for girls that want such assistance.'[388] In contrast Studley College struggled through the war. Dr Lillias Hamilton had been a medic before taking over as Principal at Studley in 1908. When war broke out, she felt compelled to return to medicine and served in a typhoid hospital in Montenegro from 1915 to 1918, leaving the college in the care of her sister. Although the college had been in receipt of a small annual grant from the Board of Agriculture since 1912, this was not enough to cover the gap in the college finances and the grounds deteriorated in condition during the war.

In her book, *A Woman and the War*, Lady Warwick complained that the public 'demands the impossible', expecting 'the girls' agricultural colleges to improvise the highly trained skilled article.' She declared 'in view of the growing demand for the work of women's hands the Government should make grants to the established colleges as they make grants to other educational bodies.'[389] Although small grants were given to individual colleges, regular funding was not forthcoming. Studley reached out to the RHS for support, asking if they would have a representative on their college council but the RHS decided against this, claiming it would 'create an undesirable precedent'.[390] Frances Wolseley's school at Glynde was also rejected. In August 1914, just a week after war was declared, Frances Wolseley

Student group at Glynde School for Lady Gardeners in 1916. Courtesy of the RHS Lindley Collections.

wrote to the RHS President, Lord Grenfell, to ask if the Society could 'in any way help or support her appeal for help towards her School of Horticulture for Women.' Her appeal was also rejected by the RHS Council, for 'if they were to consent to it in one case, they would be morally bound to do the same for all the similar schools, of which there are a good many scattered across the country.'[391]

The attitude of the RHS School of Horticulture based at Wisley shows the establishment's reluctance to endorse training for women most clearly. In October 1916, just over two years after the war had begun, during which time the number of students at Wisley had nose-dived as young men joined up, the question of admitting women to the RHS School was raised by the National Political League and Professor Hartog of the University of London. Dr Hartog was involved in setting up a degree in Horticulture to be awarded by the University of London and he wrote to Frederick Keeble, the Director of the Gardens at Wisley, to suggest that

Wisley should accept women students. Keeble replied in a lengthy letter that 'to make provision for women students at Wisley at the present time would be to affect very gravely the prospects of Wisley as a place of training for practical gardening.' His argument was that even horticultural training for men was still viewed with scepticism amongst 'large growers' in the trade, who doubted its quality and practical application. 'To throw Wisley open to women students at the moment when we are endeavouring to destroy this adverse opinion of the large growers would result in increasing instead of weakening the belief that such schools of horticulture are not the places to which to send their sons. For these men know that it is only in exceptional cases that women can follow with success the arduous practice of horticulture.' He went on to argue that women had their own schools and that Wisley did not have a hostel. Wisley students lived in lodgings in the village, which apparently was not a respectable option for single women, who needed the additional security of dedicated accommodation with a warden. According to Keeble, if the RHS were to build a hostel, it should be for male students; to prioritise women would be 'grossly unjust since in my own opinion and that of most horticulturists, though it is important to provide horticultural instruction for women, it is more important to provide it for men.'[392] The RHS Council endorsed Mr Keeble's opinions, stating at its meeting on October 24, 1916, that it was 'committed to a programme of horticultural instruction for men, and until that is carried out, the present is not an opportune time for extending the Society's work in the direction suggested.'[393] As it turned out, no 'opportune time' was to occur for another 58 years. Women were not admitted to study at Wisley on the same footing as men until 1974 and the passing of the Equalities Act. The depressing thing about this exchange was that even in wartime, the men at the top of British horticulture could not bring themselves to allow the daily evidence of women taking on large gardens and horticultural businesses to dismantle the brick wall of their prejudices.

The combination of lack of official support, lack of coordination between the various voluntary organisations and widespread scepticism from farmers hampered efforts to bring trained women onto farms in sufficient numbers. By the end of 1916 it was apparent that the current arrangements were simply insufficient. There was deadlock on the Western Front, more and more men were conscripted and the German U-boat blockade on merchant shipping was posing a real threat to food supplies. With rising food prices and shortages on the horizon, the government became seriously worried about the prospect of social unrest. In December 1916 David Lloyd George became Prime Minister, determined to bring a more centralised and concerted approach to the war effort and he appointed Roland Protheroe as President of the Board of Agriculture. Protheroe established a new department for Food Production with a special Women's Branch staffed entirely by women under the direction of Meriel Talbot. She was a prominent figure in the WFGU, a supporter of women smallholders and Secretary to the Victoria League, which had promoted women emigrating to farm in British colonies. She was a no-nonsense energetic organiser, known to her friends as 'Slasher' Talbot in honour of her batting style on the cricket field. In March 1917 Meriel Talbot announced the creation of the Women's Land Army. Paid women officers were established in every county and training centres at existing colleges and farm institutes were established to deliver special four-week courses. Well-qualified horticultural and agricultural instructors were recruited, and the government was able to draw on the services of the experienced women who had been trained up by the independent female colleges and schools before the war. For instance, Dr Winifred Brenchley, an expert in weed ecology, gave lectures on 'Our Enemy the Weed' to members of the Women's Land Army. Winifred Brenchley had studied horticulture at Swanley from 1901 to 1903, winning the RHS Silver Gilt medal for the highest marks in its examination. After leaving Swanley, she studied Botany at University College London and then won a scholarship to research at Rothampsted, the first woman scientist in the country to work at an agricultural research institute. With this system in place, volunteers, who became known as Land Girls, could be registered, trained and placed in farms, market gardens and forestry estates. Many of the Land Girls were women who had previously volunteered with the WFGU's National Land Service Corps and other existing schemes. Altogether, by the end of the war, it was estimated that 29,000 women had served in the Women's Land Army. This was still a tiny fraction of the estimated 300,000 women who worked in one way or another in food production during the war, most of them the unsung 'village women' already living and working in rural areas who often fitted agricultural work around childcare. Nevertheless, although relatively small in number, the Land Girls did successfully undertake work that was not traditionally seen as women's work and made a significant contribution to the continuity of food production.

The Women's Land Army was also immensely successful as a propaganda measure, drumming up public support for female agricultural workers who now became seen as heroines rather than busybody nuisances to farmers. Uniforms made the female agricultural workers visible and gave them status as an official part of the national war effort. Regular rallies and marches were organised in large towns up and down the country. Land Girls would parade and attend award ceremonies in which local dignitaries handed out awards and certificates. These recruiting events were often focused on urban areas, particularly London. One report remarked, 'There is nothing the recruiters have not dared. They stop girls at railway stations and eating houses, they board buses, they raid queues, they dart on likely looking victims in the shopping centres.'[394] The Women's Land Army even had its own newspaper, *The Landswoman*, which was full of rousing propaganda. In May 1918 the paper announced that 30,000 women would be needed that summer at harvest time. Under the headline 'Save the Harvest' it trumpeted, 'It is up to the women of England to show the Germans that there is such stuff in this nation that not all the guile and cunning of their statesmen, not all the atrocities of their soldiers, and not all the ruthlessness of their Gothas and U-boats can hope to bring us to our knees. Thirty thousand women can save us!'[395]

Although it was the Land Army that grabbed the headlines,

women were also heavily involved in boosting food production in domestic gardens. In its letter to its members in the first days of the war, the RHS had noted that 'garden produce may in the winter and early spring become of inestimable value' and recommended that members ensure that 'no waste is incurred and that all Fruits and Vegetables not required for the household are stored or preserved for the use of their less fortunate neighbours.'[396] As war progressed and food shortages loomed, avoiding waste was not enough; it was determined that every effort should be made to increase domestic food production wherever possible. Nurseries and seedsmen switched from supplying flower seeds to vegetables. The Department for Food Production supported domestic gardeners and allotment holders to grow more food to reduce reliance on imported food supplies. Women gardeners were a key target and the Department relied heavily on female volunteers and paid organisers across the country. The Board of Agriculture, too, appointed women for the first time to act as Agricultural Organisers who supervised female horticultural inspectors and instructors. Bertha La Mothe, Edith Bradley's old colleague from Studley College and co-author with her of *The Lighter Branches of Agriculture*, was appointed as a Chief Woman Agricultural Organiser with the Department for Food Production. Horticultural inspectors monitored the work of farm institutes and supported them in setting up and promoting model allotments. These model allotments were used to pass on the latest techniques to professional growers, domestic gardeners and allotment holders. Horticultural instructors also gave short talks to allotment and horticultural society meetings and evening classes. One example was Edna Gunnel, who studied at Lady Warwick Hostel from 1898 to 1900 and then joined Kew as gardener apprentice. After leaving Kew, she worked as a horticultural tutor at various horticultural schools in Germany – she had to escape across the border on returning troop trains when war broke out. After a short period teaching at Swanley, she became a Horticultural Inspector for Devon County Council, based at a farm institute in Exeter.

This was the area of the war effort that Edith Bradley became involved in rather than the Land Army. In May 1917 she accepted the post of Horticultural Representative (or Inspector) for the districts of Maidstone and Hollingbourne, under the Horticultural Section of the Department for Food Production. She tackled this role with her usual boundless energy, the good people of Maidstone and Hollingbourne being subject to a stream of lantern-slide lectures and potato-spraying demonstrations. One area where she was particularly well qualified to lead was food preservation. Her days running the jam-making workshop at Studley were recalled and she set up a jam factory at her farm, Greenway Court. She collected fruit from local gardens and transported them in her motor car back to the jam works, set up in a 'delightful little old-world cottage adjoining the Court'. The jam-making year began in July with strawberries and ended in October with marrow jam. In 1918 the local paper reported that 'with the aid of two village women who worked like Trojans, always willingly and well, Miss Bradley has been responsible for 17,000 lbs of jam, made solely of sugar and fruit and placed mostly in 2lbs pots supplied by the Registers of the 14 villages which are sharing in the distribution.'[397] Although it is now overshadowed by the 'Dig for Victory' campaign of the Second World War, this drive to grow and preserve food did capture the public imagination. Allotment-keeping became a craze and in 1917 local authorities were given powers to seize vacant land to convert into allotments. The Archbishop of Canterbury lent his weight to the campaign by announcing that it was not a sin to work on an allotment on a Sunday. Even the women who gardened all week at Kew wanted to do their bit. They agitated with the Kew management to be given land to work as allotments in their spare time. Each woman was given 5 rods of land on a plot near the garden's Pathology Department, on condition that they grew potatoes in one half of it that could be used in experiments by the Department.

The net result was that, whether you lived in the town or in the countryside, women were to be seen growing, tending crops in fields and gardens in a hands-on way. Even as early as 1916, the suffragette Emmeline Pethwick-Lawrence felt able to claim that 'a modern revolution' was underway. In *Votes for Women*, she wrote, 'Today it must be apparent to all whose eyes are open that we are living in the midst of a revolution.' Whilst she made mention of the women and girls 'who hasten to turn the great wheels of industry', her main focus was on female growers: 'Girls are depicted in tunic, knickerbockers and gaiters, engaged in the management and stabling of horses, or in digging, planting, market gardening, hoeing turnips, ploughing the furrows, loading carts for the harvest or even spreading manure over the fields and nobody has a word of criticism or disapproval to speak.' This was not a superficial point; Emmeline Pethwick-Lawrence argued that, 'The acceptance by the mass mind of the revolution in woman's dress means a complete revolution in thought about women's position and function in the community.' The earlier efforts of the women's movement had, she acknowledged, played a part, but really it was the war which had changed things. 'The eyes of the great mass of people in this country are opened by war experience as no appeal to mere reason could have opened them,' she wrote. 'They see for themselves the absurdity of the idea of dividing the community of adult human beings into two sections determined by the accident of sex – the male half essential to the nation, the female half accessory.' But this would not have been the case 'if women had been devoid of public spirit, lacking in efficiency, incapable of sustained effort, deficient in organising ability or insusceptible to organisation.'[398] The training and experience gained by pioneering women in the run-up to the war was the essential foundation that had enabled women to take the opportunity.

The conviction that strong, independent and capable women were a key part of the nation's success in the war was echoed by prominent public figures such as the industrialist and philanthropist Lord Leverhulme. In 1918 he was interviewed in *The Landswomen* and said, 'Think of what our women have done in the war! They are not the dull household chattels you find in Germany. They are emancipated women inured to discipline, conscious of their rights, inclined to regard life as a great adventure, full of good spirits and light-heartedness.'[399] This enthusiasm also spread to the mainstream press and media. Manufacturers jumped on the bandwagon with adverts aimed at the practical, outdoors working woman for everything from boots to hand cream, to clothing. Unlike the 1890s when practical garden clothing caused such a stir, now journalists were full of praise for utilitarian and even masculine clothes for women. The fashion correspondent of *The Clifton Society* criticised a white-and-red-ribbon-trimmed gardener's smock on sale in the shops because 'nothing less practical could possibly be imagined … the present day has little use for the type of girl who looks like an illustration in the old nursery rhyme of "Mary, Mary quite contrary" – she must be willing as an enthusiastic lady gardener to look like "nothing on earth".'[400] The article went on to praise a plain blue overall which could be the 'inseparable companion' of a female gardener.

When troops from the United States eventually started to arrive on the Western Front and victory seemed possible, thoughts began to turn to the future. The longstanding proponents of women gardeners and farmers hoped that women could capitalise on the progress made in the war. In 1916 Frances Wolseley had written, 'The world now looks to women to do work for the nation whilst men are away fighting: but when the war is at an end they still will have to remain at their posts, for fewer men will be there, and more work will have to be done.'[401] In 1918 there was much talk of social renewal, of making a new and better world in peacetime. Could that mean a world where women gardeners would be wanted and needed as fellow workers for a brighter future?

12

AT THE END OF THE DAY

In the spring, at the end of the day,
you should smell like dirt.

Margaret Attwood, *Bluebeard's Egg*, 1982

In one respect, at least, peacetime did herald a new world for women. The war highlighted the economic and strategic value of women's work to such an extent that political and public opinion shifted strongly in favour of extending the franchise to women. The extension was only partial; although young single women made up most of the wartime workforce, the vote was only offered to older women who could be relied on to use the vote in a 'mature' way. The Representation of the People Act 1918 gave the vote to women over the age of 30 who met a property qualification, or whose husband did. The same act extended the vote to all men over 21, whether they owned property or not. Still, it was real progress and once the principle was established, the gradual extension of the franchise regardless of gender became inevitable. Meanwhile in the world of horticulture, it seemed reasonable that women growers might also expect their contribution in the war years to be rewarded by more acceptance in the profession. After all, women had risen to the challenge, taking on work that many had stubbornly denied they were capable of. The reality was to fall short of these hopes, however, and within a decade it appeared that, in the garden at least, the status of women had failed to progress from the early 1900s when girl gardeners first donned knickerbockers at Kew Gardens.

At first peace brought with it a hopeful determination that the very fabric of the nation's life must be rewoven after four years of sacrifice and hardship. Only a new world built out of the ashes of the old could justify the bloodshed of the war years. A revitalised rural economy was part of this optimistic vision of the future, delivering a healthier population, a more sustainable food supply and a more egalitarian society. The old arguments for modernisation and diversification of the rural economy with greater openings for women were dusted down and brought out again. During the war, Lady Warwick saw an explicit link between a food system based on imports and the martial, defensive focus of nation states – an attitude that only made wars more likely. In her book *A Woman and the War* she wrote, 'At present we only produce about 20 per cent of the food we eat. For the rest, we depend upon our mercantile marine and our power to hold not only the seas, but the skies above.'[402] Once more she made the case for rural regeneration based on cooperative smallholdings, run by well-trained women.

Creating smallholdings for women was not top of the list for mainstream politicians, however, who were much more focused on the immediate needs of the hundreds of thousands of men waiting to be demobilised. There were real fears that unless ex-servicemen were provided with decent jobs and housing, they could be drawn towards radical and revolutionary movements. The threat of Bolshevism was taken very seriously, and this spurred both the government and the national press to urge women to leave the workplace to make space for men returning from the war. Women in the Land Army continued to work until August 1919 while men were demobbed, but then were expected to leave. The most that the Women's Land Army recruits were offered were scholarships in a Free Passage programme to enable emigration, a clear message that the government saw no place for them in the British countryside. It appeared that, instead of being seen as a demonstration of women's new capabilities, the widespread sight of women working the land in wartime was read by many as a sign of the abnormality of the times, an aberration that should be abandoned when peace returned. Newspapers that had described the Women's Land Army as 'our gallant girls' now urged that it was their patriotic duty to down tools and return to their domestic duties. By and large, this is exactly what happened, though there were some isolated exceptions. Eve Balfour, niece of the Conservative Prime Minister Arthur Balfour, worked with the Women's Land Army on a small farm in Monmouthshire. She stayed on the land after the war, renting her own farm whilst finding time to learn to fly and write detective novels. More significantly, she ran experiments in organic farming, publishing the results in 1943 in a book called *The Living Soil*, one of the classic early works on organic growing. She went on to become one of the founding members of the Soil Association. Any officially sponsored efforts to create smallholdings, however, were exclusively designed for ex-servicemen, not 'de-mobbed' Land Girls. The Land Settlement (Facilities) Act of 1919 empowered county councils to purchase and lease land for the provision of smallholdings with financial support from central government, but these were only offered to ex-servicemen. For instance, Surrey provided smallholdings for 257 ex-servicemen and their families between 1919 and 1926.

Even in the middle of the war, many women gardeners had realised that the male establishment was likely to forget them once they had served their purpose. Frances Wolseley had urged, 'We have to look ahead to realise that, when the war is terminated, many soldiers will return to the posts they held before the war, and that those women who have done their working during these months of fighting should be given every facility for continuing in the profession that they entered, for their country's sake, at a time of crisis.'[403] During the war, the Women's Farm and Garden Association (WFGA) had also begun thinking about ways to support the women who had answered the call to farm the land once peace returned. In November 1917 the Council of the WFGA decided that a cooperative community for women smallholders would be a key post-war project. In 1921 it set up a 'Smallholding Colony for Women' on a 91-acre estate called Wire Mill Lane near Lingfield in Surrey. The £10,000 needed to purchase the estate was lent by two wealthy suffragists,

Miss Margaret Ashton of Manchester and Miss Renee Courtauld, cousin of WFGA founder and Essex farmer, Katherine Courtauld. Prospective tenants were expected to have agricultural expertise and a private income of not less than £25. This reflected both the WFGA's longstanding focus on middle-class women growers and a realistic assessment that income would be needed as a buffer against poor harvests. It was also an acknowledgement of the fact that single-women smallholders, unlike their married male counterparts, could not rely on the free labour of a wife and children. The estate was split into thirteen smallholdings and tenants included Miss Wake Walker, an ex-Women's Land Corps volunteer, and Miss Miller who had trained in horticulture at the University of Reading. However, a combination of high tenant turnover, high costs to refurbish accommodation, drought and failing agricultural prices meant that the colony never prospered. As a charity, the WFGA could not subsidise the scheme indefinitely and by April 1929, the Council was forced to agree to sell the estate and wind up the project.

Other initiatives for women farmers met with a similar fate. In 1912 a company called the Women Cooperative Farmers Ltd had been set up by the radical Liberal MP Richard Denman to buy 200 acres of land at Heathfield in Sussex, with a view to renting part of it to women smallholders. The set-up was very much along the lines envisaged by Edith Bradley: a total of eight smallholdings were created with bungalows, outbuildings and glasshouses and the idea was that the cooperative would rent out equipment and market the produce grown by the tenants. The organisers declared their aim was 'to bring uncultivated land into cultivation, to allow women with small capital to become productive smallholders, and to give women wishing to take up agriculture a sound practical training. The system working at Heathfield enables the smallholder to have expert help in the stocking of her farm, buying her seeds, selling her produce, and scientific advice in the dressing of her soil; it enables her to secure labour for a short period, and to hire the implements needed.'[404] The scheme managed to survive the war years by training women from the Women's Land Corps. But by 1919 it was clear that, despite frequent appeals and meetings, the scheme could not attract enough shareholders to invest in the scheme and the company was wound up and the land sold off.

The picture was no easier when it came to women seeking employment in private or public gardens. Again, the expectation was that women would surrender the posts they had filled when male gardeners returned from the war. The truth was, times were tough for both male and female gardeners as the owners of the great country-house gardens had to make cutbacks. Wartime had disrupted the social life of the upper classes, forcing the closure of country houses and London homes, some of which had been put to use as hospitals and convalescent homes. After 1918 it proved impossible to restore many to their former condition. Experienced staff were laid off, and houses and gardens went into decline. Many aristocratic families had neither the money nor inclination to maintain their properties the way they had done in Edwardian times; elaborate ornamental gardens or large kitchen gardens were expensive and labour-intensive. The enormous national debt built up during the war forced the government to raise income tax and death duties. Add to this the drop in land values and agricultural rent income and many landowners decided to abandon their country seats entirely. Between 1920 and 1938 over one hundred country houses were demolished by owners who could no longer afford to keep them, and with each house demolished a garden was also often lost. It was not to be until 1940 when the Marquis of Lothian presented Blickling Hall to the National Trust that a viable strategy to save country houses and gardens emerged. Even if country residences were kept, the owners' relationship with them had changed: motor cars made it possible to use country houses for fleeting weekend visits rather than spending a 'season' in the country. In an environment where garden owners were looking to make cutbacks, a female gardener, who required separate accommodation and possibly more help with heavy work than a male gardener, looked like an expensive luxury. Even women who had built valuable work experience during the war found it hard to secure good positions in large gardens and most bothies became all-male preserves again. At the Royal Botanic Gardens at Kew, women workers had managed to secure equal pay to men by the end of the war, but by December 1919 only six women remained working there. At the end of March 1922 Kew ceased employing women as gardeners altogether and was not to resume until the Second World War.

The women we have followed through this book were also facing the challenges of growing older in these tough economic times. They did not abandon their hard-won horticultural careers, but they all had to deal with the reality of working in middle and old age in a physical outdoor occupation that had never paid particularly well. Her campaigning days over, Edith Bradley focused her efforts on her farm at Greenway Court, breeding pigs, growing fruit and running a dairy. The mixed smallholding continued to take pupils after the war. The 1921 census showed that in addition to the permanent residents, Edith Bradley, Cecily Baillie Hamilton and Stella Ellis who was employed for dairy and stock work, there were six other people staying described as 'visitors' who were probably pupils. They included Commander Richard Evan William Kirby RN, aged 37, and five women aged between 19 and 56. The 1920s were a very hard time for farms of all shapes and sizes and it does not seem that Greenway Court thrived in these years. After the war the government removed the price guarantee for farm produce and prices plummeted. The country returned to its reliance on cheap imported and processed food and few farmers could afford to invest in modern equipment or techniques that might help them compete. By this time, Edith Bradley was in her sixties. Her considerable energies had been dedicated to the broader cause of women's advancement, often at the expense of her own health and financial wellbeing, and now she faced an impoverished old age. In 1924 Studley College appointed Emily Ekins, an ex-pupil, as the new principal. In 1913, she reached out to Edith Bradley; there was clearly a strong feeling that Edith Bradley had been poorly treated by the college that owed her so much. Past and present pupils of Studley felt moved to organise a whip-round to raise money in appreciation of her role in the foundation and establishment of the college. Later, in 1936 it seems that Lady Warwick, too, became concerned about Edith Bradley's welfare, even though they had been estranged for over thirty years. On August 13, 1936, she wrote a 'private and very confidential' letter to Edith's brother:

> Dear Mr Bradley
>
> I hope you will forgive me for writing to you direct about your sister, Edith Bradley. She seems to be in financial difficulties, and I have written to the Prime Minister to see if it is possible to get a grant from the Civil List, but they have looked into her circumstances and have declined any assistance in that way. The Studley students, I now see, are giving her an allowance of £52 with an additional £10 each Christmas, making £62 for the last two years, and they cannot possibly do more as the sum is all raised amongst the old students of Studley.
>
> I find it such a difficult matter to find out exactly how things are with your sister. I know she has £20 from another source, but I am quite unable to know what is really her difficulty. I rather think privately that Miss Baillie Hamilton is somewhat of a burden. Perhaps you could kindly advise me in strict confidence what the position is. Forgive me for the enquiry.
>
> Yours sincerely
>
> Frances Evelyn Warwick[405]

I have not been able to locate any reply to this letter and it is not clear whether Lady Warwick's intervention resulted in any practical financial help. It was certainly a sad postscript to a relationship that had been begun with such high hopes of changing the world. Lady Warwick herself was not in the best shape financially by this time. Despite inheriting enormous wealth at a very young age, her philanthropic activity and personal extravagance meant that by the 1920s she was running out of money. Facing bankruptcy, she rented out Warwick Castle to an American family, sold parts of the Easton Lodge estate and finally even King Edward VII's love letters. She continued to live in the west wing of Easton Lodge but in 1918 her home was badly damaged in a fire caused by a typically eccentric set of circumstances. A small monkey, one of her large coterie of exotic pets, fell ill. It was wrapped in a blanket and placed on a stove for extra warmth but unfortunately the blanket caught fire. The monkey understandably panicked and ran around the room with the burning blanket in its wake, igniting the curtains and upholstery. Despite the efforts of the local fire brigade, the fire spread so quickly that the private quarters in the west wing, the kitchen and the servants' quarters were all gutted by fire, with the loss of numerous letters and papers. Thankfully there was no loss of either human or animal life. Lady Warwick had grand plans to rebuild but there was never the money to complete the refurbishment. Nevertheless, in the 1920s and 30s she still managed to live a reduced but colourful lifestyle, keeping old circus ponies and a white peacock on the lawn and charming guests such as Charlie Chaplin and H. G. Wells. Frances 'Daisy' Greville, Countess of Warwick, died in 1938 at the age of 77. Edith Bradley retired from farming in the 1930s and went to live in the village of Littledean in Gloucestershire, where she died in 1943, at the age of 84.

In about 1920 Gertrude Cope finally left her post as head gardener at Northwood after twenty years working there. She was in her mid-forties and like many head gardeners before her, she was probably starting to think about providing for her old age. The usual path for ageing gardeners, in times before the state pension, was to capitalise on a lifetime of gardening skill and careful saving to set up an independent business which could provide a gardener with an income into old age. This would pre-empt a potentially disastrous situation in which an employer was forced to evict an aged head gardener from their tied accommodation when they became too old and frail to work. Gertrude Cope set up a small market garden called Pinewood Gardens in Chandler's Ford in Essex, the county where she began her horticultural training as a young girl. She set up the business with another woman, Modwyn Bainbridge. Born in London in 1893, she was the daughter of a clergyman; she may have worked with Gertrude at Northfield but unfortunately, I have not been able to find any record of how they met. The 1921 census shows Gertrude Cope and Modwyn Bainbridge living at Pinewood Gardens, Park Road, Chandler's Ford. The business employed one full-time employee: a 29-year-old gardener named Robert Cooper. It also employed more casual, part-time labour and it is from the journal of one of these, a local lady named Joan Goater, that we learn that Gertrude Cope's market garden had glasshouses surrounded by acacia trees and also grew cabbages, broccoli and flowers including arum lilies. Gertrude became an active member of the local community, carrying on the interest in charitable and educational groups that the Cadbury family had shown at Northwood. She supported local Boys' and Girls' Clubs, the Boy Scouts and other social activities including the local Gardeners' Club and Women's Institute. However, running a market garden was hard physical work with long hours and as the years passed, the work took its toll and Gertrude suffered badly from arthritis. By 1953 she was confined to a wheelchair and the business was in decline. When she finally died in 1959, Joan Goater wrote a touching tribute to her old boss in her journal: 'I went to the funeral service for Miss Cope at St Boniface Church and was very moved by it. She was quite without relatives, but devoted friends had come to Church to be present with her in spirit and to pray for her lasting rest and peace. I walked home through the village that has lost one of its best-known and respected residents and there will be an emptiness for a long time to come.'[406]

It seems that the Pinewood Gardens business died with Gertrude Cope – this was the fate of most of the market gardens, nurseries and private gardens set up by women in the early years of the century. Their businesses had not grown to the extent that they could outlast their owner-operators. The Allen-Brown nursery, thanks to its diversification into violet products, had weathered the war rather better than most – its violet-scented products must have been an affordable comfort for women at a time of high stress. Although Ada Brown died in 1915, Decima Allen was able to expand her nursery at Henfield, buying an additional 3.5 acres about a quarter of a mile away from the original garden they had set up. After the war she ran the nursery with a new partner, Rachel Ellen Dyce Sharp. As they both aged, they naturally took more of a back seat. A British Pathé newsreel film of 1935 survives which records scenes from the Allen-Brown nursery at Henfield. Although the film shows women working in the nursery, the workforce had clearly changed – there are many men working in the violet fields and the newsreel commentary makes no mention of the female ownership and management. Instead, the commentator refers to the way that 'throughout the winter, the violets flourish under the nurseryman's constant care'. In 1947 the business was still trading under the name Allen-Brown, even though Ada Brown had been dead for over thirty years. An advert in *The West Sussex Gazette* in May 1947 stated, 'The Misses Allen-Brown: Although they have given up their violet nurseries continue to sell their violet toilet preparation. Allen-Brown, Henfield.'[407] By this time, Decima Allen was 78 years old and Rachel Ellen Dyce Sharp was in her early sixties. The nursery was eventually sold to Allwood Brothers of nearby Wivelsfield, a business that specialised in growing carnations. Rachel Ellen Dyce Sharp died in 1950 aged 64 in the new Sussex Hospital for Women that had been founded by Ada's and Decima's friend Elizabeth Robins and Octavia Wilberforce. Decima Allen died in 1951 aged 81. All three women, Ada Brown, Decima Allen and Rachel Dyce Sharp are buried in Henfield Cemetery.

J. S. Turner's colonial training school continued through the war, even though emigration to the colonies had been in a state of suspended animation. J. S. Turner's students in these years were able to apply their skills at home. When war ended, the question of 'surplus' women gained new urgency as people contemplated the impact of the loss of around 750,000 young men in the war. The original emigration societies had been private charitable organisations run by women for women; now the concern about surplus single women and the need to strengthen the British Empire in a new world order was such that the government became involved. In 1919 the government set up and funded the Society for the Overseas Settlement of British Women. The President was Miss Gladys Potts, former secretary and spokeswoman for the National League for Opposing Women's Suffrage. Meriel Talbot, ex-leader of the Women's

Land Army, worked as an Intelligence Officer for the Society. Yet despite this official backing, this new emigration drive was no more effective than the earlier ones had been. The colonies and dominions had no real interest in taking female immigrants, except for domestic servants, of which there was a continuing shortage. It is telling that the advertisements placed by the Canadian Pacific Railway Company in the WFGU journal in the 1920s no longer featured women driving ploughs over rolling prairies. Instead, an advert headed 'New Opportunities' was illustrated by a woman standing at a kitchen sink. Hardly surprisingly, few women sought to travel thousands of miles to do the washing up in a different setting.

The 1921 census reveals that J. S. Turner's Strathcona Gardening School at Huntsmoor near Iver in Buckinghamshire had only twelve students in residence; eight were English and four were born abroad, in France, Australia, Palestine and Luxembourg. Dorothea Kitson, who had been taken on as a teacher when the school was based at Arlesey, was now listed as co-principal alongside J. S. Turner. By1923, J. S. Turner's ill health led her to retire from teaching and wind the school up. She and Dorothea retired to a cottage in Madehurst in Sussex and after leasing the Huntsmoor property to various tenants, eventually the pair sold it to Buckinghamshire County Council in 1937 and the house was demolished the following year. Dorothea Kitson and J. S. Turner continued to live together in Sussex until J. S. Turner's death in 1942 at the age of 85. This was a common picture amongst the smaller private gardening schools. As the principals aged, private gardening schools were not financially viable enough to support a new generation of teachers and students. Many of the private schools struggled financially as the economic depression deepened; the market gardens and floristry businesses run by students to subsidise the school fees saw their sales and profits fall. All-female horticultural colleges and private schools were never as well-endowed or supported as male counterparts. By 1926 there were only three privately owned gardening schools still in business (Aldersley Hall near Chester, the Practical Gardening School for Ladies in Regent's Park and the School of Nature Study and Gardening at Clapham). In 1932 they were joined by the Waterperry School of Horticulture for Ladies in Oxfordshire, run by the indomitable Beatrix Havergil, who was reputed to be the inspiration for the appearance of the character of Miss Trunchbull in Roald Dahl's *Matilda*. Even the larger colleges like Swanley and Studley struggled; they spent the inter-war years perpetually lobbying government for support with limited effect.

The demand for training places at these schools fell dramatically after the war. In contrast to the Edwardian years, horticulture had dropped down the list of potential careers for ambitious and active young women. The Sex Disqualification Act of 1919 made it somewhat easier for women to go to university and take up professional jobs as teachers, nurses and doctors. Growing numbers of women began to get jobs in the civil service, accounting for about a quarter of all such posts by 1935. There was also a growing generation gap between the women who had pioneered horticultural training and the new generation of young women coming of age in the 1920s. Where the press had previously been obsessed with the 'girl garden boys' of the 1890s and 1900s, now they carried long articles on the antics of 'flappers' with their short haircuts, short skirts and racier attitude to sex. Older women, who had fought hard to be freed from corsets and other trappings of femininity that hampered their freedom to move and do serious work, were often appalled at the dress and life choices of the younger generation. Sylvia Pankhurst voiced this disapproval when she complained of 'the emancipation of today (which) displays itself mostly in cigarettes and shorts, painted lips and nails … absurdities of dress which betoken the slave woman's sex appeal rather than the free woman's intelligent companionship.'[408] For the new generation of women, brought up on the movies and with the prospect of better-paid work in factories and offices, life on a farm or garden no longer represented independence and modernity.

The inter-war years were disappointing ones for the women who had fought so hard to establish the right of women to train and work as gardeners and farmers. Frances Wolseley described how she

52

Golden Opportunities

AWAIT WOMEN IN CANADA

There is always considerable demand in Canada for women prepared to undertake household work. Good wages are obtainable and advantage can be taken of the reduced rates to Canada of £2 upwards :: ::

For full particulars apply to

CANADIAN PACIFIC

62-65 CHARING CROSS, S.W. 1
103, LEADENHALL ST., E.C.3.
LONDON.
or *Local Agents Everywhere.*

Advertisement placed by the Canadian Pacific Railway Company in the WFGA magazine, 1923. Courtesy of the RHS Lindley Collections.

and her fellow women gardeners 'have been looked askance by their neighbours as leading profitless lives or verging upon eccentricities which should neither be countenanced nor assisted by reasonable people.'[409] Even the most fervent supporter of women gardeners could be forgiven for wondering if it had all been worth it. By 1923, thirty years after women first sat the RHS National Examination in Practical Horticulture, women were no closer to conquering the heights of the horticultural profession.

Writing back in 1899, Ada Goodrich Freer had predicted of graduates of Swanley, 'The chances are very great against her rising to the top of the tree ... she may make up her mind to the anomalous position of gardener plus governess or the like, or to gardening of the villa or institution class, for the rest of her days; to the care of 'bedding out' plants and a conservatory, with perhaps a boy to help with the roller or mowing machine.'[410] This is exactly what most women gardeners did. Of the 600 women I have been able to identify in the RHS examination lists between 1893 and 1914, I have only been able to find evidence in the national census and other sources for 183 (30 per cent) obtaining paid or self-employed positions as gardeners after they sat their examinations. The majority of these were jobbing gardeners in suburban areas or lived at home with their parents selling small surpluses from their own gardens.

Frances Wolseley, with characteristic upper-class hauteur, attributed this apparent lack of progress to the type of women that were attracted to train at the female horticultural schools. In 1916 she wrote: 'On the whole, the majority of those who during the past twenty years have studied garden craft are town-bred, delicate, or devoid of the powers of leadership that are so essential to the profession.'[411] In her book, *In a College Garden,* she identified other shortcomings in the women who aspired to be gardeners. Rather than too delicate, now she said they were too rough! 'The somewhat rough-mannered, undisciplined middle-class woman who in early days emerged as gardener from some of the training centres ... has done more harm to the calling than can perhaps be realised by any excepting those who have lived for a while in an educational gardening atmosphere. Her untidy general appearance, disorder of clothes, unkempt hair, unbusiness-like habits and bad manners have caused her employer many a mental shudder.'[412] This was both unfair and inaccurate, based as it was on Frances Wolseley's prejudices and preference for women in her own image and from her own social class. Whilst some of the graduates of gardening colleges and schools may have fallen short of Frances Wolseley's exacting sartorial standards, many were serious about gardening and well trained. It is also a picture which completely ignores the barriers women faced in building a career in horticulture and the real progress they made in overcoming them. These barriers were not only misogyny, though there was certainly plenty of that. Even for men, horticulture as a profession was low in confidence and status and as a result it was very defensive and resistant to change. Horticulture had been on a journey of increasing professionalisation since the mid-nineteenth century, with more specialised training, proficiency tests and structured qualifications, yet despite this, professional gardeners were still not rewarded with pay or respect in line with the skills and knowledge the job required. Instead, completely unintentionally, this process of professionalisation had created openings for women in what had once been a closed male-oriented system. To their horror, male professional gardeners now found themselves competing with assertive, articulate middle-class women. It was not lost on male horticulturalists that in some occupations, notably shop work and clerical work, single women had squeezed men out of employment altogether; they would work for lower wages and employers argued that they did not need to pay single women as much, as they did not have to support a family. This phenomenon had seen a drop in status for these occupations, a lesson not lost on the male horticultural establishment. Thus, even though women had demonstrated comprehensively that they were physically capable of doing the job, the horticultural profession still did not welcome them. For the very top positions, the garden gates remained resolutely shut, and any woman who achieved high standards was dismissed as the exception that proved the rule. As

Ada Goodrich had predicted, most women professional gardeners worked in small gardens, institutional gardens or small horticultural businesses. Denied significant progression opportunities in their horticultural careers, unless they were already relatively well off, women gardeners of this era simply had no opportunity to save for their old age. As many of the women found, the culmination of many years of work could be an impoverished old age.

However, it would be wrong to dismiss the achievements of the women in this book just because few of them attained high-profile head gardener posts or are household names today. If we only look for 'stars' and only listen out for the sound of glass ceilings smashing, we risk missing more subtle, but no less real, signs of progress. The hundreds, possibly thousands, of women who undertook horticultural training of one sort or other before the First World War did have an impact. In her novel *Time is Whispering*, written in 1923, Elizabeth Robins described the limited prospects for ordinary single women who did not possess extraordinary abilities. The heroine, a woman gardener, says, 'I've been thinking, people like us ought to be making that clear to more girls … The great women – they'll find their way. The artists, even the little artists, they'll find their way. But there is a whole world left for the ordinary kind of woman – like me. I wish those millions knew!'[413] Even Edith Bradley, who had such bold ambitions for women growers, came to realise the lasting value of more modest contributions. She may not have achieved her dream of feminist revival of the British countryside but, she reflected, progress had been made:

> The history of the Women's Movement is the history of every other progressive movement. The leaders go forward and make tracks in the dark woods for themselves but they do not see that the tracks are not wide enough or smooth enough for the rank and file of their followers … Distressing as their slowness may be to the ardent spirits in front, their mode of procedure is useful and sustaining to the General Cause, because average every-day people do not care to be whirled off their feet by the glamour of great enterprise … All honour to these useful people; they become the backbone of

> the whole scheme and help to lay the dust raised by the clatter and hurry of the advanced guard.[414]

The women who worked as jobbing gardeners, garden teachers, gardeners in therapeutic institutions or ran modest horticultural businesses and smallholdings, might not make the headlines but they were significant figures in their local communities. Their quiet presence normalised the idea that women could do strenuous outdoor work without demeaning themselves. Even the modest, practical adjustments they made to their clothing helped in cementing the revolution in women's dress which freed them from clothing that had literally restricted and confined them.

They were quiet revolutionaries hidden in plain sight in suburbs, small towns and villages up and down the country. Women gardeners working in local institutions such as schools and hospitals or running small horticultural businesses, gave themselves licence to live a life that deviated from social and gender conventions. The market gardener Anna Bateson was a highly unusual figure for her day in an ordinary English country district in Hampshire. She was described as 'physically big and strong, she wore boots, overall and breeches, worked the land like a labourer and enjoyed her glass of beer and pipe of tobacco.'[415] But she was at the heart of her community in Mew Milton in the New Forest and active in public affairs, and the competent way she ran her business meant she was both respected and accepted by her neighbours. In contrast with the days when they were radical young women, shocking the nation with their willingness to dig and get their hands dirty in skirts that showed their ankles, women gardeners became almost invisible as they entered middle age. The same clothes that had seemed so outlandish in their youth – manly Norfolk jackets, short tweed skirts and sturdy boots – came to be seen as dowdy and respectable, at most a little eccentric. The First World War and the glamour of the Women's Land Army, backed as it was with all the might of government propaganda, overshadowed these earlier pioneers. Historians have tended to credit the First and Second World Wars with bringing about the change in perceptions about what was and was not women's work, but this is to overlook the foundations that our early gardeners laid. The success of the wartime mobilisation of women workers in agriculture and horticulture depended on the leadership and guidance of these experienced women who had trained in the early years of the century.

In 1921 Madeline Agar designed the Richardson Evans Memorial Playing Fields, in Wimbledon, close to where she grew up. The playing fields included a war memorial set in the centre of a circular hedged area that carries the inscription 'Nature provides the best memorial'. But of course, one of the difficulties of gardens as a form of memorial is that they are not static. Gardens change over time. The types of gardens our women designed, created or nurtured were rarely the large, prestigious ones, likely to be commemorated or preserved. Women were entrusted with small urban parks rather than large public landscapes, suburban private gardens rather than large country estates and small one- or two-women businesses rather than large conglomerates. It is still possible to locate some of the small city gardens designed by Fanny Wilkinson and Madeline Agar, but many of Madeline Agar's designs do not survive intact. In 1910 she worked on designs to renovate the south-west corner of the churchyard of Southwark Cathedral, the oldest surviving Gothic church in London. In 2001 her designs were altered in subsequent renovations, and a new garden was laid down by Elizabeth Banks, a landscape architect who was to become the first female President of the RHS in 2010.

But the fact that, decades later women such as Elizabeth Banks reached the pinnacle of the RHS (the Society now has its second female Director General, Clare Matterson, who followed Sue Biggs in 2022) is testament to a more perceptible legacy left by these early female professional gardeners. They were very committed to passing their skills on to other women and building supportive female networks. Madeline Agar is a case in point. Her first opportunity for paid work as a designer came as an assistant to Fanny Wilkinson. Later, Madeline nurtured a new generation of gardeners when she

The war memorial gardens designed by Madeline Agar in the Richardson Evans Memorial Playing Fields, April 2022. Courtesy of P. Bateson.

combined her design practice with teaching a course on landscape design at Swanley. One of her pupils was Brenda Colvin who joined Swanley in 1919 after a peripatetic education in India, England and France where she had taken art classes. Brenda Colvin became intrigued by Madeline Agar's lessons, realising that landscape design would allow her to bring together her interest in design and plants. When Madeline stood down from teaching at Swanley because she was too busy with her own practice, Brenda Colvin took private tuition with her, and soon afterwards she was employed by Madeline Agar as her clerk of works and site assistant, just as Madeline had once been given a chance at the Metropolitan Public Gardens Association by Fanny Wilkinson. One of the first projects Brenda Colvin worked on was Madeline Agar's war memorial garden at Wimbledon. After two years learning the business at Madeline's side, Brenda Colvin left to establish her own practice. Sylvia Crowe was another pupil of Madeline Agar's at Swanley. After she left she got a job as a garden designer at William Cutbush's nursery in Barnet and, after success at the Chelsea Flower Show in the 1930s, she set up a practice at Gloucester Place near Baker Street with her old friend, Brenda Colvin. Colvin was to become the first female President of the Institute of Landscape Architects. Sylvia Crowe served as President of the Institute of Landscape Architects from 1957 to 1959. Both women were to become enormously influential landscape architects, working at scale to shape landscapes around reservoirs, nuclear power stations, motorways, universities, hospitals and New Towns.

You can see women gardeners linking muddy, calloused hands across the generations almost everywhere you look, and it is fun to track these connections through the years. Lily Hughes Jones studied at Lady Warwick Hostel in 1901 when Edith Bradley was warden. When Hughes Jones left, she set up the Thatcham Fruit and Flower Farm which took in female pupils. One of these pupils was Beatrix Havergil who went on to set up the Waterperry School of Horticulture for Ladies in 1932. The school ran for forty years and in that time taught many influential gardeners including Mary Spiller, presenter on BBC Gardeners' Question Time, and Pamela Schwerdt, who became head gardener for Vita Sackville-West at Sissinghurst. Another Waterperry alumnus was Valerie Finnis, who stayed on as an instructor in the Alpine Department. Valerie Finnis was a highly respected plantswoman who created the Merlin Trust, a foundation which has supported many young horticulturists with grants for travel and research projects.Valerie Finnis was something of a mentor for Carol Klein at the beginning of her career as owner of Glebe Cottage Plants. Apparently, at one Chelsea Flower Show, when the RHS judges had only seen fit to award Carol Klein's stand a silver medal, Valerie Finnis gave her a banana inscribed 'Gold Medal winner'.[416] Later she was. Carol Klein went on to win many awards and medals and today is a TV presenter and writer who, in turn, informs and inspires millions more gardeners.

One reading of the stories of the women who took up gardening in the early years of the century is a depressing one – of high hopes dashed, frustrating hours in pointless committees, unanswered pleas for support, cold shoulders and low returns. Certainly, this has not been a simple story of unstoppable progress. Even today, the latest workforce survey shows that women make up only 30 per cent of the horticultural workforce, though this rises to 44 per cent in public gardens. Nonetheless, Madeline Agar would have been delighted to know that the record for the most gold medals won at the RHS Chelsea Flower Show is held by a female garden designer, Sara Eberle. Looking back at the stories of the pioneering women, what impresses me most, however, is the ambitions they had for their gardening. The Edwardian era was a time when people grappled with the gross inequalities and environmental damage arising from rapid industrialisation. Women sought to play a role in responding to these challenges and it is striking how often they turned to horticulture to find solutions. Tracking their life stories, I'm struck that gardening offered these women much more than just financial independence or self-expression. Training and working as gardeners offered them a degree of empowerment and autonomy, not solely for individualistic purposes, but also to make the world a better place. Whether this was by rural revival, extending the franchise, greening cities, healing the sick or educating others, the women of this generation sought to put their horticultural skills and abilities to practical use to make a difference.

In an earlier chapter, we left Helen Nussey heartbroken after the death of Olive Cockerell in 1910. She could not face going back to the French garden in Sussex they had built together and returned to life in London as a social worker. In 1914, in her late thirties, Helen Nussey was appointed by the London County Council (LCC) as one of two principal assistant organisers of the school care service, which aimed to ensure that poor schoolchildren in London were sufficiently fed and clothed to benefit from their schooling. In 1930 she was promoted to run the service and under her leadership the care service flourished: by 1939 there was a care committee in every elementary school in London and about 5,000 volunteers. Despite this busy workload, she found time to be drawn back to nature and gardening, this time in a very urban context. In 1939 she became an honorary organiser for the London Gardens Society which aimed 'to make a permanent contribution towards beautifying London by the growing of flowers and shrubs thus improving the urban environment'. The Society, which still operates today, gave away free seeds to encourage the citizens of London to grow flowers to brighten up the areas where they lived and worked. At the end of the Second World War, when many parts of the city had been devastated by the Blitz and many Londoners were living in temporary accommodation, Helen Nussey reached out to her fellow gardeners. Writing in a letter to *The Times* she asked,

> Now that spring seems really on its way, we suppose that many of your readers will be dividing their herbaceous plants. We would therefore appeal for some of the less rampageous throw-outs to be sent to our distributing centres to help tenants to make gardens round their prefabricated houses or to resuscitate old gardens spoilt by bombing or neglect owing to war work and evacuations … Another of our urgent needs is for voluntary workers to help in organising small pot plant shows for old people in every borough in London. Signed Helen G. Nussey.[417]

In 1938 she wrote a book, *London Gardens of the Past* (reissued in 1948). The book is a celebration of the histories and stories behind London's gardens through the ages, but it also contains a picture of a garden on a modern LCC housing estate, one of the gardens Helen supported to brighten the lives of ordinary Londoners. The caption Helen wrote to go with the image reveals a lot about her values and approach to gardening. She wrote, 'Like children, those [gardens] that have needed the most care, are often the best loved.'[418]

Today this feels one of the most powerful points to take away from this story. With worries about climate change, biodiversity collapse, social inequality and mental health challenges, we are once more looking to garden with a purpose. Gardening can be so much more than outdoor housework, prettifying our own private spaces. In 2021, while researching this book, feeling rather depressed with the state of the world, like many other people, I turned to gardening to try to make a small positive change, volunteering in a local community greenspace. I was amazed and delighted to find that the Finchley Way Open Space was the site of an Edwardian housing experiment with a kitchen garden at its centre. Just before the First World War, a plot of land in Finchley, North London, was purchased by the Brent Garden Village Company Ltd., established by Alice Melville, one of the many female supporters of the Garden City movement. The idea was to create a communal living initiative where tenants would share servants, a kitchen, laundry, dining room and other communal services, including a large kitchen garden and orchard. This cooperative scheme did not prosper financially and eventually most of the land was sold for private housing development. The remaining land was bequeathed to the local community but over the years became overgrown and a spot for fly-tipping. A small group of volunteers have gradually cleared the rubbish and planted native trees, bulbs and wildflowers, hoping to create a space for people and nature. The hours I have spent knee-deep in ivy, extracting bed frames and lager cans have been enormously satisfying, made more so by the knowledge that this kind of small-scale urban renewal would have pleased women like Fanny Wilkinson, Madeline Agar, Octavia Hill and Helen Nussey.

The women in this book may now be long forgotten, but there is no denying that they managed to live rich and fulfilling lives on their own terms. In doing so, they changed expectations of what a gardener could look like, and what a gardener could do.

NOTES

1 Sir Joseph Hooker letter to Miss Symonds, 20 March, 1906, Royal Botanic Gardens Kew, letters from J. D. Hooker, vol 13, f261 [JDH/2/3/12 f261] Sarah A. M. Brown writing to Miss Symonds on behalf of Sir Joseph Hooker 20 March, 1906.

2 'Canada for Women', *Daily Mail*, 1910, from Carter, S. (2016) *Imperial Plots: Women, Land and the Spadework of British Colonialism on the Canadian Prairies*, University of Manitoba Press, Winnipeg, p. 142.

3 Ruskin, J. (1865) *Sesame and Lilies* were published lectures that Ruskin delivered in December 1864, at the town halls at Rusholme and Manchester.

4 Johnson, L. (1852) *Every Lady Her Own Flower Gardener*, C. M. Saxton, New York, p. 11.

5 Perry, A. J. (1858) *The Afternoon of Unmarried Life*, Longmans and Roberts, London, p. 142.

6 Elizabeth Carter, 'A Series of Letters between Mrs Elizabeth Carter and Miss Catherine Talbot from the Year 1744 to 1770', quoted in Horwood, C. (2010) *Gardening Women: Their Stories from 1600 to the Present*, Virago, London p. 99.

7 Loudon, J. (1840) *Instructions in Gardening for Ladies*, John Murray, London, p. 8.

8 Austen, J. (1813) *Pride and Prejudice.*

9 *Lincolnshire Chronicle*, 29 August, 1884.

10 *The Bystander*, 16 September, 1908.

11 The Beckenham Directory for 1887, T. W. Thornton Steam Press, Beckenham, p.192.

12 Bradley, E. and La Mothe, B. (1903) *The Lighter Branches of Agriculture*, Chapman and Hall, London, p. 7.

13 Letter from Theodore Cockerell to Annie Fern, 25 March, 1889, from Weber, W. A. (ed.) (2004) *The Valley of the Second Sons: Letters of Theodore Dru Alison Cockerell*, Pilgrim's Progress Inc, p. 350.

14 Letter Cockerell, O. to Cockerell, S., 19 July, 1895, quoted in Blunt, W. (1964) *Cockerell: Sydney Carlyle Cockerell, Friend of Ruskin and William Morris and Director of the Fitzwilliam Museum*, Hamish Hamilton, London, pp. 115–6.

15 Letter Hill, O. to Cockerell, S., 15 February, 1895, Letters of Octavia Hill, City of Westminster Archive Centre, ref: OH/M:Acc 0374.

16 *The Lady: A Journal for Gentlewomen*, 6 August, 1891, p. 198.

17 *Belfast News*, 18 May, 1891.

18 Quoted in Opitz, D. L., 'A Triumph of Brains over Brute', *Isis*, vol 104, no 1, March 2013, p. 43.

19 Ibid, p. 40.

20 Ibid, p. 41

21 *East Anglian Daily Times*, 10 November 1893.

22 'Gardening for Women', *The Examiner*, 30 August, 1879.

23 Chamberlain, Edith (1892) *The Gentlewoman's Book of Gardening*, Henry and Co., London, p. 208.

24 Women's Branch of the Horticultural College, Swanley Kent, Second Annual Report' December, 1893, in Reports 1892–1912, p. 7, SWAN00015, Hextable Heritage Centre.

25 *The Scottish Review*, July, 1900, p. 95

26 Wolseley, F., (1908) *Gardening for Women*, Cassell & Co., London, p. 78.

27 Ibid, p. 2

28 Quoted in Carter, Sarah (2016) *Imperial Plots: Women, Land and the Spadework of British Colonialism on the Canadian Prairies*, University of Manitoba Press, Canada, p. 97.

29 Horwood, C. (2010) *Gardening Women: Their Stories from 1600 to the present*, Virago, London, p. 286.

30 *Journal of the Kew Guild*, 1894.

31 *The Queen*, 29 June, 1895

32 Goodrich Freer, A. (1899) 'Horticulture as a profession for the educated', *The Nineteenth Century*, p. 769.

33 Smith, J., 'History of the College IV: Reminiscences of the First Year of college for Women Students', *Horticultural College Magazine,* May 1917, pp. 13–14.

34 Dean, Arthur, letter to *The Gardening World*, 1 August, 1903, p. 658.

35 *The Queen*, 29 June, 1895.

36 Earle, C. W. (1897) *Pot-Pourri from a Surrey Garden*, Smith, Elder & Co., London, p. 39.

37 Jekyll, G. (1899) *Wood and Garden: Notes and thoughts, practical and critical, of a working amateur*, Longmans, Green & Co., London.

38 Von Arnim, E. (1899) *The Solitary Summer*, Macmillan & Co., London, p. 21.

39 Vere Boyles, E. (1884) *Days and House in a Garden*.

40 *Journal of the Kew Guild*, 1901.

41 Advertisement for gardening school, cutting from T. P. Weekly, 18 November, 1904, Frances Wolseley Commonplace Book, 182, Wolseley Archive, Hove Library.

42 *The Gardening World*, 21 November, 1903, p. 979.

43 *The Common Cause*, 9 December, 1909.

44 Sanecki, K. N., 'Hard Work in High Society', *Hortus*, 2, 1987.

45 *The Journal of Horticulture*, 18 February, 1897, p. 114.

46 Ibid, 4 July, 1907, p. 2.

47 *Journal of the Kew Guild*, 1894, p. 13.

48 Goodrich Freer, 'A. Horticulture as a Profession for the Educated', *The Nineteenth Century*, Vol 1899, p. 774

49 Letter from Broade, F. M., *Swanley Student Magazine*, 1900, Swanley Archives, Hextable Heritage Centre.

50 Letter from Ford, E., Ibid.

51 *The Common Cause*, 5 August, 1913.

52 Society for Promoting Employment of Women, Report of 41st Annual Meeting, 22 May, 1900.

53 Inscription by Rev. Wilks on Pamphlet on the RHS Examination in Horticulture and Scholarships 1898, RHS Archive RHS/P2/6.

54 Thistelton Dyer, W., *Journal of the Kew Guild*, 1895, p. 22.

55 *The Queen*, 1 February ,1896.

56 'An Amazon of Kew', *The Gardening World*, 30 May, 1903, p. 480.

57 *Yorkshire Evening Post*, 20 February, 1896.

58 *Bognor Regis Observer*, 29 January, 1896.

59 *Daily Gazette for Middlesbrough*, 25 January, 1896.

60 *The Northern Echo*, 18October, 1897.

61 *Journal of the Kew Guild*, 1900, p. 21.

62 Letter from Miss Powell, *Swanley Student Magazine*, 1900, Swanley Archives, Hextable Heritage Centre.

63 *The Northern Echo*, 18 October, 1897.

64 Letter from Miss Hutchings, *Swanley Student Magazine*, 1900, Swanley Archives, Hextable Heritage Centre.

65 *Journal of the Kew Guild*, 1896.

66 Letter from Miss Hutchings, *Swanley Student Magazine*, 1900, Swanley Archives, Hextable Heritage Centre.

67 *Journal of the Kew Guild*, 1897.

68 https://sceptical.scot/2016/03/erased-from-history-women-gardeners/

69 Letter from Miss Hay-Currie, *Swanley Student Magazine*, 1900, Swanley Archives, Hextable Heritage Centre.

70 After completing the course, Lina Baker and Annie Morrison went on to found their own gardening school in Corstorphine called The Edinburgh School of Gardening.

71 Quoted in Sanecki, K. N., 'The Ladies and the Gentlemen', *Hortus*, vol 8, no 4, 1994, p. 63.

72 Quoted in Horwood, C. (2010) *Gardening Women: Their Stories from 1600 to the Present*, Virago, London, p. 313.

73 Obituary of Rhoda Anstey, *Anstey Physical Training College Magazine*, no 38, Autumn 1936, p. 38.

74 Ibid.

75 'Gardening as a Career for Women', *The Common Cause*, 7 October, 1909.

76 Letter from Madeline Agar, *Swanley Student Magazine*, 1900, Swanley Archives, Hextable Heritage Centre.

77 Agar, Madeline (1909) *A Primer of School Gardening*, George Philip & Son Ltd, London, p. 18.

78 Ibid, p. 99.

79 Ibid, p. 106.

80 *The Woman's Signal*, 20 February, 1896.

81 https://white-ribbon.org.uk/2021/06/09/outdoor-life-at-duxhurst-inebriate-farm-colony-in-the-1890s/

82 Amherst Archive at the Chelsea Physic Garden quoted in Sanecki, K. N. 'The Ladies and the Gentlemen', *Hortus,* vol 8, no 4, 1994, p. 64.

83 Quoted in Le Lievre (1980) *Miss Wilmott of Warley Place: Her Life and Her Gardens*, Faber and Faber, London, p. 209.

84 Smith, Laura Alex, 'Gardening for Women', Clifton Society, June 27, 1901.

85 *Journal of the Kew Guild*, 1898, p. 11.
86 *Journal of the Kew Guild*, 1897, p. 9.
87 Ibid, 1898, p. 11.
88 Ibid, 1898, pp. 11–12.
89 *Journal of the Kew Guild*, 1897, p. 9.
90 Ibid, 1898, p. 11.
91 Ibid, 1898, p. 13.
92 Ibid, 1899.
93 Goodrich Freer, A. 'Horticulture as a Profession for the Educated', *The Nineteenth Century*, 46, November, 1899, p. 777.
94 Cadbury Alexander, H. (1920) *Charles M Alexander: A romance of song and soul winning*, London, p. 92.
95 Letter from C. F. Fellows, *Swanley Student Magazine*, 1900, Swanley Archives, Hextable Heritage Centre.
96 Letter from Olive Harrisson, Ibid.
97 Wolseley, F. (1908) *Gardening for Women*, Cassell & Co. Ltd, p. 55.
98 Ibid, p. 58.
99 Ibid, pp. 65–6.
100 *Journal of the Kew Guild*, 1900.
101 Letter from Olive Harrisson, *Swanley Student Magazine*, 1900, Swanley Archives, Hextable Heritage Centre.
102 Letter from Lilian Deane, Ibid.
103 Letter from Albert R. Gould, *Journal of Horticulture*, 8 August, 1907, p. 140.
104 Burbidge, F. W., 'The Lady Gardener', *The Gardening World*, 25 July 1903, p. 635.
105 Letter from Lilian Deane, *Swanley Student Magazine*, 1900, Swanley Archives, Hextable Heritage Centre.
106 Letter from Ada Cassidy, Frances St Barbe, Frances Meadmore, Emily Boorman, *Swanley Student Magazine*, 1900, Swanley Archives, Hextable Heritage Centre.
107 Wolseley, F. (1908) *Gardening for Women*, Cassell & Co. Ltd, London, p. 34.
108 Wolseley, F. (1916) *In a College Garden*, John Murray, London, p. 104–5.
109 *Journal of the Kew Guild*, 1900, p. 21.
110 Ibid, 1903, p. 103.
111 *The Gardening World*, 10 January, 1903, p. 25.
112 'The Work of a Woman Gardener', *Votes for Women*, 5 August, 1910.
113 *The Times*, 21 November, 1892.
114 *The Queen*, 22 September, 1895.
115 *The Lady's Pictorial*, 4 April, 1896
116 *The Queen*, 22 September, 1895..
117 Warwick, Countess of (1929) *Life's Ebb and Flow*, Hutchinson & Co., London.
118 Warwick, Countess of (1897) *Progress in Women's Education*, p. 144–5.
119 Ibid, pp. 127–8.
120 'The New Woman and the Old Acres', *The Woman's Agricultural Times*, vol 1, no 1, 1899, p. 2.

121 Bradley and La Mothe (ed.) (1903) *The Lighter Branches of Agriculture*, Chapman & Hall, London, p. 340.

122 Quoted in McKay, G. (2011) *Radical Gardening – Politics, Idealism, Rebellion in the Garden*, Frances Lincoln, London, p. 138.

123 Quoted in Verdon, N., 'Business and Pleasure: Middle Class Women's Work and the Professionalisation of Farming in England 1890–1939', *Journal of British Studies*, vol 51, no 2, April 2012, Cambridge University Press, pp. 393–415.

124 *Fortnightly Review*, 63, no 374, February 1898, Letter to the editor in response to article by Janet E. Hogarth, 'The Monstrous Regiment of Women', *Fortnightly Review*, 62, no 372, December 1897.

125 *The Times*, 17 August, 1898.

126 Blunden, M. (1967) *The Countess of Warwick: A Biography*, Cassell & Co. Ltd, London, p. 136.

127 Alexander Dean, letter in *The Gardening World*, 1 August, 1903, p. 658

128 'New Women and Old Acres', *The Women's Agricultural Times*, vol 1 (1) 1899.

129 Letter to W. T. Stead, quoted in Anand, S. (2009) *Daisy: The Life and Loves of the Countess of Warwick*, Piatkus Books, London, p. 161.

130 Warwick, Countess of (1929) *Life's Ebb and Flow*, Hutchinson & Co., London, pp. 172–6.

131 Warwick, Countess of (1916) *A Woman and the War*, George H. Doran Co., New York, p. 89.

132 Quoted in Warwick, Countess of (1929) *Life's Ebb and Flow*, Hutchinson & Co., London, p. 244

133 Bradley, E., 'Lady Warwick Hostel: A New Direction', *The Woman's Agricultural Times*, vol 4, no 1, 1902, p. 2.

134 Lady Warwick College Warden's Report, 31 October, 1904, MERL Archives.

135 'A London Letter', *West Australian*, 6 February, 1905, p. 5.

136 Letter from E. Bradley to Miss Hart, April 1905, MERL Archives, Letter Book Lady Warwick Hostel, ref: FR WAR 5/1/1.

137 Letter from E. Bradley to Miss White, 6 May, 1905, MERL Archives, Letter Book Lady of Warwick Hostel, ref: FR WAR 5/1/1.

138 Lady Warwick College, Minutes of Executive Committee, 16 March, 1904, MERL Archives, ref: FR WAR 5/7/3

139 'Women and Agriculture', *Country Life*, 25 July, 1903.

140 'New Women and The Old Acres', *The Woman's Agricultural Times* vol 1, no 1, 1899.

141 Bradley and La Mothe (ed.) (1903) *The Lighter Branches of Agriculture*, Chapman & Hall, London, p. 340.

142 Lady Warwick College Warden's Report, 31 October, 1904.

143 Letter from Lady Warwick to Joe Laycock, August 1904, quoted in Annand, S. (2009) *Daisy: The Life and Loves of the Countess of Warwick*, Piatkus Books, London, p. 161.

144 Lady Warwick College Minutes of Executive Committee 9 September, 1905, MERL Archives, ref: FR WAR 5/7/3.

145 Letter from E. Bradley to Dr L. Hamilton, 31 January, 1909, MERL Archives, ref: FR WAR 5/1/25.

146 *Northern Whig*, 29 August, 1905.

147 Stinchcombe, O. (2000) *American Lady of the Manor, Bredon's Norton: The Later Life of Victoria Woodhull Martin*, Adprint, Cheltenham, p. 13.

148 *Cheltenham Examiner*, 11 July, 1906.

149 *The Common Cause*, 9 September, 1909.

150 Bradley, E. and Crooke, M. (1907) *The Book of Fruit Bottling*, John Lande, New York, p. viii.

151 *Tewkesbury Recorder*, 23 February, 1907.

152 *The Gloucester Graphic*, 25 August, 1906.

153 *The Daily News*, 19 June, 1907.

154 Stinchcombe, O. (2000) *American Lady of the Manor, Bredon's Norton: The Later Life of Victoria Woodhull Martin*, Adprint, Cheltenham, p. 42.

155 *The Times*, 19 July, 1909.

156 *The Times*, 25 July, 1910.

157 *The Times*,16 April, 1913.

158 *The Spectator*, 29 January, 1881, p. 3.

159 Agar, M. (1912) *Garden Design, Theory and Practice*, J. B. Lippencott, Philadelphia, p. ix.

160 *The Horticultural Record*, vol 3, no 5, 14 May, 1903, pp. 3–4.

161 Hill, Octavia (1875) *Homes of the London Poor*, Macmillan, London, pp. 211–212.

162 *The Medical Times and Gazette*, quoted in Crawford, E., *A Woman Professional in Bloomsbury: Fanny Wilkinson, Landscape Gardener*, The Bloomsbury Project, University College London.

163 MPGA Minute Book 6, p. 36, London Metropolitan Archives, ref: CLC/011/MS/11097/006.

164 St Ann Blackfriars site record, London Parks and Gardens Trust: https://londongardenstrust.org/conservation/inventory/site-record/

165 Agar, M. (1912) *Garden Design, Theory and Practice*, J. B. Lippencott, Philadelphia, p. 200.

166 Ibid, p. 202.

167 Wolseley, F. (1908) *Gardening for Women*, Cassell & Co., London, p. 18.

168 Advertisement in *Common Cause*, 27 June, 1913.

169 Earle, C. W. (1897) *Pot-Pourri from a Surrey Garden*, Smith, Elder & Co., p. 22.

170 Lady Warwick Hostel Student Register, MERL Archives.

171 Hill, O. quoted: https://www.nationaltrust.org.uk/discover/history/people/octavia-hill-her-life-and-legacy

172 Earle, C. W. (1897) *Pot-Pourri from a Surrey Garden*, Smith, Elder and Co., London, p. 40.

173 *Common Cause*, 14 November, 1912.

174 Wolseley, F. (1908) *Gardening for Women*, Cassell & Co., London, p. 22.

175 *Gardeners' Chronicle*, 51, 1912, p. 399.

176 Robinson, William, 'A Sign of the Times', *The Garden*, June 1872(a), pp. 651–2.

177 'Women as Gardeners', *Country Life*, 7 February, 1914.

178 Agar, M. (1912) *Garden Design, Theory and Practice*, J. B. Lippencott, p. 183.

179 Ibid, p. 24.

180 *Lady's Pictorial*, 2 November, 1912.

181 Agar, M. (1912) *Garden Design, Theory and Practice*, J. B. Lippencott, p. 43.

182 Ibid, p. 37

183 Wolseley, F., *Gardening for Women*, Cassell & Co. London, 1908, p. 71.

184 Allen-Brown, D. and A. (1913) *The Violet Book*, The Bodley Head, London, p. 87.

185 Webster, C. (ed.) (1981) *Biology, Medicine and Society, 1840–1940*, Cambridge University Press, Cambridge.

186 Wolslely, F. (1908) *Gardening for Women*, Cassell & Co., London, p. 74.

187 Studley Student Register 1898–1916, MERL FR STU 1/1

188 Letter from Miss Lutley, *Swanley Student Magazine*, 1900, Swanley Horticultural College Archives, Hextable Heritage Centre.

189 Bromwich, D. (ed.) (2000) *The Diary and Memoirs of John Allen Giles*, Somerset Record Society, Taunton, p. 405.

190 Ibid, p. 412.

191 'Women in Horticulture', *The Queen*, 9 July, 1910.

192 *Isle of Wight Observer*, 25 July, 1908.

193 'Horticulture as a Career For Women', *The Times*, 26 December, 1907.

194 Colt, H., 'Gardening as a Health Cure', *Common Cause*, 23 June, 1910.

195 Allen-Brown, D. and A. (1913) *The Violet Book*, The Bodley Head, London, p. 87.

196 'Gardening for Women', Clifton Society, 27 June, 1901.

197 Allen-Brown, D. and A. (1913) *The Violet Book*, The Bodley Head, London, p. 64.

198 Ibid, p. 88.

199 Ibid, p. 88.

200 Ibid, p. 89.

201 Ibid, pp. 89–90.

202 Ibid, pp. 90–91.

203 Report of lecture by A. D. Hall, Director of Rothampsted Experimental Station in *The Gardening World*, 7 November, 1903.

204 Allen-Brown, D. and A. (1913) *The Violet Book*, The Bodley Head, London, p. 92.

205 Ada and Decima were not the only professional female violet growers. Evelyn D'Ombrain and Mary Foster, who had both been students at Studley, set up a violet-growing business at Poplar Hall, in Hawkhurst, Kent.

206 Mrs Loftie quoted in Hoyles, M. (1991) *The Story of Gardening*, Journeyman Press, London, p. 226.

207 Allen-Brown, D. and A. (1913) *The Violet Book*, The Bodley Head, London, p. 92.

208 Ibid, p. 23.

209 Ibid, p. 102.

210 Ibid, p. 93.

211 Ibid, p. 99.

212 Ibid, p. 95.

213 Ibid, p. 97.

214 Ibid, pp. 36–7.

215 Ibid, pp. 74–5.

216 *The Bystander*, 19 October, 1904.

217 Allen-Brown, D. and A. (1913) *The Violet Book*, The Bodley Head, London, pp. 95–6.

218 Ibid, p. 95.

219 Ibid, p. 101.

220 Ibid, p. 62.

221 *The Graphic*, 26 November, 1910.

222 Allen-Brown, D. and A. (1913) *The Violet Book*, The Bodley Head, London, p. 105.

223 Advert in *The Queen*, 1 December, 1906.

224 Allen-Brown, D. and A. (1913) *The Violet Book*, The Bodley Head, London, pp. 253–4.

225 https://womanandhersphere.com/2017/03/03/suffrage-stories-sussex-violets-and-votes-for-women/

226 John, A. V. (1995) *Elizabeth Robins: Staging a Life*, Routledge, London, p. 154.

227 Robins, E. (1923) *Time is Whispering*, Hutchinson & Co, London, p. 316.

228 Allen-Brown, D. and A. (1913) *The Violet Book*, The Bodley Head, London, p. 98.

229 'Horticulture as a Career for Women', from A Correspondent, *The Times*, December 26, 1907.

230 Saxby, J. M, 'West Nor West', quoted in Carter, S. (2016) *Imperial Plots: Land and the Spadework of British Colonialism on the Canadian Prairies*, University of Manitoba Press, Winipeg, pp. 5–6

231 Optiz, D., 'A Triumph of Brains over Brute', *ISIS*, vol 104 no 1, 2013.

232 Tarif Reform Meeting, *Biggleswade Chronicle*, 17 December, 1909.

233 'Training Girls for the Colonies', *The Girls' Realm*, 1907, pp. 968–972.

234 Ibid.

235 Carter, S. (2016) *Imperial Plots: Land and the Spadework of British Colonialism on the Canadian Prairies*, University of Manitoba Press, Winnipeg, p. 280.

236 J. S. Turner, Letters to the Editor, *Country Life*, 8 June, 1907.

237 Wolseley, F. (1916) *In a College Garden*, J. Murray, London, p. 4.

238 'The Training for Colonial and Country Life', *The Queen*, 10 October, 1908.

239 *The Manchester Guardian*, 6 July, 1910

240 'Woman's Work', *Every Woman's Encyclopaedia*, London, 1910, pp. 344–5.

241 'Training for Colonial and Country Life', *The Queen*, 10 October, 1908

242 Quoted in Bennett, S. (2000) *Five Centuries of Women and Gardens*, NPG, London, p. 100.

243 Quoted in Bennett, S. (2000) *Five Centuries of Women and Gardens*, NPG, London, p. 100.

244 Pember Reeves, Mrs, 'What Clever Men and Women are Saying', *Pearson's Weekly*, 12 January, 1905.

245 *The Bystander*, 16 September, 1910.

246 Wolseley, F. (1908) *Gardening for Women*, Cassell & Co. Ltd, London, p. viii.

247 *Imperial Colonist*, no 1, January 1902, quoted in Carter, S. (2016) *Women, Land and the Spadework of British Colonialism on the Canadian Prairies*, University of Manitoba Press, Winnipeg, p. 116.

248 *The Queen*, 9 July, 1910.

249 Wolseley, F. (1908) *Gardening for Women*, Cassell & Co. Ltd, London, p. 93.

250 Quoted in Opitz, D. L., 'A Triumph of Brains over Brute', *Isis*, vol 104, no 1, March 2012, p. 52.

251 Grosvenor, C. 'Women Farmers in Canada: British Farm Settlement', *The Times*, 27 February, 1913.

252 Carter, S. (2016) *Imperial Plots: Land and the Spadework of British Colonialism on the Canadian Prairies*, University of Manitoba Press, Winnipeg, p. 117.

253 Ibid, p. 4.

254 Ibid, p. 24.

255 Cran, M. (1911) *A Woman in Canada*, W. J. Ham Smith, London, p. 22.

256 Carter, S. (2016) *Imperial Plots: Land and the Spadework of British Colonialism on the Canadian Prairies*, University of Manitoba Press, Winnipeg, p. 280.

257 'Woman's Work', Every Woman's Encyclopaedia, London 1910 pp. 344–5

258 Carter, S. (2016) *Imperial Plots: Land and the Spadework of British Colonialism on the Canadian Prairies*, University of Manitoba Press, Winnipeg, p. 117.

259 Ibid, p. 131.

260 Ibid, p. 280.

261 'Training for Colonial and Country Life', *The Queen*, 10 October, 1908.

262 *Liverpool Evening Express*, 2 March, 1914.

263 Opitz, D. L., 'A Triumph of Brains over Brute: Women and Science at Horticultural College Swanley', *Isis*, vol 104, no 1, March 2012, p. 51.

264 'A Farming Hostel for Girls: An Appeal by Lady Warwick', *The Review of Reviews*, 26, no 152, August 1902.

265 'The Woman at Home', *The Review of Reviews*, 40, no 239, November 1909, p. 114.

266 *Illustrated London News*, 1 December, 1900.

267 Letter Hill, O. to Cockerell, C., 22 August, 1897, Letters of Octavia Hill, City of Westminster Archive Centre, ref: OH/M: Acc 0374.

268 Letter from Morris, J. to Cockerell, S., 26 October, 1901, quoted in Sharp, F. C. and Marsh, J. (ed.) (2012) *The Collected Letters of Jane Morris*, The Boydell Press, Woodbridge, p. 346.

269 Parkins, W. (2013) *Jane Morris: The Burden of History*, Edinburgh University Press.

270 Letter from Morris, J. to Price, C., 27 December, 1902, quoted in Sharp, F. C. and Marsh, J. (ed.) (2012) *The Collected Letters of Jane Morris*, The Boydell Press, Woodbridge, p. 360.

271 Ibid, vol 17, pp. 106–7.

272 Letter Hill, O. to Cockerell, C., 8 June, 1887, Letters of Octavia Hill, City of Westminster Archive Centre, ref: OH/M: Acc 0374.

273 Letter from Cockerell, S. to Hill, O., quoted in Blunt, W. (1964) *Cockerell: Sydney Carlyle Cockerell, friend of Ruskin and William Morris and Director of the Fitzwilliam Museum*, Hamish Hamilton, London, p. 40.

274 Letter Hill, O. to Cockerell, S., 8 June, 1887, Letters of Octavia Hill, City of Westminster Archive Centre, ref: OH/M: Acc 0374.

275 Ibid.

276 Letter Hill, O. to Cockerell, S., 7 December, 1904, Letters of Octavia Hill, City of Westminster Archive Centre, ref: OH/M: Acc 0374.

277 Nussey, H. 'Medical Treatment for the Working Classes', *Monthly Review*, vol XIX, no 57, John Murray, London, 1905.

278 Letter Hill, O. to Cockerell, O., 10 November, 1906, Letters of Octavia Hill, City of Westminster Archive Centre, ref: OH/M: Acc 0374.

279 Morris, W. 'News from Nowhere' in Clive Wilmer (ed.) (1993) *News from Nowhere and Other Writings*, Penguin Classics, London.

280 Chesterton G. K. (1905) *Heretics*, John Lane, London.

281 Cockerell, O. and Nussey, H. (1909) *A French Garden in England*, Stead's Publishing House, London, p. 8.

282 Letter from Hill, O. to Cockerell, S., 4 January, 1907, Letters of Octavia Hill, City of Westminster Archive Centre, ref: OH/M: Acc 0374.

283 Letter from Morris, J. to Cockerell, S., 23 December, 1906, Sharp, F. C. Marsh, J. (ed.) (2012) *The Collected Letters of Jane Morris*, The Boydell Press, Woodbridge.

284 Cockerell, O. and Nussey, H. (1909) *A French Garden in England*, Stead's Publishing House, London, pp. 10–12.

285 Ibid, pp. 13–14.

286 Ibid, pp. 23–9.

287 Ibid, p. 7.

288 Ibid, p. 18.

289 Ibid, p. 23.

290 Ibid, p. 68.

291 Ibid, p. 14.

292 Ibid, p. 146.

293 Ibid, p. 148.

294 Ibid, pp. 148–9.

295 Ibid, pp. 75–7.

296 Ibid, p. 30.

297 Ibid, pp. 85–8.

298 Ibid, pp. 132–5.

299 Ibid, p. 138.

300 Ibid, p. 32.

301 Ibid, p. 21.

302 Ibid, pp. 13–4.

303 Ibid, pp. 20–1.

304 Ibid, p. 78

305 'Lady Gardeners in Brittany', *The Gardening World Illustrated*, vol 17, 1900–1901, p. 537.

306 Advertisement in *Field*, 3 October, 1908.

307 *The Clarion*, 26 March, 1909.

308 Letter from Hill, O. to Cockerell, S., 15 March, 1909, Letters of Octavia Hill, City of Westminster Archive Centre, ref: OH/M: Acc 0374.

309 Cockerell, O. and Nussey, H. (1909) *A French Garden in England*, Stead's Publishing House, London, p. 145.

310 Ibid p. 154.

311 Letter from Nussey, N. to Blunt, W. S., July 1910, West Sussex Records Office, Letters to W. S. Blunt folder ref Blunt/1/Nussey.

312 Ibid, 23 July, 1910.

313 Ibid, 13 July, 1910.

314 Ibid, 23 July, 1910.

315 Ibid.

316 Ibid, 22 September, 1910.

317 Nightingale, F. Quoted in Ross, E., *Slum Travellers: Ladies and London Poverty 1860–1920*, University of California Press, 2007, p. 21.

318 Cockerell, O. and Nussey, H. (1909) *A French Garden in England*, Stead's Publishing House, London, p. 154.

319 *The Times*, 15 July, 1910.

320 Inglis, E. quoted in Robinson, J. (2018) *Hearts and Minds,* Transworld Publishers, London, p. 263.

321 Frances, Countess of Warwick (1929) *Life's Ebb and Flow*, Hutchinson & Co. Ltd, London, p. 244.

322 *South East Gazette*, 3 December, 1918.

323 *Maidstone Telegraph*, 14 December, 1918.

324 *Longford Journal*, 4 December, 1909.

325 Robins, E. (1907) *The Convert*, Macmillan, New York, p. 119.

326 McFarland, F. K. (2013) *Women's Suffrage memorabilia: an illustrated historical study*, p. 92.

327 *Common Cause*, 22 December, 1910.

328 *The Suffragette*, 14 March, 1913.

329 *Common Cause*, 28 April, 1910.

330 *Votes for Women*, 30 April, 1909.

331 Ibid, 16 July, 1908.

332 Ibid, 2 April, 1909.

333 Letter from Stillington to Wolseley, F., Commonplace Book 182, Wolseley Archive, Hove Library.

334 Crawford, E., www.womenandhersphere.com.

335 *Votes for Women*, 8 July, 1910.

336 Horwood, C. (2010) *Gardening Women: Their Stories from 1600 to the present*, Virago, London, p. 285.

337 Godfrey, J. (2019) *Suffragettes of Kent*, Pen and Sword Books, Barnsley, p. 45.

338 'The Organisation of Women in Agriculture', Archive Museum of English Rural Life, Folder ref: WAR 5/1/25.

339 Letter from Bradley, E. to Wolseley, F., 8 July, 1910, Commonplace Book 186, Frances Wolseley Archive, Hove Library.

340 Ibid.

341 Riddell, F. (2018) *Death in Ten Minutes: The forgotten life of radical suffragette Kitty Marion*, Hodder and Stoughton, p. 137.

342 *Common Cause*, 17 July, 1914.

343 *Votes for Women*, 18 July, 1913.

344 Ibid, 17 July, 1913.

345 Ibid, 14 February, 1913.

346 West, R., 'The Mildness of Militancy', *The Clarion*, 28 February, 1913.

347 *The Suffragette*, 29 August, 1913.

348 Ibid, 30 May, 1913.
349 Ibid, 25 April, 1913.
350 Ibid, 30 May, 1913.
351 Ibid, 13 March, 1914.
352 Carter, S. (2016) *Imperial Plots: Women, Land and the Spadework of British Colonialism on the Canadian Prairies, University of Manitoba Press*, p. 144.
353 *Warwick and Warwickshire Advertiser*, 18 July, 1914.
354 Robinson, J. (2018) *Hearts and Minds* Transworld Publishers, London, p. 19.
355 RHS Council Minutes, 25 August, 1914, RHS Archives, RHS Lindley Library.
356 Wolseley, F. (1916) *Women and the Land*, Chatto and Windus, London, p. 202.
357 *Journal of Horticulture*, 11 February, 1915.
358 Ibid, 18 February, 1915.
359 Ibid, 25 February, 1915.
360 Ibid, 11 March, 1915.
361 Ibid, 25 March, 1915.
362 Joshua, L., 'Women Gardeners at Kew During the War 1914–18', *Journal of the Kew Guild*, 1944, p. 392.
363 *Gardeners' Chronicle*, 6 January, 1917.
364 *Oxfordshire Weekly News*, 5 June, 1918.
365 *Suffolk and Essex Free Press*, 24 May, 1916.
366 *Nantwich Guardian*, 26 May, 1916.
367 *Bradford Weekly Telegraph*, 9 February, 1917.
368 Wolseley, F. (1916) *In a College Garden*, J. Murray, London, p. 106.
369 *Common Cause*, 20 June, 1916.
370 British Red Cross Volunteers Register 1914–19, https://www.redcross.org.uk/about-us/our-history/first-world-war-volunteers
371 *Ealing Gazette and West Middlesex Observer*, 13 November, 1915.
372 Royal Horticultural Society, *Economy in the Garden*, 1916, p. 1.
373 Wolseley, F. (1916) *Women and the Land*, Chatto and Windus, London, p. 202.
374 Ibid, p. 204.
375 *Common Cause*, 11 September, 1914.
376 White, B., 'Feeding the War Effort: agricultural experiences in First World War Devon', *Agricultural History Review*, 58, p. 95.
377 *Common Cause*, 29 January, 1915.
378 *Kent Messenger and Gravesend Telegraph*, 10 April, 1915
379 Letter Bradley, E. to Hamilton, L., 19 March, 1915, Museum of English Rural Life, Archive Collection, FR WAR.
380 *Common Cause*, 15 October, 1915.
381 *Illustrated War News*, 29 November, 1916
382 Wilkins, L., Letter to the Editor, *The Times*, June 1, 1916.
383 Letter from Hamilton, L. to Bradley, E., 8 May, 1915, Museum of English Rural Life, Archive Collection, FR WAR.
384 Wolseley, F. (1916) *Women and the Land*, Chatto and Windus, London, p. 65–6.

385 *South Eastern Gazette*, 1 February, 1916.
386 *Kent Messenger and Gravesend Telegraph*, 6 May, 1916.
387 *South Eastern Gazette*, 10 October, 1916.
388 *The Daily Telegraph*, 4 December, 1915.
389 Greville, F. (1916) *A Woman and the War*, George H. Doran and Co., New York, pp. 88–90.
390 RHS Council Minutes, 16 June, 1914, RHS Archive, RHS Lindley Library.
391 RHS Council Minutes, 11 August, 1914, RHS Archive, RHS Lindley Library.
392 Letter from Keeble, F. to Hartog, M., October 1916, pasted into RHS Council minutes 24 October, 1916, RHS Archive, RHS Lindley Library.
393 RHS Council Minutes, 24 October, 1916, RHS Archive, RHS Lindley Library.
394 *The Landswoman*, June 1918, p. 118.
395 *The Landswoman*, May 1918, pp. 90–2.
396 RHS Council Minutes, 25 August, 1914, RHS Archives, RHS Lindley Library.
397 *Kent Messenger and Gravesend Telegraph*, 26 October, 1918.
398 *Votes for Women*, 1 September, 1916.
399 *The Landswoman*, vol 1, May 1918, pp. 90–2.
400 Clifton Society 29 April, 1915.
401 Wolseley, F. (1916) *Women and the Land*, Chatto and Windus, London, p. 220.
402 Greville, F. (1916) *A Woman and the War*, George H. Doran & Co., p. 14.
403 Wolseley, F. (1916) *Women and the Land*, Chatto and Windus, London, p. 38.
404 *Common Cause*, 4 August, 1916.
405 Letter from Lady Warwick to Mr Bradley, 13 August, 1936 (Lot 269 in Sale Catalogue, Spring Autograph and Manuscript Sale, 30 March, 2011, Alexander Historical Auctions).
406 www.chandlersfordtoday.co.uk/tag/joan-adelaide-goater/
407 *The West Sussex Gazette,* 29 May, 1947.
408 Pankhurst, S. quoted in Pugh, M. (2009) *We Danced All Night: A Social History of Britain between the Wars*, Vintage, London, p. 187.
409 Wolseley, F. (1916) *Women and the Land*, Chatto and Windus, London p. 4.
410 Goodrich Freer, A., 'Horticulture as a Profession for the Educated', *The Nineteenth Century*, vol 46, November, 1899, p. 777.
411 Wolseley, F. (1916) *Women and the Land*, Chatto and Windus, London, p. 207.
412 Wolseley, F. (1916) *In a College Garden*, J. Murray, London, p.103.
413 Robins, E. (1923) *Time is Whispering*, Hutchinson & Co., London, p. 311.
414 Bradley, E. (1903) 'The Lighter Branches of Agriculture', *The Women's Library*, vol VI, Chapman & Hall, London, p. 5.
415 Creese, M. R. S., (1988) *Ladies in the Laboratory: American and British Women in Science 1800-1900*, Lanham, p. 42
416 Horwood, C (2010) *Gardening Women: Their Stories from 1600 to the Present*, Virago Press, London, p. 351
417 Nussey, H., Letter to the Editor, *The Times*, 5 April, 1947.
418 Nussey, H. (1939) *London Gardens of the Past*, John Lane, London.

SELECT BIBLIOGRAPHY

Agar, M., *A Primer of School Gardening*, George Philip & Son Ltd, London, 1909.

Agar, M. *Garden Design, Theory and Practice*, J. B. Lippencott, Philadelphia, 1912.

Allen-Brown, D. and A., *The Violet Book*, The Bodley Head, London, 1913.

Anand, S., *Daisy: The Life and Loves of the Countess of Warwick*, Piatkus Books, London, 2009.

Blunt, W., *Cockerell: Sydney Carlyle Cockerell, Friend of Ruskin and William Morris and Director of the Fitzwilliam Museum*, Hamish Hamilton, London, 1964.

Bradley, E. and La Mothe, B. ed., *The Lighter Branches of Agriculture*, Chapman and Hall, London, 1903.

Carter, S. *Imperial Plots: Women, Land and the Spadework of British Colonialism on the Canadian Prairies*, University of Manitoba Press, Winnipeg, 2016.

Chamberlain, Edith, *The Gentlewoman's Book of Gardening*, Henry and Co., London, 1892.

Cockerell, O., and Nussey, H., *A French Garden in England*, Stead's Publishing House, London, 1908.

Crawford, E., *A Woman Professional in Bloomsbury: Fanny Wilkinson, Landscape Gardener*, The Bloomsbury Project, University College London.

Earle, C. W., *Pot-Pourri from a Surrey Garden*, Smith, Elder & Co., London, 1897.

Geffrey, J., *Suffragettes of Kent*, Pen and Sword Books, Barnsley, 2018.

Horwood, C., *Gardening Women: Their Stories from 1600 to the Present*, Virago, London, 2010.

Hoyles, M., *The Story of Gardening*, Journeyman Press, London 1991.

John, A. V., *Elizabeth Robins: Staging a Life*, Routledge, London, 1995.

Johnson, L., *Every Lady Her Own Flower Gardener*, C. M. Saxton, New York, 1852.

Loudon, J., *Instructions in Gardening for Ladies*, John Murray, London, 1840.

Meredith, A., 'A Horticultural Education in England 1900–1940', *Garden History*, vol 31 no 1, The Gardens Trust, Spring 2003.

McKay, G., *Radical Gardening – Politics, Idealism, Rebellion in the Garden*, Frances Lincoln Ltd, London, 2011.

Nussey, H., *London Gardens of the Past*, John Lane, London, 1939.

Opitz, Donald L., 'A Triumph of Brains over Brute', *Isis*, vol 104, no 1, 2013.

Parkins, E., *Jane Morris: The Burden of History*, Edinburgh University Press, Edinburgh, 2013.

Robins, E., *Time is Whispering*, Hutchinson & Co., London, 1923.

Robins, E., *The Convert*, The MacMillian Company, New York, 1907.

Robinson, J., *Hearts and Minds: The Untold Story of the Great Pilgrimage and How Women Won the Vote*, Doubleday, London, 2018.

Sanecki, K. N., *Hard Work in High Society*, Hortus, vol 2, (1987).

Sanecki, K. N., *The Ladies and the Gentlemen*, Hortus, vol 8, no 4 (1994).

Short, A., *The French Gardening Craze, 1908–1914: Horticulture, politics and the media in Edwardian Britain*, Masters Thesis, University of London, 2017.

Stinchcombe, O., *American Lady of the Manor, Bredon's Norton: The Later Life of Victoria Woodhull Martin,* Adprint, Cheltenham, 2000.

Verdon, N., 'Business and Pleasure: Middle Class Women's Work and the Professionalisation of Farming in England 1890–1939', *Journal of British Studies*, vol 51, no 2 (April 2012) Cambridge University Press.

Von Arnim, E., *Elizabeth and Her German Garden*, Macmillan & Co., London, 1898.

Warwick, Countess of, *A Woman and the War,* George H. Doran Co.,1916.

Warwick, Countess of, *Life's Ebb and Flow*, Hutchinson & Co., London, 1929.

Weber, W. A. ed., *The Valley of the Second Sons: Letters of Theodore Dru Alison Cockerell*, Pilgrim's Progress Inc., 2004.

Wolseley, F., *Gardening for Women*, Cassell & Co., London, 1908.

Wolseley, F., *In a College Garden*, J. Murray, London, 1916.

Wolseley, F., *Women and the Land*, Chatto and Windus, London, 1916.

INDEX

People

Places

Organisations

Topics

ACKNOWLEDGEMENTS

This book started with a chance encounter with a bundle of letters uncovered during a cataloguing project at the RHS Lindley Library. In the bundle was a letter written to the RHS to claim a scholarship to train at its Chiswick Garden for O. Harrisson, who had come top in the RHS National Examination in Horticulture in 1898. Buried in a general file of the Director's correspondence, an eagle-eyed archivist spotted a handwritten comment from the Director that made it clear that the RHS would reject O. Harrisson's claim as she was a woman and that the reason that this exclusion was not made clear in the published rules was that 'it was never anticipated that a woman would try.' This inspired me to find out more about Olive Harrisson to see if she was an isolated case. From that first question a project spiralled, as I tried to find all the women that sat the RHS examination and what became of them. This is a long-winded way of saying thank you to all the archivists and library staff who reveal hidden histories by careful documentation of collections. In addition to the team at the RHS Lindley Library, I would also particularly like to say thank you to the team at Hove Library, archivists at the Museum of English Rural Life, Royal Botanic Gardens, Kew, Wimbledon High School, City of Westminster Archives and Henfield Museum. Thanks also to Mr Derek Turner who kindly shared with me the findings of his research into the story of his grandmother, Annie Gulvin. I would like to say particular thanks to Mr Graham Mitchell whose late wife Sharon did so much to protect and preserve the history and archive of the Swanley Horticultural College. While we were still facing COVID-19 restrictions, Mr Mitchell most kindly allowed me to access the Swanley papers at the Hextable Heritage Centre and I want to thank him sincerely for his time and kindness.

Lots of people (knowingly or not!) have fed into my thinking as I started to write. I am very grateful to Dr Suzanne Moss, the marvellous Head of Education at the RHS for thought-provoking conversations in the Wisley coffee shop about gardening lesbians through the ages. Of course, in looking at the topic of women gardeners, I am following in the footsteps of a number of writers and historians and I have relied on their work.

A rambling three-year research project does not turn itself into a book without a team effort and I would like to thank Adrian, Gracie, Graham and Jon of Little Toller Books for all their hard work. Thanks as ever to my ace agent, Rebecca Winfield of Luxton Associates, who has been an unflappable and positive advocate for me and the book throughout. Finally, love and thanks to Patrick, Liam and Joel for their supportive interest in my self-indulgent projects.

F. D.
London, 2023

THE ARRIVAL OF THE BELLS

Oliver Rackham Library
THE ASH TREE
ANCIENT WOODS OF THE HELFORD RIVER
ANCIENT WOODS OF SOUTH-EAST WALES

Richard Mabey Library
NATURE CURE
THE UNOFFICIAL COUNTRYSIDE
BEECHCOMBINGS
GILBERT WHITE: A BIOGRAPHY

Nature Classics
THROUGH THE WOODS *H. E. Bates*
WANDERERS IN THE NEW FOREST *Juliette de Bairacli Levy*
MEN AND THE FIELDS *Adrian Bell*
THE ALLOTMENT *David Crouch & Colin Ward*
ISLAND YEARS, ISLAND FARM *Frank Fraser Darling*
AN ENGLISH FARMHOUSE *Geoffrey Grigson*
THE MAKING OF THE ENGLISH LANDSCAPE *W. G. Hoskins*
A SHEPHERD'S LIFE *W. H. Hudson*
WILD LIFE IN A SOUTHERN COUNTY *Richard Jefferies*
FOUR HEDGES *Clare Leighton*
DREAM ISLAND *R. M. Lockley*
RING OF BRIGHT WATER *Gavin Maxwell*
COPSFORD *Walter Murray*
THE FAT OF THE LAND *John Seymour*
IN PURSUIT OF SPRING *Edward Thomas*
THE NATURAL HISTORY OF SELBORNE *Gilbert White*

Field Notes & Monographs
AUROCHS AND AUKS *John Burnside*
ORISON FOR A CURLEW *Horatio Clare*
SOMETHING OF HIS ART: WALKING WITH J. S. BACH *Horatio Clare*
BROTHER.DO.YOU.LOVE.ME *Manni and Reuben Coe*
HERBACEOUS *Paul Evans*
THE SCREAMING SKY *Charles Foster*
THE TREE *John Fowles*
TIME AND PLACE *Alexandra Harris*
EMPERORS, ADMIRALS AND CHIMNEY SWEEPERS *Peter Marren*
DIARY OF A YOUNG NATURALIST *Dara McAnulty*
THE WATER'S EDGE *Louisa Adjoa Parker*
LOVE, MADNESS, FISHING *Dexter Petley*
THE LONG FIELD *Pamela Petro*
SHALIMAR *Davina Quinlivan*
ELOWEN *William Henry Searle*
SNOW *Marcus Sedgwick*
WATER AND SKY, RIDGE AND FURROW *Neil Sentance*
BLACK APPLES OF GOWER *Iain Sinclair*
ON SILBURY HILL *Adam Thorpe*
GHOST TOWN: A LIVERPOOL SHADOWPLAY *Jeff Young*

Anthology & Biography
ARBOREAL: WOODLAND WORDS *Adrian Cooper*
MY HOUSE OF SKY: THE LIFE OF J. A. BAKER *Hetty Saunders*
NO MATTER HOW MANY SKIES HAVE FALLEN *Ken Worpole*

Little Toller Books
W. littletoller.co.uk E. books@littletoller.co.uk